THE LAST GENERATION

How Nature Will Take Her Revenge for Climate Change

FRED PEARCE

TRANSWORLD PUBLISHERS
61–63 Uxbridge Road, London W5 5SA
a division of The Random House Group Ltd
www.booksattransworld.co.uk

First published in Great Britain in 2006 by Eden Project Books
a division of Transworld Publishers

This edition published in 2007

A CIP catalogue record for this book
is available from the British Library.

ISBN 9781903919880

Addresses for Random House Group Ltd companies outside the UK
can be found at: www.randomhouse.co.uk
The Random House Group Ltd Reg. No. 954009

Typeset in 11/13pt Sabon by
Falcon Oast Graphic Art Ltd.

Printed and bound in Great Britain by
Cox & Wyman Ltd, Reading, Berkshire.

2 4 6 8 10 9 7 5 3

Mixed Sources

Product group from well-managed
forests and other controlled sources

www.fsc.org Cert no. TT-COC-2139
© 1996 Forest Stewardship Council

'This is the most frightening book that I have ever read . . . everyone should read this book to find out what is going wrong with the world.'   John Gribbin, *the Independent*

'A crystal clear wake-up call from one of the finest science writers in the world.'   Dr Jeremy Leggett

'Pearce's book does a superb job of surveying the evidence which demonstrates that we are changing the world's climate. He gives an engaging, lucid and balanced account, with emphasis on both the certainty that "business as usual will produce basically a different planet" and the uncertainties as to details, particularly time scales. This is a powerful book about the most important event in human history. Read it.'
Professor Lord May OM FRS, Oxford University

'Do we really need another book telling us that doom is imminent? In this case, the answer has to be yes. Pearce is no idle Jeremiah, and his book signals a shift of tone in the popular debate . . . *The Last Generation* makes you feel that we know enough now to conceive of the problems ahead. And anticipating a problem is half way to being able to do something about.'
James Flint, *Daily Telegraph*

'Apocalyptic in its vision, but never scare-mongering, *The Last Generation* superbly explains and dramatizes both the causes and the consequences of climate change. One reads it both gripped, and deeply alarmed.'   Robert Macfarlane

'One of Britain's finest science writers, Pearce is a sceptic of the best sort, saying nothing until he has seen the truth of it for himself.'   Richard Girling, *Sunday Times*

Fred Pearce has reported on environment, science and development issues from sixty-four countries. He is environment consultant of *New Scientist* magazine and is a regular contributor to the *Independent*, the *Guardian*, *Prospect*, *Focus*, *Times Higher Education Supplement* and *Country Living*. He was UK environment journalist of the year in 2001 and is a past recipient of the Peter Kent Conservation Book Award. Author of thirteen previous books including *Deep Jungle* and *When the Rivers Run Dry* for Eden Project Books, he is also a regular broadcaster on environmental issues. Fred Pearce is based in London.

'We are on the precipice of climate system tipping points beyond which there is no redemption.'

James Hansen, Director, NASA Goddard Institute
for Space Studies, New York, December 2005

ACKNOWLEDGEMENTS

Where to start? In my twenty years of reporting on climate change for *New Scientist* magazine and others, innumerable scientists (and not a few editors and fellow journalists) have helped me get things mostly right. To all of them, thanks. I hope this book brings their work together in a form that many of them will find enlightening.

My greatest debt is to the synthesizers within the scientific community – the people who have tried to see the whole picture and to put their work into what seems to me to be an ever-more-frightening context. Their names recur throughout this book. But those who have especially helped me in person include Jim Hansen, Paul Crutzen, Jim Lovelock, Wally Broecker, Peter Cox, Peter Wadhams, Mike Mann, Richard Lindzen, Will Steffen, Richard Alley, Lonnie Thompson, Terry Hughes, Jack Rieley, Sergei Kirpotin, Euan Nisbet, Peter Liss, Torben Christensen, Crispin Tickell, Richard Betts, Myles Allen, Meinrat Andreae, Tim Lenton, Chris Rapley, Peter deMenocal, Joe Farman, Gavin Schmidt, Keith Briffa, John Houghton, Dan Schrag, Bert Bolin, Jesse Ausubel, Drew Shindell, Stefan

Rahmstorf, Mark Cane, Arie Issar, Hans Joachim Schellnhuber and the late Charles Keeling and Gerard Bond.

One always gets ideas from fellow writers. So thanks, too, to John Gribbin, Mark Lynas, Bill Burroughs, Doug Macdougall, Mark Bowen, Jeremy Leggett, Gabrielle Walker and two historians of the climate change debate, Gale Christianson and Spencer Weart, whose books I have referred to in preparing this work. Thanks also to the organizers of the Dahlem conferences for making me welcome at an important event; to Carl Petter Niesen in Ny-Alesund; and to the many people who have helped turn a germ of an idea into a completed book, including my agent Jessica Woollard and editors Susanna Wadeson and Sarah Emsley.

CONTENTS

CHRONOLOGY OF CLIMATE CHANGE

5 billion years ago Birth of planet Earth

600 million years ago Last occurrence of 'Snowball Earth', followed by warm era

400 million years ago Start of long-term cooling

65 million years ago Short-term climate conflagration after meteorite hit

55 million years ago Methane 'megafart' from ocean depths causes another short-term conflagration

50 million years ago Cooling continues as greenhouse gas levels in air start to diminish

25 million years ago First modern ice sheet starts to form on Antarctica

3 million years ago First ice sheet formation in the Arctic ushers in era of regular ice ages

100,000 years ago Start of most recent ice age

16,000 years ago Most recent ice age begins stuttering retreat

14,500 years ago Sudden warming causes sea levels to rise 20 metres in 400 years

12,800 years ago Last great 'cold snap' of the ice age,

known as the Younger Dryas era, is triggered by emptying glacial lake in North America; continues for around 1,300 years before very abrupt end

8,200 years ago Abrupt and mysterious return to ice age conditions for several hundred years, followed by stable Holocene warm era

8,000 years ago Storegga landslip in North Sea, probably triggered by methane clathrate releases that also bolster the warm era

5,500 years ago Sudden drying of Sahara

4,200 years ago Another bout of aridification, concentrated on the Middle East; widespread collapse of civilizations

1,200 to 900 years ago Medieval warm period in northern hemisphere; megadroughts in North America

700 to 150 years ago Little ice age in northern hemisphere, peaking in 1690s

1896 Svante Arrhenius calculates how rising carbon dioxide levels will raise global temperatures

1938 Guy Callendar provides first evidence of rising carbon dioxide levels in the atmosphere, but findings ignored

1958 Charles Keeling begins continuous monitoring programme that reveals rapidly rising carbon dioxide levels in the atmosphere

1970s Beginning of strong global warming that has persisted ever since, almost certainly attributable to fast-rising carbon dioxide emissions; accompanied by shift in state of key climate oscillations such as El Niño and the Arctic Oscillation, and increased melting of Greenland ice sheet

Early 1980s Shock discovery of Antarctic ozone hole brings new fears of human influence on global atmosphere

1988 Global warming becomes front-page news after Jim Hansen's presentations in Washington, DC, during US heatwave

1992 Governments of the world attending Earth Summit promise to prevent 'dangerous climate change' but fail to act decisively

1998 Warmest year on record, and probably for thousands of years, accompanied by strong El Niño and exceptionally 'wild weather', especially in the tropics; major carbon releases from burning peat swamps in Borneo

2001 Government of Tuvalu in the South Pacific signs deal for New Zealand to take refugees as its islands disappear beneath rising sea levels

2003 European heatwave with more than 30,000 dead – later described as the first extreme-weather event attributable to global warming; reports of a third of the world being now at risk of drought – twice the amount in the 1970s

2005 Evidence of potential positive feedbacks accumulates with exceptional hurricane season in the Atlantic, reports of melting Siberian permafrost, possible slowing of ocean conveyor, escalating loss of Arctic sea ice and faster glacier flow on Greenland

THE CAST

Richard Alley, Penn State University, Pennsylvania – glaciologist and leading analyst of Greenland ice cores. He revealed how in the past huge global climate changes have occurred over less than a decade and is one of the most articulate interpreters of climate science.

Svante Arrhenius, Swedish chemist. In the 1890s, he was the first to calculate the likely climatic impact of rising concentrations of carbon dioxide in the atmosphere and thus invented the notion of 'global warming'. Modern supercomputers have hardly improved on his original calculation.

Gerard Bond, formerly of Lamont-Doherty Earth Observatory, Columbia University, New York – geologist, one of the first analysts of deep-sea cores and, until his death in 2005, advocate of the case that regular pulses in solar activity drive cycles of climate change on Earth, such as the little ice age and the medieval warm period.

Wally Broecker, Lamont-Doherty Earth Observatory, Columbia University, New York – oceanographer and one of the most influential and controversial US climate scientists for half a century; discoverer of the ocean conveyor, a global thousand-year circulation system that begins off Greenland and ends in the Gulf Stream that keeps Europe warm.

Peter Cox, UK Centre for Hydrology and Ecology, Winfrith – innovative young climate modeller of the likely impacts of aerosols in keeping the planet cool and the risks of land plants turning from a 'sink' to a 'source' for carbon dioxide later this century.

James Croll – nineteenth-century Scottish artisan and self-taught academic. Through many years of study, he uncovered the astronomical causes of the ice ages, which were later attributed to the Serbian mathematician Milutin Milankovitch.

Paul Crutzen, Max Planck Institute for Chemistry, Mainz, Germany – atmospheric chemist who won the Nobel Prize for Chemistry in 1995 for his work predicting destruction of the ozone layer. He pioneered thinking in stratospheric chemistry, the role of man-made aerosols in shading the planet and the 'nuclear winter'; and he coined the term Anthropocene.

Joe Farman, formerly of British Antarctic Survey, Cambridge. His discovery of the ozone hole over Antarctica was a triumph for the dogged collection of seemingly useless data.

Jim Hansen, director of NASA's Goddard Institute for Space Studies, New York – President George W. Bush's top climate modeller. His unimpeachable scientific credentials have kept him in his post (at the time of this book going to press), despite his outspoken warnings that the world is close to dangerous climate change, which have clearly irked the Bush administration.

Charles Keeling, formerly of Scripps Institution of Oceanography, La Jolla, California. He made continuous measurements of atmospheric concentrations of carbon dioxide on top of Mauna Loa in Hawaii from 1958 until his death in 2005. The resulting 'Keeling curve', the most famous graph in climate science, shows a regular annual rise superimposed on a season cycle as the Earth 'breathes'.

Sergei Kirpotin, Tomsk State University, Russia – ecologist who told the world about the 'meltdown' of the permafrost of the West Siberian peatlands, raising fears of massive methane releases to the atmosphere.

Michael Mann, director of Earth System Science Center, Penn State University, Pennsylvania – climate modeller and creator of the 'hockey stick' graph, a reconstruction of past temperatures showing recent warming to be unique in the last two millennia. Though he is the butt of criticism from climate sceptics, he gives as good as he gets. He is the co-founder of the RealClimate website.

Peter deMenocal, Lamont-Doherty Earth Observatory, Columbia University, New York – climate historian who has charted megadroughts, the sudden drying of the Sahara and other major climate shifts of the past 10,000 years, and their role in the collapse of ancient cultures.

John Mercer, formerly of Ohio State University, Columbus – glaciologist who first proposed that the West Antarctic ice sheet has an Achilles' heel and that a 'major disaster' there may be imminent. He also pioneered research on tropical glaciers.

Drew Shindell, NASA's Goddard Institute for Space Studies, New York – ozone layer expert and climate modeller. He is doing ground-breaking research on unexpected links between the upper and the lower atmosphere, revealing how the stratosphere can amplify small changes in surface temperature.

Lonnie Thompson, Byrd Polar Research Institute, Ohio State University, Columbus – geologist who has probably spent more time above 6,000 metres than any lowlander alive, all in the pursuit of ice cores from tropical glaciers that are rewriting the planet's climate history.

Peter Wadhams, head of polar ocean physics at the University of Cambridge. He rode British military submarines to provide the first data on thinning Arctic sea ice and discovered the mysterious 'chimneys' off Greenland that are the start of the global ocean conveyor.

PREFACE: THE CHIMNEY

The Greenland Sea occupies a basin between Greenland, Norway, Iceland and the Arctic islands of Svalbard. It is an ante-chamber between the Atlantic and the Arctic Oceans: the place where Arctic ice flowing south meets the warm tropical waters of the Gulf Stream heading north. Two hundred years ago, the sea was a magnet for sailors intent on making their fortunes by harpooning its great schools of bowhead whales. For a few decades, men such as the Yorkshire whaling captain and amateur Arctic scientist William Scoresby sailed north each spring as the ice broke up and dodged the ice floes to hunt the whales that congregated to devour the spring burst of plankton. Scoresby was the star of the ice floes, landing a world record thirty-six whales at Whitby harbour after one trip in 1798. He was the nimblest navigator round a great ice spur in the sea known as the Odden tongue, where the whales gathered.

Scoresby was too clever for his own good, and boom turned to bust when all the whales were gone. What was once the world's most prolific and profitable whaling ground is still empty of bowheads. But just as the unique mix of warm tropical waters and Arctic ice was the key to the Greenland Sea's whaling bonanza, so it is also the key to another hidden secret of these distant waters.

They call it 'the chimney'. Only a handful of people

have ever seen it. It is a giant whirlpool in the ocean, 10 kilometres in diameter, constantly circling anticlockwise and siphoning water from the surface to the sea bed 3 kilometres below. That water will not return to the surface for a thousand years. The chimney, once one of a family, pursues its lonely task in the middle of one of the coldest and most remote seas on Earth. And its swirling waters may be the switch that can turn the heat engine of the world's climate system on and off. If anything could trigger the climatic conflagration shown in the Hollywood movie *The Day After Tomorrow*, it would be the chimney.

The existence of a series of these chimneys was discovered by a second British adventurer, Cambridge ocean physicist Peter Wadhams. In the 1990s, he began hitching rides in Royal Navy submarines beneath the Arctic ice. Like Scoresby, he too was fascinated by his journeys to the Odden tongue – not for its long-departed whales, but because of the bizarre giant whirlpools he found there. He concluded that they were the final destination for the most northerly flow of the Gulf Stream. The waters of this great ocean current that drives north through the tropical Atlantic, bringing warmth to Europe, are chilled by the Arctic winds in the Greenland Sea and start to freeze round the Odden tongue. The water that was left became ever denser and heavier until it was entrained by the chimneys and plunged to the ocean floor.

This was a dramatic discovery. The chimneys were, Wadhams realized, the critical starting point of a global ocean circulation system that oceanographers had long hypothesized but had never seen in action. It travelled the world's oceans, passing south of Africa, round Antarctica and through the Indian and Pacific Oceans, before gradually resurfacing and sniffing the air again as it returned to the Atlantic, joined the Gulf Stream and returned north once again to complete a circulation dubbed by oceanographers the 'ocean conveyor'.

But, even as he gazed on these dynamos of the ocean circulation, Wadhams knew that they were in trouble. For the Arctic ice was disappearing. Sonar data he had collected from the naval submarines revealed that the entire ice sheet that once covered the Arctic was thinning and breaking up. By the end of the 1990s, the Odden ice tongue was gone. The Gulf Stream water still came north, but it never got cold enough to form ice. The ice tongue has never returned.

'In 1997, the last year that the Odden tongue formed, we found four chimneys in a single season and calculate there could have been as many as twelve,' says Wadhams. Since then, they have been disappearing one by one. Except for one particularly vigorous specimen. Wadhams first spotted it out in the open ocean at 75 degrees north and right on the Greenwich Mean Line during a ship cruise in March 2001. By rights, without the ice, it should not have been there, he says. But it was. Hanging in there, propelled downward perhaps by the saltiness created by evaporation of the water in the wind.

He found the same chimney again later that summer, twice the following year and a final time in spring 2003, before the British government scandalously pulled the plug on his research funds. Over the two years he had tracked it, the last great chimney moved only about 30 kilometres across the ocean, like an underwater tornado that refused to go away. Wadhams measured it and probed it. He sent submersible instruments down through it to measure its motion at depth. It rotated, he said, right to the ocean floor, and such was the force of the downward motion that it could push aside a column of water a kilometre high. 'It is amazing that it could last for more than a few days. The physics of how it did it is not understood at all,' says Wadhams.

The great chimney had in May 2003 one dying companion, 70 kilometres to the north-west. But that chimney no longer reached the surface and was, he says, almost certainly in its death throes. That left just one remaining chimney in the Greenland Sea. 'It may be many decades old or just a transitory phenomenon. But either way, it too may be gone by now. We just don't know,' Wadhams told me in late 2005. Like Scoresby's bowheads, it may disappear unnoticed by the outside world. Or we may come to rue its passing.

INTRODUCTION

Some environmental stories don't add up. I'm an environment journalist, and sometimes the harder you look at some new scare story, the less scary it looks. The science is flaky, or someone has recklessly extrapolated from a small local event to create a global catastrophe. Ask questions, or go and look for yourself, and the story dissolves before your eyes. I like to question everything. I am, I hope in the best sense, a sceptical environmentalist. Sometimes it is bad for business. I have made enemies by questioning theories about advancing deserts, by pointing out that Africa may have more trees than it did a century ago, and by condemning the politics of demographic doomsday merchants.

But climate change is different. I have been on this beat for eighteen years now. The more I learn, the more I go and see for myself, and the more I question scientists, the more scared I get. Because this story does add up, and its message is that we are interfering with the fundamental processes that make the Earth habitable for humans. It is our own survival that is now at stake, not that of a cuddly animal or a natural habitat.

Don't take my word for it. Often in environmental science it is the young, idealistic researchers who become the impassioned advocates. But here I find it is the people who have been in the field the longest, the researchers with the best reputations for doing good science and the professors with the biggest CVs and longest lists of published papers who are the most fearful, often talking in the most dramatic language. People like President George W. Bush's top climate modeller Jim Hansen, the Nobel Prize-winner Paul Crutzen and the late Charles Keeling, begetter of the Keeling curve of rising carbon dioxide levels in the atmosphere. They have seemed to me not so much old men in a hurry as old men desperate to impart their wisdom, and their sense that climate change is something special.

Nature is fragile, environmentalists often tell us. But the lesson of this book is that that it is not so. The truth is far more worrying. She is strong and packs a serious counter-punch. Nature's revenge for man-made global warming will very probably unleash unstoppable planetary forces. And they will be sudden and violent. The history of our planet's climate shows that it does not do gradual change. Under pressure, whether from sunspots or orbital wobbles or now from the depredations of humans, it lurches – virtually overnight. We humans have spent four hundred generations building our current civilization in an era of climatic stability – a long, generally balmy spring that has endured since the last ice age. But this tranquillity looks like the exception rather than the rule in nature. And if its end is inevitable one day, we seem to be triggering its imminent and violent collapse. Our world may be blown away in the process.

The idea for this book came while I sat at a conference, organized by the British government in early 2005, on 'dangerous climate change' and how to prevent it. The scientists began by adopting neutral language. They made a distinction between Type I climate change, which is gradual and follows the graphs developed by climate modellers for the UN's Intergovernmental Panel on Climate Change (IPCC), and Type II change, which is much more abrupt and results from the crossing of hidden 'tipping points'. Type II change is not in the standard models. During discussions, this temperate language gave way. Type II climate change became, in the words of Chris Rapley, director of the British Antarctic Survey, the work of climatic 'monsters' that were even now being woken.

Later in the year, Jim Hansen spoke in even starker terms at a meeting of the American Geophysical Union, saying: 'We are on the precipice of climate system tipping points beyond which there is no redemption.' The purpose of this book is to introduce Rapley's monsters and Hansen's tipping points and to ask the question: how much time have we got?

The monsters are not hard to find. As I was starting work on this book, scientists beat a path to my door to tell me about them. I had an e-mail out of the blue from a Siberian scientist alerting me to drastic environmental change in Siberia that could release billions of tonnes of greenhouse gases from the melting permafrost in the world's biggest bog. Glaciologists, who are more used to seeing things happen with glacial slowness, told me of dramatic events in Greenland and Antarctica, where they are discovering huge river systems of meltwater beneath the ice sheets, and of events in Pine Island Bay, one of the most remote spots in Antarctica, that they discussed with a shudder. Soon, they said, we could be measuring sea level rise in metres rather than centimetres.

Along the way, I learned too about solar pulses, about the 'ocean conveyor', about how Indian village fires may be melting the Arctic, about a rare molecule that runs virtually the entire clean-up systems for the planet's atmosphere, and above all about the speed and violence of past natural climate change. Some of this, I admit, has the feel of science fiction. On one plane journey, I re-read John Wyndham's sci-fi classic *The Kraken Wakes*, and was struck by the similarities between events he describes in that and predictions for the collapse of the ice sheets of Greenland and Antarctica. It is hard to escape the sense that primeval forces lurk deep in the ocean, in ice caps, in rainforest soils and in Arctic tundra. Hansen says that we may have only one decade, and one degree of warming, before the monsters are fully awake. The worst may not happen, of course. Nobody can yet prove that it will. But, as one leading climate scientist put it when I questioned his pessimism, how lucky do we feel?

I hope I have retained my scepticism through this journey. One of the starting points, in fact, was a re-examination of whether the climate sceptics – those who question the whole notion of climate change as a threat – might be right. Much of what they say is political hyperbole of more benefit to their paymasters in the fossil fuel lobby than to science. Few of them are climate scientists at all. But in some corners of the debate, they have done good service. They have, for instance, provided a useful corrective to the common assumption that all climate change must be man made. But my conclusion from this is the opposite of theirs. Far from allowing us to stop worrying about man-made climate change, it underlines how fickle climate can be and how vulnerable we may be to its capricious changes. As Wally Broecker, one of the high priests of abrupt planetary processes, says, 'Climate is an angry beast, and we are poking it with sticks.'

This book is a reality check about the state of our planet. That state scares me, just as it scares many of the scientists I have talked to – sober scientists, with careers and reputations to defend, but also with hopes for their own futures and those of their children, and fears that we are the last generation to live with any kind of climatic stability. One told me quietly: 'If we are right, there are really dire times ahead. Having a daughter who will be about my present age in 2050, and will be in the midst of it, makes the issue more poignant.'

PART ONE

WELCOME TO THE ANTHROPOCENE

1

THE PIONEERS

THE MEN WHO MEASURED THE PLANET'S BREATH

This story begins with a depressed Swedish chemist, alone in his study in the sunless Nordic winter after his marriage to his beautiful research assistant Sofia had collapsed. It was Christmas Eve. What would he do? Some might have gone out on the town and found themselves a new partner. Others would have given way to maudlin sentiment and probably a few glasses of beer. Svante Arrhenius chose neither release. Instead, on 24 December 1894, as the rest of his countrymen were celebrating, he rolled up his sleeves, settled down at his desk and began a marathon of mathematical calculation that took him more than a year.

Arrhenius, then aged thirty-five, was an obdurate fellow, recently installed as a lecturer in Stockholm but already gaining a reputation for rubbing his colleagues up the wrong way. As day-long darkness gave way to months of midnight sun, he laboured on, filling book after book with calculations of the climatic impact of changing concentrations of certain heat-trapping gases. 'It is unbelievable that so trifling a matter has cost me a full year,' he later confided to a friend. But with his wife gone, he had few distractions. And the calculations became an obsession.

What initially spurred the work was the urge to answer a popular riddle of the day: why the world cooled during the ice ages. Geologists knew by then that much of the northern hemisphere had for thousands of years been covered by sheets of ice. But there was huge debate about why this might have happened. Arrhenius reckoned that the clue lay in gases that could trap heat in the lower atmosphere, changing the atmosphere's radiation balance and altering temperatures.

He knew from work half a century before by the French mathematician Jean Baptiste Fourier and an Irish physicist called John Tyndall that some gases, including carbon dioxide, had this heat-trapping effect. Tyndall had measured the effect in the lab. Put simply it worked like this. The gases were transparent to ultraviolet radiation from the sun, but they trapped the infrared heat that the Earth's surface radiated as it was warmed by the sun. Arrhenius deduced that if the amount of these heat-trapping gases in the air was reduced for some reason, the world would grow colder. Later dubbed 'greenhouse gases' because they seemed to work like the glass in a greenhouse, these gases acted as a kind of atmospheric thermostat.

Tyndall, one of the most famous scientists of his day and a friend of Charles Darwin, had himself once noted that if heat-trapping gases were eliminated from the air for one night 'the warmth of our fields and gardens would pour itself unrequited into space, and the sun would rise upon an island held fast in the iron grip of frost.' And that sounded to Arrhenius very much like what had happened in the ice ages. Sure enough, when he emerged from his labours, he was able to tell the world that a reduction in atmospheric carbon dioxide levels of between a third and a half would cool the planet by 4 to 5 degrees Celsius (C) – enough to cover most of north Europe, and certainly every scrap of his native Sweden, in ice.

Arrhenius had no idea if his calculations reflected what had actually happened in the ice ages. There could have been other explanations for the big freeze, such as a weakening sun. It was another eighty years before researchers analysing ancient air trapped in the ice sheets of Greenland and Antarctica found that ice-age air contained just the concentrations of carbon dioxide that Arrhenius had predicted. But as he reached the end of his calculations, Arrhenius also became intrigued by the potential of rising concentrations of greenhouse gases, and how they might trigger a worldwide warming. He had no expectation that this was going to happen, but it was the obvious counterpart to his first calculation. And he concluded that a doubling of atmospheric carbon dioxide would raise world temperatures by an average 5 to 6 degrees C.

How did he do these calculations? Modern climate modellers, kitted up with some of the biggest super-computers, are aghast at the labour involved. But in essence, his methods were remarkably close to theirs. Arrhenius started with some basic formulae on the ability of greenhouse gases to trap heat in the atmosphere. These were off the shelf from Tyndall and Fourier. That was the easy bit. The hard part was deciding how much of the solar radiation the Earth's surface absorbed, and how that proportion would alter as the Earth cooled or warmed under alterations to carbon dioxide concentrations.

The absorbing capacity of different surfaces across the globe varies from ice, which absorbs 20 per cent or less, to dark ocean, which absorbs more than 80 per cent. There are values in between for dark forest and light desert, grasslands, lakes and so on. So, armed with an atlas, he divided the surface of the planet into small squares and assessed the capacity of each segment to absorb and reflect solar radiation, and how factors like melting ice or freezing ocean would alter things as greenhouse gas concentrations rose or fell. By the end he had produced a series of temperature predictions for different latitudes and seasons determined by atmospheric concentrations of carbon dioxide.

It was a remarkable achievement. In the process he had virtually invented the theory of global warming, and with it the principles of modern climate modelling. Not only that: his calculation that a doubling of carbon dioxide levels would cause a warming of around 5 to 6 degrees C almost exactly mirrors the IPCC's most recent assessment, which puts 5.8 degrees C at the top of its likely warming range for a doubling of carbon dioxide levels.

Arrhenius presented his preliminary findings 'On the Influence of Carbonic Acid in the Air upon the Temperature of the Ground' to the Stockholm Physical Society in December 1895 and, after further refinements, published them in the *London, Edinburgh and Dublin Philosophical Magazine and Journal of Science*. There he offered more predictions that modern computer models also reproduce. High latitudes would experience greater warming than the tropics, he said. Warming would also be more marked at night than in the day, in winter rather than summer and over land rather than sea.

But he had cracked an issue that seemed to interest no one else. The world forgot all about it. Luckily for Arrhenius, this labour was but a sideshow in his career. A few years after completing it, he found fame as the winner of the 1903 Nobel Prize for Chemistry, for entirely un-related work on the electrical conductivity of salt solutions. Soon, too, he had a new wife and child, and other interests – he dabbled in everything from immunology to electrical engineering. He was an early investigator of the Northern Lights and a popular proponent of the idea that the seeds of life could travel through space.

But after the First World War, his mood changed. The optimism of his generation, which believed that science and technology could solve every problem, crumbled in the face of a war that killed so many of its sons. He railed against the wastefulness of modern society. 'Concern about our raw materials casts a dark shadow over mankind,' he wrote, in an early outburst of twentieth-century environmental concern. 'Our descendants surely will censure us for having squandered their just birthright.' His great fear was that oil supplies would dry up, and he predicted that the US might pump its last barrel as early as 1935. He advocated energy efficiency and proposed the development of renewable energy, such as wind and solar power. He sat on a government commission that made Sweden one of the first countries to develop hydroelectric power.

Many Swedes today see Arrhenius as an environmental pioneer and praise his efforts to promote new forms of energy. He would have been bemused by this appreci ation. For one thing, he never made the connection between his work on the greenhouse effect and his later nightmares about disappearing fossil fuels. He knew from early on that burning coal and oil generated greenhouse gases that would build up in the air. But he rather liked the idea, writing in 1908: 'We may hope to enjoy ages with more equable and better climates, especially as regards the colder regions of the Earth, ages when the Earth will bring forth much more abundant crops for the benefit of a rapidly propagating mankind.' But he had concluded with some sadness that it would probably take a millennium to cause a significant warming. And when he later began to perceive the scale of industrial exploitation of fossil fuels, his fear was solely that the resources would run out.

The prevailing view for half a century after Arrhenius's calculations continued to be that man-made emissions of carbon dioxide were unlikely to be sufficient to have a measurable effect on the climate any time soon. Nature would easily absorb any excess. From time to time, scientists did go out measuring carbon dioxide in the air, but there was too much local variability to be able to identify any clear trends in concentrations of the gas.

The only man to take the prospect of greenhouse warming seriously was a British military engineer and amateur meteorologist, Guy Callendar. In a lecture to the Royal Meteorological Society in 1938, he said that what few measurements of carbon dioxide levels in the atmosphere there were suggested a 6 per cent increase since 1900; that this must be due to fossil fuel burning; and that the implication was that the warming 'is actually occurring at the present time'. Like Arrhenius, he thought this on balance rather a good thing. Like Arrhenius, too, his findings were pretty much ignored.

The next person to make a serious effort to measure

carbon dioxide in the atmosphere was Charles David Keeling, a young student at the Scripps Institution of Oceanography in La Jolla, California. He began work in the mid-1950s, first in the bear-infested hills of the state's Yosemite National Park, where he liked to go hiking, and later, in the hope of getting better data, in the clean air 4,200 metres up on top of Mauna Loa, a volcano in Hawaii. It was the first time anybody had attempted to monitor carbon dioxide levels in one place continuously. Keeling was so serious about his four-hourly measurements that he missed the birth of his first child to ensure there wasn't a gap in his logbook.

The results proved a sensation. Very soon, Keeling had established that in such a remote spot as Mauna Loa, above weather systems and away from pollution, he could identify a stable background carbon dioxide level of 315 parts per million (ppm). Around this average there was an annual fluctuation between summer and winter caused by the seasonal cycling of carbon dioxide. Plants and other organisms that grow through photosynthesis consume carbon dioxide from the air, especially in spring. But during autumn and winter, photosynthesis largely stops and the photosynthesisers are eaten by soil bacteria, fungi and animals. They exhale carbon dioxide, pushing atmospheric levels back up again. Because most of the vegetation on the planet is in the northern hemisphere, the atmosphere loses carbon dioxide in the northern summer and gains it again in the winter. The Earth, in effect, breathes in and out once a year.

But Keeling's most dramatic discovery was that this annual cycle was superimposed on a gradual year-on-year rise in atmospheric carbon dioxide levels, a trend that has become known as Keeling's curve. From the 315 ppm figure that Keeling found on Mauna Loa in 1958, the background concentration steadily rose to 320 by 1965, 331 by 1975 and so on up to 380 ppm today.

The implications of Keeling's curve were profound. 'By early 1962,' he later wrote, 'it was possible to deduce that approximately half of the CO_2 [carbon dioxide] from fossil fuel burning was accumulating in the air,' with the rest absorbed by nature. By the late 1960s he had noticed that the annual cycling of carbon dioxide was growing more intense. And the spring downturn in atmospheric levels was beginning earlier in the year – strong evidence that the slow annual increase in average levels was warming temperatures and creating an earlier spring.

Keeling personally supervised the meticulous measurements on Mauna Loa until his death in 2005. In his final year, this generally mild man picked up the public megaphone one last time to warn that, for the first time in almost half a century, his instruments had recorded two successive years, 2002 and 2003, in which background carbon dioxide levels had risen by more than 2 ppm. He warned that this might be because of a weakening of the planet's natural ability to capture and store carbon in the rainforests, soils and oceans – nature's 'carbon sinks'. He feared that nature, which had been absorbing half the carbon dioxide emitted by human activity, might be starting to give it back – something which, in his typically understated way, he suggested 'might give cause for concern'.

On his death, Keeling's bosses at Scripps were kind enough to note that the Keeling curve was 'the single most important environmental data set taken in the 20th century'. Nobody disagreed. One writer called him the man who 'measured the breathing of the world'.

Thanks to Keeling's curve, the ideas of Arrhenius and Callendar were rescued from the dustbin of scientific history. It seemed they were right that people could tamper with the planetary thermostat. Climatologists, many of whom in the 1960s had been predicting that natural cycles were on the verge of plunging the world into a new ice age, began instead to warn of imminent man-made global warming. Even in the early 1970s, Pentagon officials had been asking their scientists how to stop the Arctic sea ice from becoming so thick that nuclear submarines could not break through. But by the end of the decade, President Jimmy Carter's Global 2000 Report on the environment had identified global warming as an urgent new issue, and the National Academy of Sciences had begun the first modern study of the problem.

There has been a vast amount of research conducted since. For the past decade and a half the IPCC has produced regular thousand-page updates just to review the field and pronounce on the scientific consensus. But in some ways, mainstream thinking on how climate will alter as carbon dioxide levels rise has not come on much in the century since Arrhenius. Thanks to Keeling we know that those levels are rising, but not much else has changed.

Only perhaps in the last five years, as researchers have learned more about the way our planet works, have some come to the conclusion that changes probably won't be as smooth or as gradual as those imagined by Arrhenius, or as the scenarios of gradual change drawn up by the IPCC still suggest. We are in all probability already embarked on a roller-coaster ride of lurching and sometimes brutal change. What that ride might feel like is the central theme of this book.

2

TURNING UP THE HEAT

A SCEPTIC'S GUIDE TO CLIMATE CHANGE

Ever since the rise of concern about climate change during the 1980s, the scientists involved have been dogged by a small band of hostile critics. Every time they believe they have seen them off, the sceptics come right back. And in some quarters, their voices remain influential. One leading British newspaper in 2004 called climate change a 'global fraud' based on 'left-wing, anti-American, anti-west ideology'. And the best-selling author Michael Crichton, in his much publicized novel *State of Fear*, portrayed global warming as an evil plot perpetrated by environmental extremists.

Many climate scientists dismiss the sceptics with a wave of the hand and return to their computer models. Most sceptics, they note, fall into one of three categories: political scientists, journalists and economists with little knowledge of climate science; aggrieved and retired boffins who find their old teachings disturbed; and salaried scientists with overbearing bosses to serve, like oil companies or governments in hock to them. If the sceptics are to be believed, the evidence for global warming and even the basic physics of the greenhouse effect is full of holes. The apparent scientific consensus exists only, they say, because it is enforced by a scientific establishment riding the gravy train, aided and abetted by politicians keen to play the politics of fear. Much of this may sound hysterical. But could the sceptics be on to something?

First, the basic physics. As we have seen, much of this goes back almost two centuries. Fourier and Tyndall both knew that the atmosphere stays warm because a certain amount of the short-wave radiation reaching Earth from the sun is absorbed by the Earth's surface and radiated at longer infrared wavelengths. Like any radiator, this warms the surrounding air. They knew too that this heat is trapped by gases such as water vapour, carbon dioxide and methane that have a 'greenhouse effect', without which the planet would be frozen, like Mars. But you can have too much of a good thing. Our other planetary neighbour, Venus, has an atmosphere choked with green-house gases and is broiling at around 450 degrees C as a result. And that is a worry. For, thanks to Keeling's curve, there can be no doubt now that human activity on planet Earth is raising carbon dioxide in the atmosphere to levels that are roughly a third above pre-industrial levels.

The effect this has on the planet's radiation balance is now measurable too. In 2001, Helen Brindley, an atmospheric physicist at Imperial College London, examined satellite data over almost three decades to plot changes in the amount of infrared radiation escaping from the atmosphere into space. Because what does not escape must remain, heating the Earth, this is effectively a measure of how much heat is being trapped by greenhouse gases – the greenhouse effect. In the part of the infrared spectrum trapped by carbon dioxide – wavelengths between 13 and 19 micrometres – she found that less and less radiation is escaping. The results for the other greenhouse gases such as methane were similar.

These findings alone should be enough to establish for even the most diehard sceptic that man-made greenhouse gas emissions are making the atmosphere warmer. Climate models developed by the US government's space agency, NASA, estimate that the Earth is now absorbing nearly one watt per square metre of the Earth's surface more than it releases. This is a significant amount. You could run a 60-watt light bulb off the excess energy supplied to the area of the Earth occupied by a modest house.

More contentious is whether we can actually feel the heat. Direct planet-wide temperature records go back 150 years. They suggest that nineteen of the twenty warmest years have occurred since 1980, and that the five warmest years have all been since 1998. Could the thermometers be misleading us? That has to be a possibility. The records, after all, are not a formal planetary monitoring system; they are just a collection of all the data that happen to be available.

Two important criticisms of this thermometer record are made. One is that satellite sensors and instruments carried into the atmosphere aboard weather balloons do not back up the surface thermometers. These data suggest that, whether or not air close to the surface is warming, that warming is not penetrating through the bottom 10 kilometres of the atmosphere, known as the troposphere, in the way that climate scientists predict. If true, this is very worrying, says Steve Sherwood, a meteorologist at Yale

University in Connecticut and author of a study of the problem: 'It would spell trouble for our whole understanding of the atmosphere.'

Not surprisingly, sceptics have made great play of the suggestion that satellites 'prove' the surface thermometers to be at fault. Not so fast, says Sherwood. The satellite data are untrustworthy because they measure the temperature in the air column beneath the satellites and cannot easily distinguish between the troposphere, which is expected to be warming, and the stratosphere, which should be cooling as less heat escapes the lower atmosphere. Further, satellites do not provide direct measurements in the way that thermometers do. Temperatures have to be interpreted from other data, which creates errors. The scientists running the instruments accept that the results 'drift'. Every week, says Sherwood, they recalibrate their satellite measurements according to data from weather balloons. In effect, therefore, the long-term average data from satellites are creatures of the balloon data.

So how good is the balloon data? Here he found a surprisingly obvious flaw – obvious at any rate to anyone who has left an ordinary garden thermometer out in the sun. The sun's ultraviolet rays shining on the bulb force the temperature reading continuously upwards so that it no longer measures air temperatures. The true air temperature can only be captured in the shade, unmolested by the sun's direct rays. Thermometers on weather balloons, it turns out, are no different. They are 'basically cheap thermometers easily read by an electric circuit', says Sherwood. They too show spurious readings when in the sun.

Meteorologists have recently fixed the problem by shielding the thermometers attached to weather balloons inside a white plastic housing. But this was rarely done thirty years ago. Sherwood concludes that 'back in the 1960s and 1970s especially, the sun shining on the instruments was making readings too high.' And that, he says, is the most likely explanation for why balloon measurements do not reveal a warming trend.

Two further observations back up this interpretation. First, the spurious readings should not be a problem when the sun goes down, so 1960s and 1970s readings at night should be reliable. And sure enough, night-time balloon data over the past thirty years do show a warming trend. And second, the data from both balloons and satellites do show a strong cooling in the stratosphere – which is only likely if more heat was truly being trapped beneath it, in the troposphere.

The second serious criticism of the surface temperature trends is that measurements by surface thermometers have been biased by the growth of cities. The concrete and tarmac of cities retain more heat than rural areas, especially at night. The argument is that over the decades, more and more temperature-measuring sites have become urban and that the temperature trends reflect the urbanization of thermometers and not real warming. The 'urban heat island', as researchers more prosaically call it, is undoubtedly real. Cities do hang on to heat. But is it skewing the global data?

It seems unlikely. The 'urban heat island' effect cannot explain why the largest areas of warming have been recorded over the oceans, nor why the greatest magnitude of warming is mainly in polar regions distant from big centres of population. The sceptics should finally have been silenced by a neat piece of research by David Parker of the Hadley Centre for Climate Prediction, part of Britain's Met Office in Exeter, in 2004. He reasoned that the urban heat island effect should be most intense when there is no wind to disperse the urban heat. So he divided the historical temperature data into two sets: one made up of temperatures taken in calm weather and the other of temperatures taken in windy weather. He found no difference. So, while nobody denies that the 'urban heat island' effect exists, it is not sufficient to upset the reliability of global trends in thermometer readings.

There are other disputes between climate scientists and their critics that we might call 'second order', because they are about circumstantial evidence of climate change. Is it true, for instance, that temperatures at the end of the twentieth century were really hotter than at any time in the last millennium? That is the claim first made by US researcher Michael Mann. He produced a controversial graph dubbed the 'hockey stick' which used data from tree rings and other 'proxy' sources to show that the millennium comprised 950 years of stable temperatures and a sudden upturn at the end. The arguments, which we will look at in more detail later, seem to be going in Mann's direction. But, however the dispute goes, it doesn't change the basic science of the greenhouse effect. And in any event, it should be no part of the case for future climate change that past climate did not vary. It rather obviously did. As this book will argue, there is no comfort in past variability. Quite the contrary.

Similarly, there is room for uncertainty about the cause of the rise in temperature over the past 150 years, which is, depending on how you draw your average for recent years, put at a global average warming of between 0.6 and 0.8 degrees C. The warming itself is real enough, but that doesn't necessarily mean that humans are to blame. It could be natural.

One argument is that more radiation reaching us from the sun can account for most of the warming of the past 150 years. This case was made best by Danish scientists Knud Lassen and Eigil Friis-Christensen in 1991. They found a correlation between sunspot activity, which historically reflects the energy output of the sun, and temperature changes on Earth from 1850 onwards. Time-based statistical correlations are notoriously tricky because they can happen by chance, but the Danes' correlation looked convincing, and prominent sceptics took up the case. However, more recent data have convinced Lassen that solar activity cannot explain more recent climate change. Declining sunspot activity since 1980 should have reduced temperatures on Earth. Instead, they have been rising faster than ever.

Overall, this particular dispute has been good for science, and the sceptics can claim a 'score draw'. Climate scientists who once put the whole of global warming since 1850 down to the greenhouse effect now conceded that up to 40 per cent was probably due to the sun. Solar changes may have been the main cause of the substantial global warming in the first half of the twentieth century, for instance. But there is no way the sun's activity can explain the dramatic warming since 1970.

Both sides play one last trick. Websites run by sceptics regularly publish temperature graphs from particular places that show no warming, suggesting that the whole idea of global warming is a myth. This is clearly nonsense; they are cherry picking their data. But climate scientists are almost as guilty when they indiscriminately attribute every local warming to global trends, when well-understood local climate cycles might be the more likely cause. The case for setting up local climate 'watchtowers' in parts of the planet known to be sensitive to climate change, such as the Arctic, remains strong. And we will visit one in Chapter 5. But they will never provide unambiguous proof of global change, because global warming has not cancelled out natural variations in local climate systems. What is so remarkable about recent trends is not local events but the global reach of warming. Virtually no region of the planet is spared. The difference is that natural oscillations mostly just redistribute heat but the greenhouse effect is putting more energy into the entire climate system. Occasionally that causes cooling and other weird weather, but mostly it is causing strong warming.

To summarize the current state of affairs: the global trends are real. There is no known natural effect that can explain the 0.5-degree global warming seen in the past thirty years. In fact, natural changes like solar cycles would have caused a marginal global cooling. Only some very convoluted logic can avoid the conclusion that the human hand is evident in that climate change. Indeed, to think anything else would be to flout one of the central tenets of science. The fourteenth-century English philosopher William Ockham coined the principle of Ockham's razor when he argued that, if the evidence supported them, the simplest and least convoluted explanations for events were the best. Changes in greenhouse gases are that simple, least convoluted explanation for climate change.

This is not the end of the story, however. While we can be fairly certain that more greenhouse gases in the air will push the atmosphere to further warming, there remain big uncertainties about how the planet will respond. An assessment of the sensitivity of global temperatures to outside forcing – whether to changes in sunlight or the addition of greenhouse gases – mostly revolves around disentangling the main feedbacks – the things that an altered climate will change that will in turn feed back to influence the climate. Positive feedbacks reinforce and amplify the change, and run the risk of producing a runaway change – the climatic equivalent of a squawk on a sound system. Negative feedbacks work in the other direction, moderating or even neutralizing change.

The current climate models concur with Arrhenius that the planet will amplify the warming. But some of the more scientifically coherant sceptics make the case that nature has strong stabilizing forces that will act as negative feedbacks and head off climate change. They don't by any means agree on how this will work. Some say a warmer world will be a cloudier world, providing us with more shade from the sun. Others, like the respected Massachusetts Institute of Technology meteorologist Richard Lindzen, have argued that the higher reaches of the troposphere might actually become drier, reducing the natural greenhouse effect of water vapour. Many of these arguments reflect legitimate uncertainty among climate scientists, though some of the negative feedbacks proposed by the sceptics, like cloud processes, could equally turn into major positive feedbacks and make the IPCC projections too small.

Where does this leave us? Actually, with a surprising degree of scientific consensus about the basic science of global warming. When science historian Naomi Oreskes of the University of California in San Diego reviewed almost a thousand peer-reviewed papers on climate change published between 1993 and 2003, she found the mainstream consensus to be real and near universal. 'Politicians, economists, journalists and others may have the impression of confusion, disagreement or discord among climate scientists, but that impression is incorrect,' she concluded. The disagreements were mainly about detail. The consensus, stretching from Tyndall through Arrhenius to the IPCC, lived on.

For the true hard-line sceptics, of course, any scientific consensus must, by definition, be wrong. As far as they are concerned, the thousands of scientists behind the IPCC models have either been seduced by their own doom-laden narrative or are engaged in a gigantic conspiracy. For them, the bigger the consensus the worse the conspiracy. Maverick climatologist Pat Michaels of the University of Virginia in Charlottesville says we are faced with what the philosopher of science Thomas Kuhn called a 'paradigm problem'. Michaels, who is also the 'state meteorologist' for Virginia, one of the US's largest coal producers, and a consultant to numerous fossil fuel companies, says: 'Most scientists spend their lives working to shore up the reigning world view – the dominant paradigm – and those who disagree are always much fewer in number.' The drive to conformity, he says, is accentuated by peer review, which ensures that only papers in support of the paradigm appear in the research literature, and by public funding that gives money for research into the prevailing 'paradigm of doom'.

Even if you accept this cynical view of how science is done, it doesn't mean that the orthodoxy is always wrong. The fact that scientists universally agree that the world is round does not make it flat. Many of the same claims that are now made against the global warming 'paradigm' were once made about the 'AIDS industry' by people who disputed that the HIV virus caused AIDS. Some governments took their side for a long time, and their citizens are now living with the consequences. Where are those sceptics now? Some of them can be heard making the case against climate change.

But all that said, I do think the sceptics are important to the arguments about climate science. The desire for consensus is always likely to lead the mainstream scientific community to don blinkers. This has not only blotted out the arguments of sceptics but also sidelined results from the handful of 'rogue' climate models that keep turning up tipping points that could tumble the world into much worse than what is currently predicted by the mainstream. One scientist told me in the corridors of a conference in early 2005: 'By ignoring these outliers, IPCC has failed for ten years to investigate the possible effects of more extreme climate change.'

So, despite their sometimes cynical motives, the sceptics have served a purpose in picking away at the IPCC orthodoxy. As in politics, every good government needs a good opposition. And though the sceptics' arguments have often been opportunistic and personal, they have spotted the stifling impact of consensus-building. They are, if nothing else, helping to keep the good guys honest. The pity is that they have not done a better job and engaged in more real science and less empty rhetoric. And in their enthusiasm to debunk climate change, they have failed to grasp one alarming possibility: that the IPCC could be underestimating, not overestimating, the threat that the world faces.

3
THE YEAR

HOW THE WILD WEATHER OF 1998
BROKE ALL RECORDS

Lidia Rosa Paz was at a loss. She caught my arm and pointed despairingly into the raging river. Out there, about 50 metres into the water, was the spot where, until days before, she had lived. On the night of 28 October 1998, her shanty town of Pedro Dias, in the town of Choluteca in Honduras, had been washed away, taking more than a hundred people to their deaths. Lidia had survived, but every one of her possessions had gone. 'What will I do now?' she asked. I didn't have an answer.

Hers was one story from a night when floods and landslides ripped apart the small Central American country, leaving more than ten thousand Hondurans dead and two million homeless. It was the night that Hurricane Mitch, the most vicious hurricane to hit the Americas in 200 years, came calling, and dumped a year's rain in just a few hours. Choluteca is in southern Honduras, on the Pacific coast, far from the normal track of Caribbean hurricanes. When the radio issued storm warnings that night, neither

Lidia nor any of her neighbours took much notice. 'Hurricanes never come here,' she told me. Or at least they never did.

I was in Honduras a couple of weeks after the hurricane had struck. The devastation was appalling. Huge floods had rushed down rivers and into the capital, Tegucigalpa, in the mountainous heart of the country, ripping away whole communities. A thousand people lost their lives beneath a single slide that landed on the suburb of Miramesi. Another stopped just short of the American embassy. Rivers changed their paths right across the country, obliterating towns. And flash floods on steep hill-sides buried whole communities under mud. Sixty per cent of the country's bridges were destroyed, along with a quarter of its schools and half its agricultural productivity, including nearly all its banana plantations. The first visitors to the southern town of Mordica reported that 'all you can see is the top of the church.' Ministers said the country's economic development had been put back twenty years.

For tens of millions of people across the world, the violence of Mitch is an omen. Many climatologists believe that Mitch, a ferocious hurricane made worse by the warm seas that allowed it to absorb huge amounts of heat energy from the ocean, was a product of global warming. And a sign of things to come for the hundreds of millions of in-habitants of flood-prone river valleys and coastal plains across the world; for those living on deforested hillsides prone to landslips; and for many millions more who do not yet know that they are vulnerable in a new era of hyper-weather. People like Lidia.

Those who do not believe that global warming is a real and dangerous threat should visit places like Choluteca and talk to people like Lidia. It may not convince them that climate change is making superhurricanes and megafloods. But it will show them the forces of nature untamed and the human havoc caused when the weather breaks its normal shackles. For hundreds of millions of people, these issues are no longer a matter for modelling in computers or debate in the corridors of Congress or future forecasts. They are about real lives and deaths now. The question is not: can we prove that events like Mitch are caused by climate change? It is: can we afford to take the chance that they are?

The year 1998 was the warmest of the twentieth century, probably the millennium. It was also a year of exceptionally wild weather, and few doubt that the two were connected. Besides the storms, it was the year that the rainforests got no rain. Forest fires of unprecedented ferocity ripped through the tinder-dry jungles of Borneo and Brazil, Peru and Tanzania, Florida and Sardinia. New Guinea had the worst drought for a century; thousands starved to death. East Africa saw the worst floods for half a century – during the dry season. Uganda was cut off for several days and much of the desert north of the region flooded. Mongol tribesmen froze to death as Tibet had its worst snows in fifty years. Mudslides washed houses off the cliffs of the desert state of California.

In Peru, a million were made homeless by floods along a coastline that often has no rain for years at a time. The water level in the Panama Canal was so low that large ships couldn't make it through. Ice storms disabled power lines through New England and Quebec, leaving thousands without power or electric light for weeks. The coffee crop failed in Indonesia, cotton died in Uganda and fish catches collapsed in the eastern Pacific.

Unprecedented warm seas caused the tiny algae that give coral their colour to quit reefs in their billions across the Indian and Pacific Oceans, leaving behind the pale skeletons of dead coral.

All a coincidence? Not according to the IPCC. Some of the damage was caused by an intense outbreak of a natural climate cycle in the Pacific known as El Niño. Every few years, this causes a reversal of winds and ocean currents across the equatorial Pacific that for a few months takes rains to drought regions and droughts to normally wet areas. But as we shall see in Chapter 30, there is growing evidence that El Niños are becoming stronger and more frequent under the influence of global warming. This is probably part of a pattern identified by the IPCC in which, all around the world, the weather is becoming more extreme and more unpredictable as the world warms. And 1998, the warmest year yet, was the epitome of the trend.

The heat is intensifying the hydrological cycle. Average annual rainfall globally increased by up to 10 per cent during the twentieth century because warming has increased evaporation. Locally the trends are even stronger. The floods that inundated Mozambique in 2000 arose because maximum daily rainfall there had risen by 50 per cent. In the eastern US, the proportion of rain falling in heavy downpours has increased by a quarter. In Britain, twice as much of the winter rain is falling in intense downpours as in the 1960s. There are similar patterns in Australia, South Africa, Japan and Scandinavia. Even the Asian monsoon has become more intense but less predictable. At the same time, dry areas in continental interiors have become drier, causing deserts to spread. The year 1998 was the first in a run of years of intense drought that stretched from the American West through the Mediterranean to Central Asia.

At the time of writing, no year has been as hot as 1998 – and no year so climatically violent. Unless, that is, you were caught in one of the record number of tropical storms in the North Atlantic in 2005. If you want to know what the first stage of climate change is shaping up to be like, look no further than 1998. But the events of one year can only tell us so much, so let's take a step back and look at the big picture . . .

4

THE ANTHROPOCENE

A NEW NAME FOR A NEW GEOLOGICAL ERA

Welcome to the Anthropocene. It's a new geological era, so take a good look around. A single species is in charge of the planet, altering its features almost at will. And what more natural than to name this new era after that top-of-the-range anthropoid, ourselves? The term was coined in 2000 by the Dutch Nobel Prize-winning atmospheric scientist Paul Crutzen to describe the last two centuries of our planet's evolution. 'I was at a conference where someone said something about the Holocene, the long period of relatively stable climate since the end of the last ice age,' he told me later. 'I suddenly thought that this was wrong. The world has changed too much. So I said: "No, we are in the Anthropocene." I just made up the word on the spur of the moment. Everyone was shocked. But it seems to have stuck.'

The word is catching on among a new breed of scientists who study Earth systems – how our planet functions. Not just the climate systems, but also related features like the carbon cycle on land and at sea, the stratosphere and its ozone layer, the ocean circulation and the ice of the cryosphere. And they are coming to believe that the current methods of functioning of some of these systems are close to breakdown because of human interference. If that is true, then the gradual global warming predicted by most climate models for the next centuries will be the least of our worries.

The big new discovery is that planet Earth does not generally engage in gradual change. It is far cruder and nastier, says Will Steffen, an Australian expert on climate and carbon cycles who from 1998 to 2004 was director of the International Geosphere Biosphere Programme, an international research agency dedicated to investigating Earth systems. A mild-mannered man not given to hyperbole, he nonetheless takes a hard-nosed approach to climate change. 'Abrupt change seems to be the norm, not the exception,' he says. We have been lured into a false sense of security by the relatively quiet climatic era during which our modern complex civilisations have grown and flourished. This security has left us unexpectedly vulnerable as we stumble into a new era of abrupt change.

We have been blind too, he says, to the extent of the damage we are doing to our planetary home. We often see our impact as limited to individual parts of the system: to trashed rainforests, polluted oceans and even raised air temperatures. We rarely notice that by doing all these things at once we are undermining the basic planetary systems. Something, he says, is going to give. 'The planet may have an Achilles' heel. And if it does, we badly need to know about it.' Without that knowledge and the will to act, he says, the Anthropocene may well end in tears.

A report from the US National Academy of Sciences in

2002, under the chairmanship of Richard Alley of Penn State University – a glaciologist with the slightly manic appearance of an ex-hippie, who has become a regular on Capitol Hill for his ability to talk climate science in plain language – sounded a similar warning. 'Recent scientific evidence shows that major and widespread climate changes have occurred with startling speed,' his report began. 'The new paradigm of an abruptly changing climate system has been well established by research over the last decade, but this new thinking is little known and scarcely appreciated in the wider community of natural and social scientists and policymakers.' Or, Alley might have added, among the citizens of this threatened planet.

We have already had one lucky break. It happened twenty years ago, when a hole suddenly opened in the ozone layer over Antarctica, stripping away the continent's protective shield against harmful wavelengths of ultraviolet radiation. We were lucky that it happened over Antarctica, and lucky that we spotted it before the hole spread too far. Many of the scientists who worked to unravel the cause of the ozone hole – including Crutzen, who won his Nobel Prize in this endeavour – are among the most vehement in issuing the new warnings about climate change. They know how close we came to disaster.

Another group who take the perils of the Anthropocene most seriously are glaciologists like Alley. In the past decade, they have analysed ice cores from both Greenland and Antarctica to map the patterns of past natural climate change. The results have been chilling. It has emerged, for instance, that around 12,000 years ago, as the last ice age waned and ice sheets were in full retreat across Europe and North America, the warming abruptly went into reverse.

For a thousand years the world returned to the depths of the ice age, only to emerge again with such speed that, as Alley puts it, 'roughly half of the entire warming between the ice ages and the post-glacial world took place in only a decade.' The world warmed by at least 5 degrees – the IPCC's prediction for the next century or so – within ten years. It beggars belief. But Alley and his co-researchers are adamant that that is what the ice cores show happened.

Similar switchback temperature changes occurred regularly through the last glaciation, and there were a number of other 'flickers' as the planet staggered towards a new post-glacial world. Stone Age man, exposed to a climatic switchback, must have found that tough. Heaven knows how modern human society would respond to such a change, which would see a North African climate in London, Mexican temperatures visited on New England and India's billion-plus population deprived of the monsoon rains that feed them.

The exact cause of the rise and fall of the ice ages still excites disputes. But it seems that the 100,000-year cycles of ice ages and interglacials that have persisted for around a million years have coincided with a minor wobble in the Earth's orbit. Its effect on the solar radiation reaching the Earth is minute and it happens only gradually. But somehow the Earth's systems amplify its impact, turning a minor cooling into an abrupt freeze and an equally minor warming into a sudden defrost. The amplification certainly involves greenhouse gases, as Arrhenius long ago surmised. The extraordinary way in which temperatures and carbon dioxide levels have moved in lockstep offers no other interpretation. It also probably involves changes to ocean currents and the temperature feedbacks from growing and melting ice.

We will return to this conundrum later. But what matters here is that a minor change in the planet's heating – much less, indeed, than we are currently inflicting through greenhouse gases – could cause such massive changes. The planet seems primed to leap into and out of glaciations and, perhaps, other states too.

Some see this hair trigger as rather precisely organized. Steffen says that for a couple of million years the Earth's climate seems to have had just two 'stable states': glacial and interglacial. There was no smooth transition between them. The planet simply jumped, at a signal from the orbital wobble, from the glacial to the interglacial state, and made the jump back again with a little, but not much, more decorum. 'The planet jumps straight into the frying pan and makes a bumpy and erratic slide into the freezer.' Steffen says the glacial state seems to have been anchored at carbon dioxide levels of around 190 parts per million, while the interglacial state, which our current world occupied until the Industrial Revolution, was anchored at about 280 ppm. The rapid flip between the two states must have involved a reallocation of about 200 billion tonnes of carbon between the oceans, land and atmosphere. Carbon was buried in the oceans during the glaciations and reappeared afterwards. Nobody knows quite how or why. But the operation of the hair-trigger jump to a much warmer state raises critical questions for the Anthropocene.

In the past two centuries, humanity has injected about another 200 billion tonnes of carbon into the atmosphere, pushing carbon dioxide levels up by a third from the stable interglacial level of 280 ppm to the present 380 ppm. The figure continues to rise by about 20 ppm a decade. So the big question is how the Earth will respond.

Conventional thinking among climate scientists from Arrhenius onwards predicts that rising emissions of carbon dioxide will produce a steady rise in atmospheric concentrations and an equally steady rise in temperatures. That's still the IPCC story. But Steffen takes a different view: 'If the ice age seemed to gravitate between two steady states, maybe in future we will gravitate to a third steady state.' Nature might, he concedes, fulfil the expectations of climate sceptics and push back down towards 280 ppm, but if it was going to do that, we would already see evidence of it. And we don't. The more likely prospect, he concludes, is that it will push back down to a new higher level.

Other scientists, including Alley, are not convinced by Steffen's sense of order in the system. Alley likens the climate system to 'a drunk, generally quiet when left alone, but unpredictable when roused'. When he is writing scientific papers or committee reports, his language is not so vivid. He talks of a 'chaotic system' vulnerable to 'forcings' from changes in solar radiation or greenhouse gases. 'Abrupt climate change always could occur,' he says. But 'the existence of forcings greatly increases the number of possible mechanisms [for] abrupt change'; and 'the more rapid the forcings the more likely it is that the resulting change will be abrupt on the timescale of human economies or global ecosystems.' Drunks, in other words, may be unpredictable, but if you shout at them louder or push them harder, they will react more vehemently. Right now, moreover, we are offering our drunk one more for the road.

The last 10,000 years, since the end of the last ice age, have not been without climate change. The Asian monsoon has switched on and off; deserts have come and gone; Europe and North America have flipped from medieval warm period to little ice age. None of these events has been as dramatic as the waxing and waning of the ice ages themselves. And most were confined to individual regions of the planet. Civilizations have come and gone in their wake. Even so, human society in general has prospered, learning to plant crops, domesticate animals, tame rivers, create cities, develop science and ultimately industrialize the planet.

But in the Anthropocene, the rules of the game are starting to change. Alley and Steffen agree that humanity is today pushing planetary life-support systems towards their limits. The stakes are higher because what is happening is global. 'Before, if we screwed up, we could move on,' says Steffen. 'But now we don't have an exit option. We don't have another planet.'

5

THE WATCHTOWER

KEEPING CLIMATE VIGIL ON AN ARCTIC ISLAND

A chill wind was blowing off the glacier. Small blue chunks of ice occasionally split from its icy face and floated down the fjord towards the ocean. In the sky above, a strange green ribbon of light flashed across the sky from an anonymous building on the foreshore. And on the snow behind, a polar bear wandered warily round a strange human settlement that had grown up on this remote fjord at the seventy-ninth parallel.

I had come to Ny-Alesund, an international community of scientists that, in the darkening days of autumn, numbered fewer than thirty people. The hardy band was there to man this Arctic watchtower on the north-west shores of Spitzbergen, the largest island of a cluster of Arctic islands called Svalbard, because it is reckoned to be one of the most likely places to witness first-hand any future climatic conflagration. Hollywood directors may have set New York as the place that would descend into climatic chaos first. But while the scientists here heartily enjoy watching their DVD of *The Day After Tomorrow*, they are convinced that Ny-Alesund is the place to be. The place where our comfy, climatically benign world might begin to end. Where nature may start to take her revenge.

Ny-Alesund is a tiny town of yellow, red and blue houses two hours' flight from the northernmost spot on mainland Europe. It is nearer Greenland and the North Pole than Norway, which administers Svalbard under an international treaty signed in 1920. It has history. This was where great Norwegian Arctic explorers such as Roald Amundsen and Graf Zeppelin set out for the North Pole, by ship, seaplane and even a giant airship assembled here. More recently, the High Arctic has been famous for its military listening posts, where staff sat in the cold silence, waiting for the first sign of a Russian or American nuclear missile streaking over the ice to obliterate New York or Moscow or London. But today the biggest business is climate science – waiting for the world to turn. Says Jack Kohler of the Norwegian Polar Institute: 'If you want to see the world's climate system flip, you'd probably best come here to see it first.'

Spitzbergen is already one of the epicentres of climate change. For a few days in July 2005, the scientists put aside their instruments, donned T-shirts and shorts and sipped lager by the glaciers in temperatures that hit a record 20 degrees C – just 1,000 kilometres from the North Pole. Even in late September, as the sun hovered close to the horizon and the long Arctic night beckoned, the sea was still ice free and tomatoes were growing in the greenhouse behind the research station kitchens. Old-timers like British station head Nick Cox, who has visited Ny-Alesund most years since 1978, marvel at the pace of change. 'It stuns me how far the glaciers have retreated and how the climate has changed,' he says. 'It used to be still and clear and cold. Now it is a lot warmer, and damper, too, because the warmer air can hold more moisture.'

Photographs in the town's tiny museum show families who used to work in coal mines here in the 1930s, huddled in warm clothes down by the shore. Looming behind them are glaciers that are barely visible today, having retreated about 5 kilometres back up the fjord. The glaciers and ice sheets that still cover two-thirds of Svalbard are some of the best-studied in the world. And visiting glaciologists leave each time with worsening news. In the summer of 2005, British glaciologists measured the nearby Midtre Lovenbreen glacier losing height by 30 centimetres in a single week as it melted in the sun. The Kronebreen glacier may be dumping a quarter of a cubic kilometre of ice into the fjord every year.

Jack Kohler is attempting a 'mass balance' of the ice of Svalbard. He reckons that 25 cubic kilometres melts and runs off into the ocean each year now. Another 4 cubic kilometres is lost from icebergs slumping into the sea from 1,000 kilometres of ice cliffs. At most, half of this loss is being replaced with new snow. That is an annual net loss of around 14 cubic kilometres – a staggering volume for a small cluster of islands, and probably second only in the Arctic to the loss from the huge ice sheet covering Greenland. And there is more to come, Kohler says. Many of Svalbard's glaciers and ice caps are close to freezing point and 'very sensitive to quite small changes' in temperature. Boreholes drilled into the permafrost show a staggering 0.4 degrees C warming in the past decade. A few more tenths of a degree could be catastrophic, he says.

* * *

Ny-Alesund is a cosmopolitan community, especially in summer, with Norwegian and Germans, Swedes and British, Spanish and Finns, Italians and French, Russians and Americans, Japanese and Chinese and Koreans. It is also quirky. Checking some equipment in the empty Korean labs, I found a pair of Spanish scientists hiding there with their bedrolls. They said they couldn't afford the accommodation fees in the main compound but couldn't bear to give up their work measuring glaciers. The Chinese had departed for the winter, but left behind a pair of 2-tonne granite lions to guard the entrance to their building. The week before, a shipload of Scotsmen, dressed in kilts and offering whisky galore, showed up at the quayside for some R&R while investigating the sediments on the bottom of the fjord; and some Yorkshiremen flew a remote-controlled helicopter the size of a small dog over glaciers to map them in 3D.

There are magnetometers and riometers and spectrophotometers probing the upper atmosphere; there are weather balloons aplenty, a decompression chamber for divers and even a big radio telescope that measures the radiation from distant quasars with such accuracy that it helps correct global positioning systems for the effects of continental drift. The scientists here measure chloro-fluorocarbons (CFCs) and carbon dioxide, mercury and ozone, water vapour and radon; they fingerprint the smoke and dust brought in on the breeze to find out where it came from; they photograph the Northern Lights and sniff for methane from the melting tundra. Some cloudless nights, German researcher Kai Marholdt sends a green shaft of laser light into the sky to probe the chemistry of the stratosphere. There is so much scientific equipment littering the tundra that nobody is sure what is still in use and what has been abandoned by long-since-departed researchers. There are plans for a clean-up because passing reindeer keep getting tangled in the cables.

Meanwhile, the bears are coming. As the sea ice disappears, polar bears that live out on the ice and hunt for seals are being forced ashore. They are becoming bold. They break into the huts dotted across the island and maintained for scientists spending a night out on the ice. They are looking for meat, but will sink their teeth into anything soft – bed mattresses and even inflatable boats have been torn to shreds. Anyone moving out of Ny-Alesund has to carry a gun.

Svalbard has long been recognized as being extremely sensitive to climate variations. In the early twentieth century, during a period of modest warming in much of the northern hemisphere, temperatures rose here by as much as 5 degrees C – a figure probably not exceeded anywhere on the planet. In the 1960s they fell again by almost as much, but the rise since has taken them back to the levels of the 1920s, with no end in sight. Climatologists warn against seeing warming here as an unambiguous sign of man-made climate change. But Svalbard does seem uniquely sensitive to nudges on the planetary thermostat. It is a place where climate feedbacks like melting sea ice and changes in winds and ocean currents work with special force. And who knows what the future will hold? Only a couple of hundred kilometres out to sea, Wadhams' last chimney may be living out its final days.

Svalbard is a place to watch like a hawk, and not just for changing climate. The ozone layer is on a hair trigger here, too. One day soon, many researchers expect a giant ozone hole to form over the Arctic, just as it did twenty-five years ago in the Antarctic. And so, on the roof of the Norwegian Polar Institute, the largest research station in Ny-Alesund, pride of place goes to a gleaming steel instrument with a grand embossed nameplate announcing that you are in the presence of Dr Dobson's Ozone Spectrophotometer No. 8. Or Dobson Meter No. 8, for short. British meteorologist Gordon Dobson, one of the first researchers into the ozone layer, built the first of his spectrophotometers in 1931 in a wooden hut near Oxford. His eighth, built in 1935, came north to Ny-Alesund and ever since has been pointing to the sky, measuring the ultraviolet radiation pouring through the atmosphere and so, indirectly, measuring the thickness of the ozone layer.

Dobson eventually produced 150 machines. They still form the core of the world's ozone layer monitoring network. Their work was considered routine, even dull, until one of them discovered an ozone hole over Antarctica in the early 1980s. Now Dobson Meter No. 8 and its minder, research assistant Carl Petter Niesen, are searching the skies above Ny-Alesund to look for a repeat here. The most northerly and among the oldest in continual service, these days the instrument needs a little help to keep going. It has a duvet and a small heater to stop it seizing up in the winter cold. Uniquely amongst the equipment here, it is not connected to a computer logger. Even in the depths of winter, Carl Petter goes up on the roof to write down its reading with a pencil in a large logbook. Not much science happens that way any more, but the Dobson Meter, with its idiosyncratic but continuous record for more than half a century, is irreplaceable.

Dobson Meter No. 8 hasn't spotted a full-blown hole in the ozone layer yet. But as the researchers wait, they have discovered other strange things happening to the chemistry of the atmosphere. Svalbard, it turns out, is on the flight path of acid fogs from Siberian factories that get trapped in thin pancake-like layers of air close to the ice and turn the clear, still air into a yellow haze. Sometimes it rains mercury here as industrial pollution cruises north and suddenly, within a matter of minutes, precipitates onto the snow.

Pesticides, too, arrive in prodigious quantities, apparently from the fields of Asia. They condense in the cold air and become absorbed in the sparse Arctic vegetation, then work their way up the food chain to fish and polar bears and birds. But the very highest concentrations occur in a lake on Bear Island in the south of the Svalbard archipelago, beneath a huge auk colony. The chemicals that have become concentrated in the Arctic air, and then concentrated again in the Arctic food web, are concentrated one more time in the urine of the auks. What at first sight seems to be just about the least polluted place on Earth turns out to be a toxic sump.

Ny-Alesund is as close to the top of the world as you can get without living under canvas. And the summit of Mount Zeppelin, 500 metres above the settlement, is the top of the top of the world – the ultimate watchtower for the world's climate. I went to the summit in the world's most northerly cable car with Carl Petter, who was taking his daily journey to tend the huge array of instruments designed to sniff every molecule of passing Arctic air. Recently, he says, increases in carbon dioxide levels in the air on Mount Zeppelin have grown more sharply than at other monitoring stations round the world. Some days he measures levels approaching 390 parts per million, fully 10 ppm above the global average. There is always some scatter in the readings. But it seems, he says, as if fast-rising emissions from power plants and cars in China and India are travelling north on the winds with the mercury and the pesticides and the acid haze. Not for the first time, he has caught a whiff of the future here at the top of the world.

PART TWO

FAULT LINES IN THE ICE

6

NINETY DEGREES NORTH

WHY MELTING KNOWS NO BOUNDS IN THE FAR NORTH

'Has anybody in history ever got to 90 degrees north, to be greeted by water and not ice?' That was the question posed by a group of scientists after returning from a cruise to the North Pole in August 2000. Sailing north from Svalbard on one of the world's most powerful icebreakers, the *Yamal*, the researchers found very little ice to break. And when they got to their polar destination, they were amazed to find not pack ice but a mile-wide expanse of clear blue water.

The story went round the world. For some, it revived the tales of ancient mariners, who said that beyond the Arctic ice there was an open ocean, and beyond that a mystical land, an Atlantis of the North. The proprietors of the *Yamal* were quick to cash in, offering summer cruises to 'the land beyond the pole'. But for the less romantically inclined, the story of the ice-free North Pole ignited panic about Arctic melting. By chance, the scientists on board the *Yamal* had included James McCarthy, an oceanographer at Harvard on summer vacation from chairing an IPCC working group on the impacts of climate change. He didn't want to be alarmist, he said on his return. The Arctic ice sheet is made up of shifting plates, so there are bound to be gaps. But there were more and more gaps. So the unexpected discovery was 'a dramatic punctuation to a more remarkable journey, in which the ice was everywhere thin and intermittent, with large areas of open water'.

The whole Arctic was remarkably ice free that summer. And that included the Holy Grail of generations of Arctic explorers, the North West Passage. The search for a northern route from the Atlantic to the Pacific and the riches of the Orient excited early explorers, but it was a deadly pursuit. The ice swallowed up hundreds of them, most notably Sir John Franklin, whose 1845 expedition disappeared with all 128 hands. But in 2000, a Canadian ship made the journey through the North West Passage without touching ice. Skipper Ken Burton said: 'There were some 'bergs, but we saw nothing to cause any anxiety.'

Inuit whalers the previous June told glaciologists meeting in Alaska that the ice had been disappearing for some years. 'Last year it stayed over the horizon the whole summer. We had to go 50 kilometres just to hunt seals,' said Eugene Brower of the Barrow Whaling Captain's Association. Recently declassified data from US and British military submarines had revealed that the Arctic ice in late summer was on average 40 per cent thinner in the 1990s than it was in the 1950s. And NASA satellites, which have been photographing the ice for a quarter-century, offer the most incontrovertible evidence. Their analyst-in-chief is Ted Scambos of the National Snow and

Ice Data Center in Boulder, Colorado, a wannabe astronaut who turned to exploring the polar regions as a second best. He reports annually on how the retreat of ice is turning into a rout. In 2005, there was just 5.3 million square kilometres of ice left in mid-September, the usual date of minimum ice cover. That was 20 per cent less than in 1978.

The Arctic is a place without half-measures. There is no mid-point between water and ice. Melting and freezing are, in the jargon of the systems scientists threshold processes. Melting takes a lot of solar energy, but once it is complete the sun is free to warm the water left behind. And, because it is so much darker, that water is also far better at absorbing the solar energy and using it to heat the air around. 'This makes the whole ice sheet extremely dynamic,' says Seymour Laxon, a climate physicist at University College London. 'The concept of a slowly dwindling ice pack in response to global warming is just not right. The process is very dynamic, and it depends entirely on temperature each summer.'

'Feedbacks in the system are starting to take hold,' Scambos says. The winter refreeze is less complete every year; the spring melt is starting ever earlier – seventeen days earlier than usual in 2005. 'With all that dark, open water, you start to see an increase in Arctic Ocean heat storage.' The Arctic 'is becoming a profoundly different place'. Most glaciologists agree with Scambos that the root cause of the great melt is Arctic air temperatures that have risen by 2–3 degrees C in the past thirty years, several times the global average. Global warming, it seems, is being amplified here. This is partly because the feedbacks of melting ice create extra local warming. And partly too because of a long warm phase in a climatic variability called the Arctic Oscillation, which brings warm winds further north into the Arctic. The Arctic Oscillation is a natural phenomenon, but there is growing evidence that it is being accentuated by global warming, as we shall see in Chapter 37.

There is another driver for the melting, again probably connected to global warming. Warmer air above the ice is being accompanied by warmer waters beneath. Weeks before Scambos published his 2005 report, Igor Polyakov from the International Arctic Research Center in Fairbanks, Alaska, reported on an 'immense pulse of warm water' that he had been tracking since it entered the Arctic in 1999. It had burst through the Fram Strait, a narrow 'throat' of deep water between Greenland and Svalbard that connects the Greenland Sea and the Atlantic to the Arctic Ocean. And since then, it had been slowly working its way round the shallow continental shelves that circle the Arctic Ocean. One day in February 2004, the pulse reached a buoy in the Laptev Sea north of Siberia. A thermometer strapped to the buoy recorded a jump in water temperature of half a degree within a few hours. The warm water stayed, the rise proved permanent and the Laptev Sea rapidly became ice free. 'It was as if the planet became warmer in a single day,' Polyakov told one journalist.

Pulses of warm water passing through the Fram Strait may be a regular feature of the Arctic. They were known to the Norwegian explorer and oceanographer Fridtjof Nansen, who a century ago used a specially strengthened ship called the *Fram* to float with the ice and monitor currents in the Arctic. But as the Atlantic itself becomes warmer, the pulses appear to become bigger, and their impact on the Arctic is growing. One theory is that some of the warm Atlantic water that once disappeared down the chimneys in the Greenland Sea now comes further north into the Arctic.

'The Arctic Ocean is in transition towards a new, warmer state,' says Polyakov. And most glaciologists working in the Arctic agree. Writing in the journal of the American Geophysical Union, *Eos*, in late 2005, a group of twenty-one of them began in almost apocalyptic terms: 'The Arctic system is moving to a new state that falls outside the envelope of glacial-interglacial fluctuations that prevailed during recent Earth history.' Soon, they said, the Arctic would be ice free in summer, 'a state not witnessed for at least a million years. The change appears to be driven largely by global warming, and there seem to be few, if any, processes within the Arctic system that are capable of altering the trajectory towards this "super-interglacial" state.'

What would a world be like with an ice-free Arctic? Oil and mineral companies and shipping magnates long for the day when they can prospect at will, build new cities and navigate their vessels at all seasons from Baffin Island to Svalbard and Greenland to Siberia. But it would be a world without polar bears and ice-dwelling seals, a world in which there was no place for the Inuit way of life. And the influence of such a change would spread around the world. Without the reflective shield of ice, the whole world would warm several more degrees; ocean and air currents driven by temperature differences between the pole and the tropics would falter; on land, methane and other gases would break out of the melting permafrost, raising temperatures further; and as the ice caps on land melted, sea levels would rise so that much of the world's population would have to move or drown. If the Arctic is especially sensitive to climate change, the whole planet is especially sensitive to changes in the Arctic.

7

ON THE SLIPPERY SLOPE
GREENLAND IS SLUMPING INTO THE OCEAN

We are on 'a slippery slope to hell'. That is not the kind of language you expect to read in a learned scientific paper by one of the US's top climate scientists, one moreover with a senior position as director of one of NASA's main science divisions, the Goddard Institute for Space Studies in New York. Not even in a picture caption. But Jim Hansen, President George W. Bush's top in-house climate modeller, though personally modest and unassuming, calls it how he sees it.

I've followed Hansen's work for a long time. He began his career investigating the greenhouse effect on Venus, and was principal investigator on the *Pioneer* space probe to the planet in the 1970s. But he soon switched to planet Earth. He was the first person to get global warming onto the world's front pages, during the long hot US summer of 1988. Half the states of the US were on drought alert, and the mighty Mississippi had all but dried up. The Dust Bowl, it seemed to many, was returning. Hansen picked that moment to turn up at a hearing of the US Senate's Energy and Natural Resources Committee in Washington and tell sweating senators: 'It is time to stop waffling so much. We should say that the evidence is pretty strong that the greenhouse effect is here.' He didn't quite say that greenhouse gases were causing the drought across the country, a claim that would have been hard to substantiate. But everybody assumed he had.

Sixteen years later, Hansen was the senior US government employee who, seven days before the 2004 US presidential election, began a public lecture with the words, 'I have been told by a high government official that I should not talk about dangerous anthropogenic interference with climate, because we do not know how much humans are changing the Earth's climate or how much change is dangerous. Actually we know quite a lot.' And he went on to describe what we know in some detail. Most fellow researchers thought that would be the end for Jim as a government employee. But a year later this outwardly diffident man – who couldn't stop apologizing for keeping me waiting when we met in his large, paper-strewn office – was still in his post. To the incredulity of many of his colleagues. 'He is saved by his science; he is just too good to be fired,' said one. 'Also, he is one of the good guys. He doesn't have enemies. If he needed saving there are a lot of people who would volunteer for the job.'

And now Hansen says the world, or more particularly Greenland, is on a slippery slope to hell. We had better listen.

The world's three great ice sheets – one over Greenland and the other two over Antarctica – contain vast amounts of ice. Leftovers from the last ice age, they are piles of compressed snow 3 kilometres high. Glaciologists divide the sheets into two parts. On the high ground inland, where the snowfall is greatest and the melting is least, they accumulate ice. But on the edges and on lower ground, where snowfall is usually less and melting is greater, they lose ice. The boundary is known as the equilibrium line.

For many centuries these great ice sheets have been in balance, with ice loss at the edge matched by accumulation in the centre, and the equilibrium line remaining roughly stationary. Glaciologists have regarded this balance as being rather secure, since such huge volumes of ice can change only very slowly. Glacially. This image of stability and longevity is reassuring. If the ice sheets all melted, or slumped into the ocean, they would make a big splash. They contain enough ice to raise sea levels worldwide by 70 metres. That would drown my house, and probably yours too. Luckily, so glaciologists have been telling us for years, this won't happen. Not even if there is fast global warming. Large ice sheets tend to maintain their own climate, keeping the air above cold enough to prevent large-scale melting, they say. And even if warming did take hold at the surface, it could only penetrate down through the tightly packed ice extremely slowly.

The scariest suggestion, made by the IPCC in 2001, was that beyond a warming of about 3 degrees C, Greenland might gradually start to melt, with a wave of warmth moving down through the ice. Once under way, the process might, it said, be unstoppable because as the ice sheet melted its surface would become lower and exposed to ever warmer air. The melting would take place very slowly, 'during the next thousand years or more'. Now that is not a nice legacy to leave to future generations, but a thousand years is forty or so generations away. So maybe it is not something to worry us today.

But Hansen is the public mouthpiece for a growing body of glaciologists who say that things could happen much faster. For ice sheets, even the biggest and slowest and most stable-looking, have a secret life involving dramatic and dynamic change. And their apparent stability could one day be their undoing. The story is told best in a single picture. Hansen's 'slippery slope' warning first appeared as a caption that accompanied a remarkable photograph of a river of water flowing across the Greenland ice sheet and pouring down a hole. The photo has an apocalyptic feel, and in the top right-hand corner a couple of researchers look on from a distance, giving an awesome sense of scale.

What is going on here? The presence of water is not entirely new. Small lakes have always formed on the surface of Greenland ice in the summer sun. And sometimes those lakes empty down flaws in the ice – whether crevasses or vertical shafts, which are known to glaciologists as moulins. But what is new is the discovery that as the surface warms, more and more water is pouring into the interior of the ice sheet. Waterfalls as much as 3 kilometres high are taking surface water to the very base of the ice, where it meets the bedrock. 'The summer of 2005 broke all records for melting in Greenland,' says Hansen. And such melting threatens to destabilize large parts of the ice sheet on timescales measured in years or decades, not millennia.

Jason Box of Ohio State University is a younger researcher who knows more about this than most. Every year, he visits Swiss Camp, a research station set up in 1990 on Greenland ice. The name was chosen by the

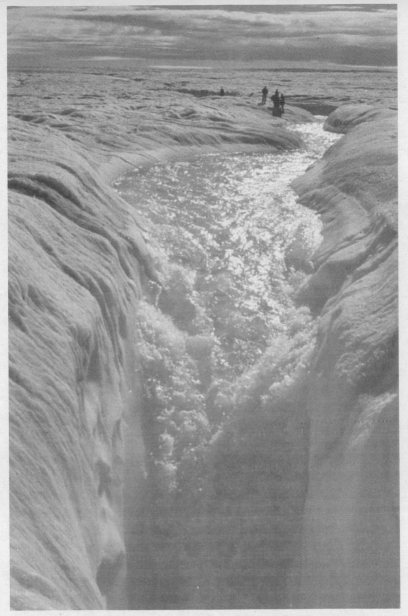

'We used to think it would take 10,000 years for melting to penetrate down to the bottom of the ice sheet. But if the water goes down a crack, it doesn't take 10,000 years, it takes ten seconds.'

camp's founder, Konrad Steffen from Zurich, so that he felt more at home. The station was originally sited on the equilibrium line, the point where the amount of ice melting in summer is exactly matched by winter accumulation of new snow. But the equilibrium line has since moved many kilometres north, as ever larger chunks of Greenland find themselves in the zone of predominant melting. These days, Box goes boating in an area close to Swiss Camp dubbed the 'Greenland Lake District'. 'Some of these lakes are six kilometres across and have lasted for a decade or more now,' he said. 'You wouldn't think it was Greenland at all.'

The lakes are more than just symptoms of melting. They are also reservoirs for the destruction of the ice sheet. 'These lakes keep growing and growing until they find a crevasse, into which they drain. Down there are extensive river systems, beneath the ice and the hard rock, that eventually emerge at the glacier snout. There may be great lakes too.'

Another regular visitor to Swiss Camp is glaciologist Jay Zwally, one of Hansen's colleagues at NASA. He made the alarming discovery that during warm years the kilometre-thick ice sheet lifts off the bedrock and floats on the water – rising half a metre or more at times. And it floats towards the ocean. Ice sheets are never entirely still, of course. But Swiss Camp is already 2 kilometres west of where it started. And Zwally found that in summer, when it is warmer at the surface and there is more water pouring down the crevasses, the velocity of the ice sheet's flow increases. Acceleration starts a few days after the melting begins at the surface. It stops when the melting ceases in the autumn.

This discovery is a revelation, admit glaciologists.

'These flows completely change our understanding of the dynamics of ice sheet destruction,' says Richard Alley from Penn State University. 'We used to think that it would take 10,000 years for melting at the surface to penetrate down to the bottom of the ice sheet. But if you make a lake on the surface and a crack opens and the water goes down the crack, it doesn't take 10,000 years, it takes ten seconds. That huge lag time is completely eliminated.'

Alley has a good analogy. 'The way water gets down to the base of glaciers is rather like the way magma gets up to the surface in volcanoes – through cracks. Cracks change everything. Once a crack is created and filled, the flow enlarges it and the results can be explosive. Like volcanic eruptions. Or the disintegration of ice sheets.' The lakes on the surface of Greenland are, he says, the equivalent of the pots of magma beneath volcanoes. 'More melting will mean more lakes in more places, more water pouring down crevasses and more disintegration of the ice.' No wonder, in a paper in *Science*, Zwally called the phenomenon 'a mechanism for rapid, large-scale, dynamic responses of ice sheets to climate warming'.

Could such processes be close to triggering a runaway destruction of the Greenland ice sheet? It is hard to be sure, but Greenland does have past form, says David Bromwich, Box's colleague at Ohio State. There is good evidence that the ice sheet lost volume around 120,000 years ago, during the warm era between the last ice age and the previous one. 'Temperatures then were very similar to those today,' he says. 'But the Greenland ice sheet was less than half its present size.' He believes that the Greenland ice sheet is a relic of the last ice age whose time may finally have run out. 'It looks susceptible, and with the drastic warming we have seen since the 1980s, the chances must be that it is going to melt, and that water will go to the bottom of the ice sheet and lubricate ice flows.'

Greenland melting seems to have set in around 1979, and has been accelerating ever since. The interior, above the rising equilibrium line, may still be accumulating snow. But the loss of ice round the edges has more than doubled in the last decade. The NASA team believe that the raging flows of meltwater may be responsible for more than half of the ice loss. In early 2006, they reported the results of a detailed satellite radar study of the ice sheet showing that it was losing 220 cubic kilometres more ice every year than it accumulated through snowfall. That was double the estimated figure for a decade before. And all this gives real substance to the evidence accumulating from Greenland's glaciers, the ice sheet's outlets to the ocean.

Swiss Camp is in the upper catchment of a glacier known as Jakobshavn Isbrae. It is Greenland's largest, flowing west from the heart of the ice sheet for 700 kilometres into Baffin Bay. It drains 7 per cent of Greenland. Jakobshavn has for some decades been the world's most prolific producer of icebergs. From Baffin Bay they journey south down Davis Strait, past Cape Farewell, the southern tip of Greenland, and out into the Atlantic shipping lanes. Jakobshavn was the likely source of the most famous iceberg of all – the one that sank the *Titanic* in 1912. But it has been in overdrive since 1997, after suddenly doubling the speed of its flow to the sea. It is now also the world's fastest moving glacier, at 12 kilometres a year.

Jason Box has installed a camera overlooking the

glacier to keep track. It takes stereo images every four hours throughout the year. As well as flowing ever faster towards the sea, he says, the glacier is becoming thinner and in 2003 a tongue of ice 15 kilometres long that used to extend from its snout into the ocean broke off. 'What is most surprising is how quickly this massive volume of ice can respond to warming,' says Box. There seems to be a direct correlation between air temperatures in any one year and the discharge of water from glaciers into the ocean. Long time lags, once thought to be the essence of glaciers, are vanishing. Jakobshavn, he estimates, could be shedding 50 cubic kilometres a year, an amount of water close to the flow of the world's longest river, the Nile. Half of that volume is water flowing out to sea from beneath the glacier, and half is calving glaciers.

Other Greenland glaciers are getting up speed, too. The Kangerdlugssuaq glacier in eastern Greenland, which drains 4 per cent of the ice sheet, was flowing into the sea three times faster in the summer of 2005 than when last measured in 1988. At an inch a minute, its movement was visible with the naked eye. Meanwhile its snout has retreated by 5 kilometres in four years. This familiar pattern of faster flow, thinning ice and rapid retreat of the ice front has also shown at the nearby Helheim glacier, where Ian Howat of the University of California in Santa Cruz concludes that 'thinning has reached a critical point and begun drastically changing the glacier's dynamics.'

Most of these great streams of ice are exiting into the ocean beneath the water line, in submarine valleys, via giant shelves of floating ice that buttress them. But as the oceans warm, these ice shelves are themselves thinning. It is, says Hansen, a recipe for rapid acceleration of ice loss from across Greenland.

* * *

The picture, then, is of great flows of ice draining out of Greenland, lubricated by growing volumes of melting water draining from the surface to the base of the ice sheet and uncorked by melting ice shelves at the coast. All this is new and frightening. 'The whole Greenland hydrological system has become more vigorous, more hyperactive,' says Box. 'It is a very non-linear response to global warming, with exponential increases in the loss of ice. I've seen it with my own eyes. Even five years ago we didn't know about this.' Alley agrees: 'Greenland is a different animal from what we thought it was just a few years ago. We are still thinking it might take centuries to go, but if things go wrong it could just be decades. Everything points in one direction, and it's not a good direction.'

'Building an ice sheet takes a long time – many thousands of years,' says Hansen. 'It is a slow, dry process inherently limited by the snowfall rate. But destroying it, we now realize, is a wet process, spurred by positive feedbacks, and once under way it can be explosively rapid.'

8

THE SHELF

DOWN SOUTH, SHATTERING ICE UNCORKS THE ANTARCTIC

Over three days in March 2002, there occurred one of the most dramatic alterations to the map of Antarctica since the end of the last ice age. It happened on the shoreline of the Antarctic peninsula – a tail of mountains 2,000 kilometres long and 2 kilometres high pointing from the southern continent towards the tip of South America. A shelf of floating ice larger than Luxembourg and some 200 metres thick that had been attached to the peninsula for thousands of years shattered like a huge pane of glass. It broke into thousands of pieces, each of them huge icebergs that floated away into the South Atlantic.

There were no casualties, except the esteem of Antarctic scientists who believed that, after a century of studying the continent's ice, they knew how it behaved. Their subsequent papers revealed their shock. 'The catastrophic break up of the Larsen B ice shelf is remarkable because it reveals an iceberg production mechanism far different from those previously thought to determine the extent of

Antarctic ice shelves,' wrote Christina Hulbe, a glaciologist from Portland State University in Oregon. Rather than the normal 'infrequent shedding of icebergs at the seaward ice front', this time 'innumerable icebergs were created simultaneously through the entire breadth of the shelf.'

The demise of the Larsen B ice shelf was not in itself a surprise. Both the air and water around the Antarctic peninsula had been warming since the 1960s. It had become one of the hotspots of global warming. Warm currents had been gradually eating away at the underside of the floating shelf, while warmer air produced pools of melting water on the surface. It was obvious that the sheet was under strain. Some cracks formed across the surface in 1994; a chunk round the edge of the shelf broke off in 1998. But nothing had prepared glaciologists for what was about to happen. During January 2002, the height of the southern summer, temperatures hit a new high and the heavy winter snow on the shelf's surface began to melt. By the end of the month, satellite pictures showed dark streaks across the shelf. Some were ponds, but others were crevasses that had filled with water.

Water is denser than ice. So, once inside the crevasses, it created pressure that levered them ever wider. There were, in effect, thousands of mechanical wedges pushing ever deeper into the ice shelf. Then, in three climactic days at the start of March, the entire structure gave way. Some 500 billion tonnes of ice burst into the ocean. In many ways, says Richard Alley at Penn State, what happened at Larsen B mirrored the processes under way in Greenland. 'Water-filled cracks more than a few tens of metres deep can be opened easily by the pressure of water. Ponding of water at the ice surface increases the water pressure wedging cracks open.' In their enthusiasm to study ice, glaciologists had forgotten about water.

Larsen B was one of a series of floating shelves formed by ice draining from the mountains of the Antarctic peninsula. The shelves are the floating front edges of glaciers, and where they meet the ocean, icebergs regularly break off. In recent years Larsen B had been moving forward by about a metre a day. Despite this constant movement the ice shelf itself, at more than 200 metres thick, was a surprisingly permanent structure. After its collapse, investigations of the diatoms in the sediment beneath the former shelf suggested that Larsen B had been there for the entire 12,000 years since the end of the last ice age.

Larsen B wasn't alone, and nor has it been alone in disappearing. In all, 13,000 square kilometres of ice shelves have been lost from around the Antarctic peninsula in the past half-century. The other side of an ice-covered headland called Seal Nunatak, the Larsen A ice shelf broke up in a storm in 1995. And before that the Wordie shelf, on the west side of the peninsula, disappeared between 1974 and 1996, triggering a dramatic thinning of the glaciers that fed it. But both were much smaller than Larsen B, and neither disappeared in the catastrophic manner of Larsen B.

'Really we don't think there is much doubt that the collapse of the Larsen B shelf was caused by man-made climate change,' says John King, chief climatologist at the British Antarctic Survey (BAS). From their base at Rothera on Adelaide Island, BAS researchers have mapped in detail how a pulse of warmer air temperatures has pushed south across the peninsula over the past fifty years, lengthening the summer melt season, sending glaciers into retreat and destabilizing ice shelves as it goes. Even so, melting is of itself a slow process. What destroyed the Larsen B shelf was not so much melting as the dynamic mechanical forces of water that the melting unleashed.

Armed with the evidence of Larsen B, glaciologists are reassessing the stability of dozens of peninsula ice shelves – starting with Larsen C immediately to the south, which is thinning and widely expected to be the next to go. Eventually, they say, the warming will reach the Ronne ice shelf, a slab of ice the size of Spain situated at the south of the peninsula. And on the other side of the continent is the Ross ice shelf, the continent's largest. It too now seems to be vulnerable, says Hulbe.

The loss of ice shelves does not contribute to sea level rise, because their ice is already floating. Their loss no more raises sea levels than an ice cube melting in a drink causes the glass to spill over. But their disappearance does change what happens inland. Ice shelves buttress the glaciers that feed them. After Larsen B disappeared, it was 'as if the cork had been removed from a bottle of champagne', says French glaciologist Eric Rignot, who works at NASA's Jet Propulsion Laboratory in California. The glaciers that once discharged their ice onto the Larsen B shelf are now flowing into the sea eight times faster than they did before the shelf collapsed. Similar acceleration has happened after other ice sheet collapses. And that faster discharge of ice from land into the ocean is raising sea levels.

9

THE MERCER LEGACY

AN ACHILLES' HEEL AT THE BOTTOM OF THE WORLD

John Mercer was an English eccentric and, frankly, somewhat disreputable. The charge sheet against him is long. He had a penchant for doing his field work in the nude and was once convicted for jogging naked near his campus at Ohio State University in Columbus. He regularly fell out with colleagues, and once abandoned two graduate students, including his acolyte and eventual successor Lonnie Thompson, high in the Andes after the money ran out on a field trip. Thompson thought it was something he had said, until he realized that 'those kind of things kept happening to John; he was the same with everyone.'

Mercer, who died of a brain tumour in 1987, is now a largely forgotten figure outside the glaciological community. But within it he is regarded by many, not least by Thompson himself, as a genius. He is credited with inventing the term 'greenhouse effect' during a symposium at Ohio in the early 1960s. In the late 1940s, he set off alone to explore the ice in distant Patagonia, mapping much of the area, and came to realize that tropical glaciers might hold clues to the history of the world's climate. But probably his greatest legacy is in Antarctica, where back in the 1960s he made a prophetic warning that may one day ensure the revival of his memory.

At a time when everyone else saw Antarctic ice as just about the most dependable glacial feature on the planet, Mercer began to argue that much of it may have entirely disintegrated during the last interglacial era, about 125,000 years ago. And, though it took him a decade to get his warning into print, he feared that it might be about to happen again. In 1978, in *Nature*, he published a paper declaring: 'I contend that a major disaster – a rapid deglaciation of West Antarctica – may be in progress . . . within about 50 years.'

The two ice sheets covering Antarctica are vast. The smaller of them, the West Antarctic ice sheet, covers around 4 million square kilometres. It is vulnerable because, unlike its larger eastern neighbour, it does not sit on dry land. Instead, like a giant ship that has foundered in the shallows, it is perched precariously on an archipelago of largely submerged mountains. Ocean currents are swirling beneath its giant ice shelves. Sea temperatures today are close to freezing, but the risk is that as they rise, melting will loosen the ice sheet's moorings.

The heart of the ice sheet has some protection from the ocean. On two sides it is buttressed by mountains and on the other two sides it is held in place by the Ronne and Ross ice shelves. But Mercer warned that if the ice shelves gave way, then the entire sheet could lift off and float away. 'Climate warming above a critical level would remove all ice shelves, and consequently all ice grounded below sea level, resulting in the deglaciation of most of West Antarctica.' Once under way, the disintegration would 'probably be rapid, perhaps catastrophically so'. Most of the ice sheet would be gone within a century. He reckoned that a warming of 5 degrees C would be enough to set the process in train. Parts of the continent have already experienced more than 2 degrees of warming. 'One warning sign that a dangerous warming is beginning will be the break-up of ice shelves in the Antarctic peninsula,' he said. Like Larsen B.

Another old acolyte of Mercer is Terry Hughes of the University of Maine. Back in 1981, he suggested that the West Antarctic ice sheet may have another vulnerability – a 'weak underbelly' in Pine Island Bay, a large inlet on the Amundsen Sea, west of the Antarctic peninsula. This is one of the most remote places on Earth. Head north from here and you don't hit land until Alaska. For the few sailors who have penetrated the bay, these are dangerous waters – deep with unusually tall icebergs breaking off the glaciers and being blown fast across the bay by fierce winds. There is a constant danger of getting trapped by the ice if the wind changes. Onshore, the terrain is rugged, and its weather is violent, with intense snow storms steered inland by the Antarctic peninsula. Even Antarctic researchers have given Pine Island Bay a wide berth. There are no bases here.

Hughes's 'weak underbelly' theory was, like Mercer's warnings a decade before, roundly ignored at the time. When I first wrote about it a few years later, other glaciologists warned me off, suggesting that it had been discredited. But today just mentioning Pine Island Bay is enough to send a shudder through the hearts of many glaciologists. Hughes, they now believe, was right on the button.

The bay is the outlet for two of Antarctica's top five glaciers: the Pine Island and Thwaites glaciers. Together, they drain about 40 per cent of the West Antarctic ice sheet. They were already the fastest-flowing glaciers in Antarctica when, in the 1990s, Pine Island began to accelerate sharply and Thwaites, while travelling at the same speed, doubled its flow by becoming twice as wide. The glaciers were responding to a rapid melting of the shelves of ice that stick out from the glaciers into the bay. The melting was in turn caused by warmer sea waters circling into the bay.

This discovery has, once again, turned conventional thinking about the dynamics of ice on its head. The old view holds that events on the coast, where a glacier meets the ocean, have little bearing on what happens inland. But at Pine Island Bay the impacts of coastal melting are swiftly being felt throughout the glaciers' network of tributaries across the ice sheet. In the past decade, the flow of the two glaciers has speeded up for 200 kilometres from the coast. NASA glaciologist Eric Rignot reported in 2004 that the two glaciers are dumping 250 cubic kilometres of ice a year into Pine Island Bay. This dwarfs even the very high rates of snowfall, which add about 160 cubic kilometres a year. The net 'mass loss' of ice from the Pine Island Bay catchment has tripled in a decade.

Since Rignot's paper was published, the news has become even more grim. Studies of the Pine Island glacier show that its ice shelf is thinning fast. As it thins, ever more warm sea water penetrates beneath the glacier. The 'grounding line', the farthest point downstream where the ice makes contact with solid rock, has been retreating by 2 kilometres a year. Once under way, the retreat of the grounding line is 'theoretically self-perpetuating and irreversible, regardless of climate forcing', says Rignot. The glacier is primed for runaway destruction.

In 2005, British and Texan researchers flew 75,000 kilometres on more than a hundred flights back and forth across Pine Island and Thwaites glaciers, using ice-penetrating radar to map the rocks beneath an area of ice the size of France and sometimes 3 kilometres high. They found that inland along its major tributaries the Pine Island glacier sits on great lakes of meltwater. There seemed remarkably little to hold back its flow. Meanwhile, the Thwaites glacier, which is a stream of ice flowing through a wider area of ice sheet, could be about to widen again, says David Vaughan of the British Antarctic Survey, who masterminded the survey.

If the Pine Island and Thwaites glaciers are on a one-way trip to disaster, the implications are global. Together they drain an area containing enough ice to raise sea levels worldwide by 1–2 metres. In all probability, the Pine Island and Thwaites glaciers are already the biggest causes of sea-level rise worldwide. Hughes believes their collapse could destabilize the entire West Antarctic ice sheet, and potentially parts of the East Antarctic ice sheet too. 'The well-documented changes happening just within the past decade are a numbing prospect,' he told me. 'And we have only hints about exactly what is going on.'

Days after Vaughan presented the first findings of the survey of the two glaciers to a conference in the US, I met Richard Alley. He had been in the audience and had been astounded by the findings. 'Thwaites just taps right into the vast reservoirs of ice in the middle of the ice sheet, and the question is whether it will drag them along with it. I think Thwaites could be absolutely critical,' he told me. 'If you pull the plug, the ice goes faster and there is thinning. The only question is whether the plug can reform a bit further back, or whether the ocean will deliver enough heat for it to just blowtorch its way to the centre. I don't think we know the answer to that yet.' There was, he said, 'a possibility that the West Antarctic ice sheet could collapse and raise sea levels by 6 metres in the next century'.

The East Antarctic ice sheet is the biggest, highest slab of ice on the planet. In the unlikely event that it all melted, sea levels would rise by 50 metres or more. But it has been in place for some 20 million years. And in 2005, Curt Davis of the University of Missouri reported, after analysing satellite data, that extra snowfall linked to global warming is raising the height of the ice by almost 2 centimetres a year – enough to shave a tenth off current rates of sea level rise. All seemed well, then, with the East Antarctic ice sheet.

But there was a slight problem. His study could cover only the flat interior. Satellite instruments are not yet good enough to establish altitude trends near the coasts where there is sloping terrain. A footnote to his paper mentions that 'mass loss in areas near the coast could be even greater than the gains in the interior.' Unfortunately, other researchers say that is precisely what may be happening.

Exhibit A in this case is the Totten glacier. It is a biggie – 100 kilometres wide at its mouth, where it calves icebergs into the Indian Ocean. Totten's network of tributary glaciers drains an area containing more ice than the whole of the West Antarctic. And since the early 1990s, says Andy Shepherd of the Scott Polar Research Institute in Cambridge, that catchment has been losing enough ice to lower its height by more than 10 metres a year. Another giant of the East Antarctic ice sheet, the Cook glacier, is doing the same.

The last bastion of glacial stability suddenly looks much less safe. And Shepherd points out that Totten and Cook have something else in common with Pine Island, Thwaites and the other troublesome glaciers on the west side – something that suggests there could be worse ahead. Both Totten and Cook have grounding lines in the ocean that are below sea level – more than 300 metres below in the case of Totten. That is, the glacier's contact with the continental land mass is so tenacious that the glacier slides 300 metres under water before the ice gives up contact with the rock and begins to float. That sounds good news: evidence of stability. The problem is that warmer waters appear to be loosening that contact. Should the grounding line start to retreat, we can expect the glacier to begin the familiar process of thinning and accelerating. It would, in other words, remove the cork from a very large bottle.

Nobody is yet saying that the East Antarctic ice sheet is vulnerable in the way that the western sheet appears to be. It remains very big and, by and large, extremely stable. But, as Rignot puts it, 'it is not immune.' And every new discovery seems to raise the stakes for the fate of the Antarctic ice. As recently as 2001, the IPCC reported a scientific consensus that it was 'very unlikely' that Antarctica would produce any significant rise in sea levels during the twenty-first century. Few glaciologists are repeating that claim with any confidence now. Most would agree with Alley that 'major changes are taking place in the Antarctic, on much shorter time scales than previously anticipated.'

The British Antarctic Survey now employs a mathematician full time to apply chaos and complexity theory to the fate of the continent's ice – a topic once considered of utmost simplicity. They are using the language of fractals, phase space and bifurcations to work out what might happen next to the ice sheets of the Antarctic peninsula and the glaciers of Pine Island Bay. They have seen Larsen B shatter in three days; they believe they are seeing the soft underbelly of the West Antarctic ice sheet ripped open before their eyes. What next?

10

RISING TIDES

SAYING TOODLE-OO TO TUVALU

The Carteret Islands are to be abandoned. Life is simply too hard for their 2,000 inhabitants, huddled on a clutch of low-lying coral islands in the South Pacific, with a total surface area of just 60 hectares, and rising sea levels threatening to wash them away. The islands, named after an eighteenth-century English explorer of the South Seas, Philip Carteret, have been under nearly constant erosion since the 1960s and the current guess is that they will be wholly submerged by 2015. Already the fields have been invaded by salt water and the crops of breadfruit have died. The people, refugees in their own land, depend on handouts.

In 2001, when strong winds and rough seas cut off the atoll and prevented them from going to sea to catch fish, many inhabitants resorted to eating seaweed. One resident on the island of Han pleaded by radio for rescue. 'Erosion is occurring from both sides and the island is getting narrow. In Piul, many families are leaving. Huene island is divided in half, and four families only are left. On Iolasa, Iosela and Iangain, when high seas occur, they stand below sea level. This is very frightening.' Indeed. In November 2005, the central government in Papua New Guinea, of which the Carteret Islands form a part, agreed that the islanders should all be moved to Bougainville, four hours' boat ride to the south-west. Ten families at a time will journey over the next few years, relinquishing their ancestral homes for ever.

For most people round the world, stories of sea level rise remain a matter of academic interest, if that. The risks seem remote. But for the inhabitants of low-lying islands like the Carterets, it is happening now and devastating their lives.

The ten thousand citizens of the nine inhabited South Pacific islands of Tuvalu are also abandoning ship. High tides regularly wash across the main street in the capital Funafuti; sea salt is poisoning their fields and killing their coconuts. Tuvalu is a fully fledged nation state. Formerly the British Ellice Islands, it won independence in 1975. But just thirty years on, it seems destined to be the first modern nation state to disappear beneath the waves. A twenty-first-century Atlantis. 'In fifty years, Tuvalu will not exist,' says the prime minister. His government has signed a deal with New Zealand, 3,000 kilometres away, that will allow the entire population to move there in the coming years, as rising tides and worsening storms destroy their homes.

One by one, the island nations of the South Pacific are drowning. Kiribati, formerly the British Gilbert Islands, won its independence on the same day as Tuvalu. It too is going under. Two uninhabited islands disappeared in 1999. The following year, Nakibae Teuatabo, a resident of Kiribati, explained their plight to me at a climate change conference in Bonn, where he had been sent to plead for his country's survival. 'Eight or nine house plots in the village that my family belongs to have been eroded. I remember there was a coconut tree outside the government quarters where I lived. Then the beach all around it was eroded, and eventually the tree disappeared. It might not sound a lot to you. But the atolls are just rings of narrow islands surrounding a lagoon, with the open ocean on the outside. Some of the islands are only a few metres wide in places. Imagine standing on one of these islands with waves pounding on one side and the lagoon on the other. It's frightening.'

Villagers on some outer islands have already moved away as the sea gobbles up their land, he said. 'Apart from causing coastal erosion, higher tides are pushing salt water into the fields and into underground freshwater reservoirs. In some places, it just bubbles up from the ground.' It was a heart-rending story. Good for journalists, but of no interest to most government negotiators at the conference. Such nations, it seems, are expendable.

The world's sea levels have been largely stable for the past 5,000 years, since the main phase of melting of ice sheets after the end of the last ice age abated. Some residual ice loss continued at about a tenth of a millimetre a year. But around 1900, the pace of sea-level rise began to increase. At first, it was most likely due to the melting of glaciers following the end of the little ice age in the mid-nineteenth century. That should have diminished through the twentieth century. But instead sea-level rise has accelerated in the past fifty years to around 2 millimetres a year. About half of this is probably due to the expansion of water in the ocean as the water becomes warmer – a process known to physicists as thermal expansion. And the rest is probably due to the resumed melting of the world's glaciers and ice caps, doubtless largely a result of man-made climate change.

The first signs of a further acceleration emerged in the early 1990s, when satellite data suggests a sudden jump to a 3-millimetres-a-year rise. Since 1999, it may have risen again to 3.7 millimetres. At the time of writing, these figures had failed to gain much attention because glaciologists remained worried about their reliability. Some think there may be a problem calibrating the satellite data; others that it may simply be a natural fluctuation. But, with every year that passes, more researchers are concluding that we may be seeing the first effects of the dramatic changes apparently under way on the ice sheets of Greenland and Antarctica.

The planet has a history of startling sea-level rise that cannot be explained by the conventional models used by glaciologists to predict future change. Consider events towards the end of the last ice age. Around 20,000 years ago, at what glaciologists call the 'glacial maximum', there was so much water tied up in ice on land that sea levels were around 120 metres lower than today. Then a thaw began. Sea levels initially rose by around 10 millimetres a year. That is four or five times faster than today, but within the traditional expectations of glaci-ologists. Then something happened. About 14,500 years ago, the tides went haywire. Within 400 years, sea levels rose by 20 metres. That's an average rate of a metre every twenty years.

It is worth thinking about those numbers. If such a rise

happened today, you could say toodle-oo to Tuvalu by 2010; most of Bangladesh would be largely under water by 2020; millions of people on the Nile delta would be looking for new homes by 2025; London would need a new Thames Barrier immediately. New Orleans? Well, forget New Orleans, and Florida, and most of the rest of the US seaboard, too. Lagos, Karachi, Sydney, New York, Tokyo, Bangkok: you name your coastal megacity and it would be abandoned by mid-century. It sounds unbelievable, but we know the rise happened. The evidence is in tide marks on ancient cliffs and in the remains of coral that can only live close to sea level.

How could such a thing have happened? It required the transfer into the oceans of 16,000 cubic kilometres of ice every year throughout the 400-year period. That is a huge amount of ice. Glaciologists believe that the West Antarctic ice sheet, which was much larger then, was the most likely source. But wherever it came from, it could only have reached the oceans in such quantities and at such speed by some process other than melting alone. Such discharges required the physical collapse of ice sheets on a grand scale. That can have happened only if the ice sheets were lubricated at their base by great rivers of meltwater and destabilized at the coasts by the shattering of ice shelves.

Go back further. In the last interglacial period, about 120,000 years ago, evidence such as wave-cut notches along cliffs in the Bahamas show sea levels 6 metres higher than they are today. During a previous interglacial some 400,000 years ago, they might have been even higher. In neither were temperatures significantly higher than they are today. On the face of it, either the West Antarctic ice sheet or the Greenland ice sheets, or both, succumbed at temperatures close to our own. Within the coming century, we can expect that temperatures could rise by 2 or 3 degrees. That, says Hansen, would make them as high as they were 3 million years ago, before the era of ice ages started. What were sea levels then? About 25 metres higher than today, plus or minus 10 metres, he says.

A first guess would be that we will very soon have set the world on a course for reaching such levels again. The models of glaciologists suggest that, if that were to happen, it would take thousands of years. Hansen doesn't believe it. 'I'm a modeller, too, but I rate data higher than models,' he says. He sees the evidence of the start of runaway melting in Greenland and Antarctica emerging today and anticipates that 'sea levels might rise by a couple of metres this century, and several more the next century.'

Some see this as alarmist. Where, they say, is the evidence of big sea-level rises so far? Hansen says that so far much of the extra melting has been camouflaged by increased snowfall on the ice sheets. 'Because of this, sea level changes slowly at first, but as global warming gets larger, as summer melt extends higher up the ice sheet, and as buttressing ice shelves melt away, multiple positive feedbacks come into play, and the non-linear disintegration wins the competition, hands down.'

The world's ice sheets 'are a ticking time bomb', he says. There is no reason why the events of 14,000 years ago should not be repeated in the twenty-first century. 'The current planetary energy imbalance is now pouring energy into the Earth system at a rate sufficient to fuel rapid deglaciation.' His hunch is that an increasing amount of global warming will be harnessed to melting the ice sheets. That could slow the heating of the atmosphere, but at the expense of faster-rising sea levels. Within a few decades, vast armadas of icebergs could be breaking off the Greenland ice sheet, making shipping lanes impassable and cooling the ocean surfaces like the ice in a gin and tonic. Sea-level rise, he concludes, 'is *the* big global issue'. It will, he believes, transcend all others over the coming century.

It is easy to forget the plight of the people of the Carteret Islands and Tuvalu. Few of us could even find these places on the map. But as the tides rise ever higher, and as the precarious state of the big ice sheets becomes more apparent, we might want to heed those people's fate. It could be that of our own children.

PART THREE

RIDING THE CARBON CYCLE

11

IN THE JUNGLE

WOULD WE NOTICE IF THE AMAZON WENT UP IN SMOKE?

The Amazon rainforest is the largest living reservoir for carbon dioxide on the land surface of the Earth. Its trees contain some 70 billion tonnes of carbon, and its soils perhaps as much again. That is about twenty years of man-made emissions from burning fossil fuels. It is also an engine of the world's climate system, recycling both heat and moisture. More than half of the raindrops that fall on the forest canopy never reach the ground but instead evaporate back into the air to produce more rain downwind. The forest needs the rain, but the rain also needs the forest.

But as scientists get to understand the importance of the Amazon for maintaining climate, they are discovering too that it may itself be under threat from climate change. We are familiar enough with the damage done to the world's biggest and lushest jungle by farmers armed with chainsaws and firebrands. But, hard as they try, they can only destroy the rainforest slowly. Despite many decades of effort, most of this jungle the size of western Europe remains intact. Climate change, on the other hand, could overwhelm the forest in a few years.

Until recently, many ecologists have thought of the Amazon rainforest much as their glaciologist colleagues conceived the Greenland ice sheet: big and extremely stable. The Greenland ice maintained the climate that kept the ice securely frozen, while the Amazon rainforest maintained the rains that watered the forest. But just as the image of the stability of the Greenland ice sheet has taken a knock, so it is with the Amazon: some researchers believe that it is in reality a very dynamic place, and that the entire ecosystem might be close to a tipping point beyond which it will suffer runaway destruction in an orgy of fire and drought. Nobody is quite sure what would happen if the Amazon rainforest disappeared. It would certainly give an extra kick to climate change by releasing its store of carbon dioxide. It would most likely also diminish rainfall across South America. It might also change weather systems right across the northern hemisphere. If the Amazon burned, Europe could suffer too.

One man trying to find out how stable the Amazon rainforest might be is Dan Nepstad, a forest ecologist nominally attached to the Woods Hole Research Center in Massachusetts but based for more than two decades in the Amazon. He doesn't just watch the forest: he conducts large experiments within it. Starting in 2001, Nepstad has created a man-made drought on a small patch of jungle in the Tapajos National Forest outside the river port of Santarem. While much of the Amazon has rain virtually every day in most years, Tapajos is on the eastern fringe of the rainforest proper, where weather cycles can shut down the rains for months. The forest here is, to some extent, adapted to drought. But there are limits, and Nepstad has been trying to find out where they lie.

He has covered the 1-hectare plot with more than five thousand transparent plastic panels that let in the sunlight but divert the rain into wooden gutters that drain to canals and a moat. Meanwhile, he has erected gantries high above the forest canopy, linked by catwalks, so that he can study the trees in detail as the artificial drought progresses. The work was all done by hand to avoid damaging the dense forest, and the scientists soon found they were not alone. The canals became 'congregating places for every kind of snake you can imagine', says Nepstad. Caimans and jaguars cruised by, just, it seemed, to find out what was going on.

The results were worth the effort. The forest, it turns out, can handle two years of drought without great trouble. The trees extend their roots deeper to find water and slow their metabolism to conserve moisture. But after that, the trees start dying. Beginning with the tallest, they come crashing down, releasing carbon to the air as they rot and exposing the forest floor to the drying sun. By the third year, the plot was storing only 2 tonnes of carbon, whereas a neighbouring control plot where the rain continued to fall held 7 tonnes. 'The lock was broken' on a corner of one of the planet's great carbon stores. Ecologist Deborah Clark of the University of Missouri, discussing the findings in *Science*, said the study showed that the Amazon is 'headed in a terrible direction. Given that droughts in the Amazon are projected to increase in several climate models, the implications for these rich ecosystems are grim.'

Everywhere in the jungle, drought is followed by fire. So back in the forest in early 2005, Nepstad started an even more audacious experiment. He set fire to another stretch of forest with kerosene torches. 'We want to know if recurring fire may threaten the very existence of the forest,' he says. The initial findings were not good. The fires crept low along the forest floor. There were no huge flames bursting through the canopy. The fires were largely invisible to the satellites that keep a constant watch overhead. But many trees died nonetheless, as their bark scorched and the flow of sap from their roots was staunched.

Nepstad's experiments are part of a huge international effort to monitor the health of the Amazon called the Large-scale Biosphere-Atmosphere Experiment in Amazonia. From planes and satellites and gantries above the jungle, researchers from a dozen countries have been sniffing the forest's breath and assessing its survival strategies. The current estimate is that fires in the forest are releasing some 200 million tonnes of carbon a year, far more than is absorbed by the growing forest. The Amazon has become a significant source of carbon dioxide, adding to global warming. More worryingly still, the experiment is discovering a generally drying trend across the Amazon that leaves it ever more vulnerable to fires. Nepstad's work suggests that beyond a certain point, the forest will be unable to recover from the fires, and will begin a process of rapid drying that he calls the 'savannization' of the Amazon.

And even as he concluded his drought experiment, nature seemed to replicate it. The rains failed across the Amazon through 2005, killing trees, triggering fires and reducing the ability of the forest to recycle moisture – thus increasing the risk of future drought. Nepstad's experiments suggest that the rainforest is close to the edge – to permanent drought, rampant burning, savannization or worse. In the final weeks of 2005 the rains returned. The forest may recover this time. But if future climate change causes significant drying that lasts from one year to the next, then feedbacks in the forest could realize Nepstad's worst fears.

The 2005 drought was caused by extremely warm temperatures in the tropical Atlantic – the same high temperatures that are believed to have caused the record-breaking hurricane season that year. The rising air that triggered the hurricanes eventually came back to earth, suppressing the formation of the storm clouds over the Amazon. And, as I discovered at Britain's Hadley Centre for Climate Prediction, that is precisely what climate modellers are forecasting for future decades.

The Hadley Centre's global climate model is generally regarded as one of the world's top three. And it predicts that business-as-usual increase in worldwide industrial carbon dioxide emissions in the coming decades will generate warmer sea temperatures that will subject the Amazon to repeated droughts, in turn creating 'threshold conditions' beyond which fires will take hold. The Amazon rainforest will be dead before the end of the century. Not partly dead, or sick, but dead and gone. 'The region will be able to support only shrubs or grass at most,' said a study published by the Hadley Centre in 2005.

Not all models agree about that. But the Hadley model is the best at reproducing the current relationship between ocean temperatures and Amazon rainfall, so it has a good chance of being right about the future, too. Nepstad himself predicts a 'mega-fire event' spreading across the region. As the forests in the more vulnerable east of the rainforest die, they will cease to recycle moisture back into the atmosphere to provide rainfall downwind. A wave of aridity will travel west, creating the conditions for fire to rip through the heart of the jungle.

With the trees gone, the thin soils will bake in the sun. Rainforest could literally turn to desert. The Hadley forecast includes a graph of the Amazon forest's future carbon. It predicts that the store of a steady 70 billion tonnes over the past half-century will shrink to 40 billion tonnes by 2050 and 15 billion tonnes by the end of the century. That, it calculates, would be enough to increase the expected rate of warming worldwide by at least 50 per cent.

The Amazon rainforest does not just create rain for itself. By one calculation, around 6 trillion tonnes of water evaporate from the jungle each year, and around half of that moisture is exported from the Amazon basin. Some travels into the Andes, where it creates clouds that swathe some mountains so tightly that their surfaces have never been seen by satellite. Some blows south to water the pampas grasslands of Argentina, some east towards South Africa and some north towards the Caribbean. The forest is a vital rain-making machine for most of South America. As much as half of Argentina's rain may begin as evaporation from the Amazon.

But the benefits of the great Amazon hydrological engine extend much further and are not restricted to rainfall. The moisture also carries energy. A lot of solar energy is used to evaporate moisture from the forest canopy. It is one reason why forests stay cooler than the surrounding plains. And when the moisture eventually condenses to form new clouds, that energy is released back into the air. It powers weather systems and high-level winds known as jets far into the northern hemisphere. Nicola Gedney and Paul Valdes, two young climate researchers at the University of Reading, have calculated that this process ultimately drives winter storms across the North Atlantic towards Europe. 'There is a relatively direct physical link between changes over the deforested region and the climate of the North Atlantic and western Europe,' they say. If the rainforest expires, the hydrological engine is likely to falter too, and the link will be cut. Dessication in the Amazon could be followed by the dessication of Europe.

12

WILD FIRES OF BORNEO

CLIMATE IN THE MIRE FROM BURNING SWAMP

The smoke billowed through Palangkaraya. One of the largest towns in Borneo was engulfed in acrid smog more dense even than one of London's old pea-soupers. It blotted out so much sun that there was a chill in the air of a town more used to the dense humid heat of the rainforest that encircled it. This was late 1997 and the rainforest was burning. The most intense El Niño event on record in the Pacific Ocean had stifled the storm clouds that normally bring rain to Borneo and the other islands of Indonesia. Landowners took advantage of the dry weather to burn the forest and clear new plantations for palm oil and other profitable crops. The fires got out of control and the result was one of the greatest forest fires in human history. The smoke spread for thousands of kilometres. Unsighted planes crashed from the skies and ships collided at sea; in neighbouring Malaysia and distant Thailand, hospitals filled with victims of lung diseases and schools were closed. The fires became a global news story. The cost of the fires in lost business alone was put at tens of billions of dollars.

But it was not just the trees that were burning. The densest smoke was in central Borneo around Palangkaraya, where the fires had burrowed down, drying and burning a vast peat bog that underlies the forest. The peat, 20 metres deep in many places, is the accumulated remains of wood and forest vegetation that has fallen into the swamps here for tens of thousands of years. Even when the rains returned, the peat continued to smoulder for months on end. When the smoke finally cleared, most of the swamp forest was burnt and black, and skeletons of trees poked from charred ground that had in places shrunk by a metre or more.

The burning of the Borneo swamp was part of a wider global assault on tropical rainforests – for timber and for land. But there were aggravating factors here. Until recently the swamps were empty of humans. Local tribes and modern farmers alike had found them inhospitable and inaccessible. But in the early 1990s, Indonesia's President Suharto decreed that an area of the central Borneo swamp forest half the size of Wales should be drained and transformed into giant rice paddy to make his country self-sufficient in its staple foodstuff. Some 4,000 kilometres of canals were dug to drain the swamp. Some 60,000 migrant farmers were brought in from other islands to cultivate the rice. The soils proved infertile and virtually no rice was ever grown. The megaproject was abandoned. But its legacy lingers, as the canals continue to drain the swamps and the desiccated peat burns every dry season. Especially during El Niños.

This is no mere local environmental disaster. Jack Rieley, a British ecologist with a love of peat bogs who has adopted the central Borneo swamps for his field studies, says the disaster is of global importance. At least half of the world's tropical peat swamps are on the Indonesian islands of Borneo, Sumatra and West Papua. And the largest, oldest and deepest of them are in central Borneo, where they cover an area a quarter the size of England and harbour large populations of sun bears and clouded leopards, as well as the world's largest surviving populations of orang-utans. They also contain vast amounts of carbon – an estimated 50 billion tonnes of the stuff. That is almost as much as the entire Amazon rainforest, which is more than ten times larger. A single hectare of Borneo peat swamp contains 2,000 tonnes of carbon.

Tropical peat swamps are a major feature of the planet's carbon cycle. They are important amplifiers of climate change, capable of helping push the world into and out of ice ages by capturing and releasing carbon from the air. For thousands of years now, they have been keeping the world cooler than it might otherwise be, by soaking up carbon from the air. To release that carbon now, as the world struggles to counter global warming, would be folly indeed. But that is what is happening. Rieley estimates that during the El Niño event of 1997 and 1998, as Palangkaraya disappeared for months beneath smoke, the smouldering swamps lost more than a half-metre layer of peat, and released somewhere between 800 million and 2.6 billion tonnes of carbon into the atmosphere. That was equivalent to up to 40 per cent of all emissions from burning fossil fuels round the world that year.

At first there was some scepticism about Rieley's figures. Few other researchers had been to Borneo to see what had been going on. But in 2004, US government researchers published a detailed analysis of gas measurements made round the world. It showed that roughly 2 billion tonnes more carbon than usual entered the atmosphere during 1998 – and two-thirds of that excess came from South East Asia. The Borneo fires must have contributed most of that, and the burning peat was almost certainly the major component. 'We are witnessing the death of one of the last wilderness ecosystems on the planet, and it is turning up the heat on climate change as it goes,' says Rieley. 'What was once one of the planet's most important carbon sinks is giving up that carbon. The whole world is feeling the effect.'

Every year the farmers continue burning forest in Borneo to clear land for farming. And whenever the weather is dry, those fires spread out through the jungle and down into the peat. During 2002 and 2003, satellite images suggest that 5 million hectares of the swamp forests were in flames at one point. These were also the first back-to-back years when the net additions to the atmosphere's burden of carbon exceeded 4 billion tonnes, and Rieley reckons that the burning swamp forests contributed a billion tonnes of that.

It looked as if smouldering bogs in remote Borneo were single-handedly ratcheting up the speed of climate change. They show, says David Schimel of the National Center for Atmospheric Research (NCAR) in Boulder, Colorado, how 'catastrophic events affecting small areas can have a huge impact on the global carbon balance.' Fire in Borneo and the Amazon may be turning the world's biggest living 'sinks' for carbon dioxide into the most explosive sources for the gas in the twenty-first century.

13

SINK TO SOURCE

WHY THE CARBON CYCLE IS SET FOR A U-TURN

It seemed too good to be true. Throughout the 1980s and 1990s, there was growing evidence that wherever forests survived around the world they were growing faster. And as they did so, they were soaking up ever more carbon dioxide from the air. Despite deforestation in the tropics, the world's forests were overall a strong carbon sink. Most researchers assumed that the extra growth happened because rising concentrations of carbon dioxide in the atmosphere made it easier for trees to absorb the gas from the air. Provided the other ingredients for photosynthesis, such as water and nutrients, were available, for growing plants the sky was the limit. It seemed as if the natural carbon dioxide cycle provided a large negative feedback to shut down global warming. The 'CO_2 fertilization effect' entered the climate scientists' lexicon.

In 1998, at the height of this enthusiasm, a group of carbon modellers at Princeton University in New Jersey scored what looked like a political as well as a scientific bull's eye. Song-Miao Fan and colleagues claimed in a paper in *Science* to have discovered 'a large terrestrial carbon sink in North America'. The US and Canada, they said, had become a hotspot for carbon absorption, as trees grew on abandoned farmland and previously logged forests, and carbon dioxide in the air boosted growth. They calculated the sink at a stunning 2 billion tonnes a year – more than enough to offset all the two countries' annual emissions from power plants, car tailpipes and the rest. Thanks to their trees, the biggest polluters on the planet were 'carbon neutral'.

It seemed to many an outrageous claim. And on examination, it involved some fairly heroic assumptions about where carbon dioxide in the atmosphere was coming from, where it was going to and how it moved around. Carbon cycle specialists poured cold water on the notion. The figure of 2 billion tonnes was not far off the total amount of carbon that North America's trees absorbed in a year in order to grow. If it were true, it meant that no North American trees were dying; they weren't even breathing out – because both processes release carbon dioxide back into the air. But the findings came less than a year after the Clinton administration had signed up to tough carbon dioxide emissions targets at Kyoto, without any clear idea how it was going to achieve them. They seemed like manna from heaven.

And yes, it was too good to be true. The authors agreed that their data were sparse and their analytical techniques largely untried. Nobody, it turned out, could repeat the results. A plethora of researchers demonstrated that US forests could never have stashed away more than a fifth of the nation's emissions. After a while, nobody stood up to defend the original results and they disappeared from view as fast as they had arrived.

The final nail entered the coffin when it emerged later that 1998, the year of the report's publication, was just about the worst on record for nature's ability to soak up carbon dioxide from the air. Forests and peat bogs had burned from the Amazon to Borneo. If there had been a big sink, it was disappearing even as it was uncovered. And it wasn't just the tropics where carbon had been seeping out of the biosphere. There were major forest fires from Florida to Sardinia and Peru to Siberia, where Russian foresters revealed that a forest conflagration on a par with Borneo had been taking place virtually unnoticed. The world's largest stretch of forest, which for 200 years had been soaking up a fraction of Europe's industrial emissions as they poured east on the prevailing winds, was giving up what it had previously absorbed. As 1998 closed, the idea of a huge carbon sink in the US or anywhere else seemed absurd.

The next episode in the story of the amazing disappearing carbon sink came in the summer of 2003. Europe suffered a massive heatwave. Temperatures averaged 6 degrees C above normal during July. In France, the mercury soared above 40 degrees C. With the high temperatures accompanied by less than half the usual rainfall, the beech trees and cornfields, grasslands and pine forests of Europe were expiring.

Philippe Ciais, a Paris-based environmental scientist, followed events. He was a key player in CarboEurope, a project begun a couple of years before to measure Europe's carbon sink. It was begun in the aftermath of the purported discovery of the large North American carbon sink. European politicians, like their US counterparts, were keen to discover if nature was helping them meet their own Kyoto Protocol targets. Ciais' initial assessment was that, thanks to warmer temperatures, raised carbon dioxide levels in the air and a longer growing season, Europe's ecosystems were absorbing up to 12 per cent of the continent's man-made emissions.

But in 2003, the carbon sink blew a fuse. During July and August that year, when Europe's ecosystems would normally have been in full bloom and soaking up carbon dioxide at their fastest, around 500 million tonnes of carbon escaped from western European forests and fields. The releases were the equivalent of roughly twice Europe's emissions from burning fossil fuels during those two months. All the carbon absorbed in recent years was being dumped back into the atmosphere in double-quick time. The rapid exhaling of the continent's ecosystems was 'unprecedented in the last century', said Ciais. But he judged it was likely to be repeated 'as future droughts turn temperate ecosystems from carbon sinks into carbon sources'.

Europe seemed to have fast-forwarded into a nightmare future strapped to a runaway greenhouse effect. And it soon emerged that Europe's carbon crisis was part of a more general story of summer stress across the northern hemisphere. Ning Zeng of the University of Maryland found an area of drought stretching from the Mediterranean to Afghanistan. It lasted from 1998 to 2002 and had eliminated a natural carbon sink across the region that had absorbed 700 million tonnes a year over the previous two decades.

Alon Angert of the University of California at Berkeley explained the big picture. Through the 1980s and into the early 1990s, the 'CO_2 fertilization effect' had been working rather well, with increased photosynthesis in the northern hemisphere soaking up ever more carbon dioxide. But sometime around 1993 that had tailed off, probably because of droughts and higher temperatures. And since the mid-1990s, the carbon sink had been in sharp decline. From the Mediterranean to central Asia and even in the high latitudes of Siberia and northern Europe, the added uptake of carbon by plants in the early spring was cancelled out by the heat and water stress of the hotter, drier summers. The findings, Angert said, dashed widespread expectations of a continuing 'greening trend' in which warm summers would speed plant growth and moderate climate change. Instead, 'excess heating is driving the dieback of forests, accelerating soil carbon loss and transforming the land from a sink to a source of carbon to the atmosphere.'

And further north, beyond the tree line, where some of the fastest warming rates in the world are currently being experienced, fear is growing about carbon stored in the thick layers of permanently frozen soil known as permafrost. The carbon comprises thousands of years of the accumulated remains of dead lichen, moss and other vegetation that never had a chance to rot before it froze. David Lawrence of NCAR reported in 2005 that he expected the top 3 metres of permafrost across most of the Arctic to melt during the twenty-first century. This will leave a trail of buckled highways, toppled buildings, broken pipelines and bemused reindeer; it will also unfreeze tens and perhaps hundreds of billions of tonnes of carbon. As the thawed vegetation finally rots, its carbon will generally return to the atmosphere as carbon dioxide. In those bogs and lakes where there is no oxygen, most of the carbon will be converted into methane which, as we will see in the next chapter, is an even more potent greenhouse gas.

We should not entirely write off the carbon sink. It won't die altogether. Especially in higher latitudes, warmer and wetter conditions will sometimes mean that trees grow faster and further north than before, at least where plagues of insects don't get them first. Right now, the best guess is that, on average, forests are still absorbing much more carbon dioxide than they release. Up to a fifth of the carbon dioxide we emit from burning fossil fuels may still be being absorbed by soils and forests. But the sink is diminishing, not rising as many anticipated. And many believe that the sink is doomed as we face more and more years like 1998 and 2003.

One of those who fear the worst is Peter Cox, a top young British climate modeller who left Britain's Hadley Centre to spend more time investigating the carbon cycle at the Centre for Ecology and Hydrology at Winfrith in Dorset. He believes he is on the trail of the disappearing carbon sink and is prepared to put a date on when it will disappear.

'Basically, we are seeing two competing things going on,' he says. 'Plants absorb carbon dioxide as they grow through photosynthesis; but they give back the carbon dioxide as they die and their wood, leaves and roots decompose. The speed of both processes is increasing.' First, the extra carbon dioxide in the atmosphere encourages photosynthesis to speed up. So plants grow faster and absorb more carbon dioxide. But that extra carbon dioxide is also warming the climate. And the warming encourages the processes that break down the plant material and release carbon dioxide back into the air. Because there is a time lag of a couple of decades before the extra carbon dioxide is converted into warmer temperatures, we have seen the fertilization effect first. Now the process of decay is starting to catch up. We are approaching the point where decay and the release of carbon dioxide will outstrip growth and absorption.

The processes do not just involve plants. Soils have their own processes of inhaling and exhaling carbon. And they too will switch from being a net sink to a net source of carbon – eventually releasing what they have absorbed in recent decades. Ultimately, Cox says, 'you can't have the one without the other. If you breathe in, eventually you have to breathe out.' And soon, most of the rainforests and soils of the world will be breathing out, pouring their stored carbon back into the air. If the climate gets drier and there are more fires, then the release of the carbon dioxide will happen even more quickly. But it will happen anyway.

The entire land 'biosphere' – the forests and soils and pastures and bogs – has been slowing the pace of global warming for some decades. Soon the biosphere will start to speed up the warming. The day the biosphere turns from sink to source will be another tipping point in the Earth system. Like collapsing ice sheets, once under way the process will be unstoppable. Potentially, hundreds of billions of tonnes of carbon in the biosphere could be destabilized, says Pep Canadell, a carbon-cycle researcher for the Australian government research agency CSIRO.

Nobody is quite sure when the tipping point might occur. 'It is possible,' says Cox, 'that the 2003 surge in carbon dioxide into the atmosphere is the first evidence.' But while some parts of the biosphere may now be irrevocably stuck as carbon sources, it is likely to be a few decades yet before the entire system switches. Depending, of course, on how fast we allow temperatures to rise.

Cox suggests that 2040 is the most likely date when the biosphere will start taking its revenge on us for relying on its accommodating nature. He calculates that by the end of the century, the biosphere could be adding 7 billion tonnes of carbon to the atmosphere each year. That is roughly the amount coming from burning fossil fuels today, and probably enough to add an extra 1 or 2 degrees C to global temperatures – 2 degrees that are not yet included in the IPCC forecasts.

Only one country, so far as I am aware, has completed anything like a national study of the current impact of these changes in the biosphere on its overall contribution to climate change. But Guy Kirk of the National Soil Resources Institute, part of Cranfield University, has done the job for Britain. He surveyed 6,000 test plots across forest and bog, heath and farmland, scrub and back gardens to see how much carbon dioxide is leaving the biosphere and how much is entering it. His conclusion is that the English biosphere is releasing about 1 per cent of its carbon store into the atmosphere every year. Enough, in other words, to turn the whole country to desert if the release continued at that rate for another century.

Kirk rules out farming methods or land use changes as the predominant cause. The changes are so universal that it can only be climate change. He puts the total release from the British biosphere at around 13 million tonnes a year. That, he points out, is roughly the amount of carbon dioxide that the British government has kept from the atmosphere each year in its efforts to comply with the Kyoto Protocol. As German researcher Ernst-Detlef Schulze of CarboEurope put it – rather gloatingly, I thought – this 'completely offsets the technological achievements of reducing carbon dioxide emissions, putting the UK's success in reducing greenhouse gas emissions in a different light.' True enough. But Britain is not alone.

14

THE DOOMSDAY DEVICE
A LETHAL SECRET STIRS IN THE PERMAFROST

One of my favourite films is *Dr Strangelove*. It was made back in 1964 when the biggest global threat was nuclear Armageddon. Directed by Stanley Kubrick and starring Peter Sellers as Dr Strangelove, a wheelchair-bound caricature of Henry Kissinger, the film was a satire of the military strategy known as Mutual Assured Destruction – or MAD, for short. The plot involved the Soviet Union building the ultimate defence, a doomsday device in the remote wastes of Siberia. If Russia were attacked, the device would shroud the world in a radioactive cloud and destroy all human and animal life on Earth. Unfortunately, the Soviet generals forgot to tell the Americans about this and, needless to say, Dr Strangelove and the American military attacked. The film ends with a deranged Major Kong sitting astride a nuclear bomb as it is released into the sky above Siberia. The end of the world is nigh, as the credits roll.

Now our most feared global Armageddon is climate change. One reason we have to fear its consequences lurks in the frozen bogs of western Siberia. There, beneath a largely uninhabited wasteland of permafrost, lies what might reasonably be described as nature's own doomsday device. It is primed to be triggered not by a nuclear bomb but by global warming. That device consists of thick layers of frozen peat containing tens of billions of tonnes of carbon.

The entire West Siberian peat bog covers a million square kilometres, an area as big as France and Germany combined. Since its formation, the moss and lichen growing at its surface have been slowly absorbing massive amounts of carbon from the atmosphere. Because it is so cold, the vegetation only partially decomposes and forms an ever-thickening frozen mass of peat beneath the bog. Perhaps a quarter of all the carbon absorbed by soils and vegetation on the land surface of the Earth since the last ice age is right here.

The concern now is that as the bog begins to thaw the peat will decompose and release its carbon. The world's largest carbon sink could become the world's largest carbon source. Unlike the tropical swamps of Borneo, which produce carbon dioxide as they burn, the Siberian bogs will degrade in the wet as the permafrost melts. In the fetid swamps and lakes, devoid of oxygen, they will produce methane. Methane is a powerful and fast-acting greenhouse gas, potentially a hundred times more potent than carbon dioxide. Its release in such quantities quickly enough would be like an atmospheric tsunami, swamping the planet in warmth. But we have to change tense here. For 'would be', read 'is'.

In the summer of 2005, I received a remarkable e-mail from a man I had neither met nor corresponded with, a young Siberian ecologist called Sergei Kirpotin at Tomsk State University in the heart of Siberia. A collaborator of his at Oxford University had suggested me as a Western outlet for what Kirpotin in his e-mail called an 'urgent message for the world'. He had recently undertaken an expedition across thousands of kilometres of the empty West Siberian peatlands between the bleak windswept towns of Khatany-Mansiysk, Pangody and Novy Urengoi. Nobody bar a few reindeer herders lives out there. It was an area that Kirpotin and his colleagues had visited several times in the past fifteen years, observing the apparently unchanging geography and biology of the tundra. This time they had found a huge change.

'We had never seen anything like it, and had not expected it,' he said. Huge areas of frozen peat bog were suddenly melting. The former soft spongy surface of lichens and moss was turning into a landscape of lakes that stretch unbroken for hundreds of kilometres. He described it as an 'ecological landslide that is probably irreversible and is undoubtedly connected to climate warming'. Most of the lakes had formed, he said, since his previous visit three years before. There was clearly a huge danger that the melting peatland would begin to generate methane.

I had come across Russian scientists before who had been left out in the tundra too long with their crackpot theories. But Kirpotin did not fit that category. He had only recently been appointed vice-rector of his university. And, the more I checked it, the more likely his story seemed. Larry Smith of the University of California at Los Angeles told me that the West Siberian peat bog was warming faster than almost anywhere on the planet. Every year, the spring melt was starting earlier and the rainfall was increasing, making the whole landscape wetter, he said.

Other researchers were finding big methane emissions in the region. Katey Walter of the University of Alaska in Fairbanks had told a meeting of the US Arctic Research Consortium just a few weeks before about 'hotspots' of methane releases from lakes in eastern Siberia that were 'unlike anything that has been observed before'. Peat on the bottom of lakes was converting to methane and bubbling to the surface so fast that it was stopping the lakes from freezing over in winter. And Euan Nisbet of London's Royal Holloway College, who oversees a big international methane-monitoring programme that includes Siberia, said his estimate was that methane releases from the West Siberian peat bog were up to 100,000 tonnes a day, which meant a warming effect on the planet greater than all the US's man-made emissions. 'This huge methane flux depends on temperature,' he said. 'If peatlands become wetter with warming and permafrost degradation, methane release from peat lands to the atmosphere will dramatically increase.'

So I wrote up Kirpotin's story for *New Scientist* magazine, emphasizing the methane angle. It went round the world. The London *Guardian* reproduced much of it the next day under the front-page banner headline 'Warming hits "tipping point"'. In *Dr Strangelove*, one nuclear device dropped on Siberia unleashed a thousand more. Here, in the real world of melting Arctic permafrost, a degree of global warming could unleash enough methane to raise temperatures several degrees.

I had visited western Siberia a few years before, travelling with Western forest and oil industry scientists to

Noyabr'sk, a large oil town on the south side of the great peat bog. On a series of helicopter rides, I had seen thousands of square kilometres of still intact swamp sitting on top of permafrost. The landscape was terribly scarred by human activity: divided into fragments by oil pipelines, roads, pylons and seismic survey routes; smeared with spilled oil; littered with abandoned drums, pipes, cables and the remains of old gulags and half-built railways; and shrouded in black smoke from gas flares. The reindeer had fled and the bears had been hunted almost to extinction. But the peat bog and the permafrost had survived. The helicopter landed regularly and we jumped out without so much as getting our feet wet on the spongy surface.

No longer. On my way to meet Kirpotin's colleagues at their research station at Pangody on the Arctic Circle, I flew for two hours over a vast bog that was seemingly going into solution. In place of the green carpet of moss and lichen there were now, as Kirpotin had told me, numberless lakes stretching to the horizon. From the air, they did not look like natural lakes of the kind that form in depressions in the landscape. They were generally circular, looking more like flooded potholes in a road. And flooded potholes were more or less what they were. The lakes had formed individually from small breaches in the permafrost. At each point where ice turned to water, a small pond of water formed. Then surrounding lumps of frozen peat slumped into the water, and the pond began to grow in an ever-widening circle, until mile after mile of frozen bog had melted into a mass of lakes.

'Western scientists cannot imagine the scale of the melting,' Kirpotin had told me. But I could see it beneath me as I flew east. It seemed to me that there was a positive feedback at work, much as in the accelerated melting of

Arctic sea ice. The new melted surface was darker than the old frozen surface, absorbed more heat and caused more warming. Kirpotin agreed. There seemed, he said, to be a 'critical threshold' beyond which 'the process of warming would be essentially and suddenly changed. Some kind of trigger hook mechanism would come into play and the process of permafrost degradation would start to stimulate itself and to urge itself onwards.' His bad English somehow made the events he was describing sound even more awesome. 'The problem concerned does not have only a scientific character: it has passed to the plane of world politics. If mankind does not want to face serious social and economic losses from global warming, it is necessary to take urgent measures. Obviously we have less and less time to act.'

I was defeated in my efforts to see these processes in Siberian bogs on the ground. Landing at Novy Urengoi with all the necessary paperwork, I was nonetheless refused admission. 'You need a special invitation from an organization in the city,' a fearsome policewoman at the airport told me as she confiscated my passport and put it in a safe. This was a company town. I later discovered that the mayor, a gas company nominee, had won approval from Moscow some months before for special rules to keep out unwanted foreigners. Novy Urengoi was one of Russia's few surviving closed cities.

It was also rather disorganized. Unsupervised, I wandered into town anyhow, and looked around one of the most desolate and inhospitable places I have ever been to. No wonder its name in the language of the local reindeer herders means 'godforsaken place'. I briefly met the scientists I had come halfway across the world to see, before being rounded up by a spook wearing a double-breasted suit and a smile like Vladimir Putin's, and driven back to the airport. He seemed to think I was a terrorist, and the fact that I was meeting scientists investigating the tundra only made him more incredulous. I could at any rate say I had been thrown out of Siberia.

Back home, there has been growing concern about the role of methane in stoking the fires of global warming. In early 2006, a dramatic study suggested that all plants, not just those in bogs, are manufacturing methane – something never previously considered by scientists. That led to headlines about trees causing global warming, which seemed a bit hard on them. If they do make methane, they also absorb carbon dioxide. And since trees have been around for millions of years, and there are probably fewer of them now than for the majority of that time, any role for them in recent warming seems unlikely. They are simply part of the natural flux of chemicals into and out of the atmosphere. Though if evidence emerged that, as a result of warming, they were emitting more methane than before, that would be a big worry. And that is precisely what seems to be happening with peat bogs in the Arctic permafrost.

There is a critical line around the edge of the Arctic that marks the zone of maximum impact from global warming. It is a 'front line' of climate change, marking the zero-degree isotherm, where the average year-round temperature is 0 degrees C, the melting point of ice. To the north of this line lie ice and snow, frozen soil and Arctic tundra. To the south lie rivers and lakes and fertile soils where trees grow. The line runs through the heart of

Siberia and Alaska – where huge blocks of frozen soil that have been stable for thousands of years are now melting – across Canada, skirting the southern shore of Hudson Bay, through the southern tip of Greenland and over northern Scandinavia.

Having failed to visit Kirpotin's field station to see the melting of the Siberian bogs close up, I went instead to northern Sweden to visit what is almost certainly the longest continually monitored Arctic peat bog in the world. In 1903, scientists took over buildings erected near Abisko during the construction of a railway to take iron ore from the Swedish mine of Kiruna to the Norwegian port of Narvik. And they have been out there ever since, through the midnight sun and the long dark winters, measuring temperatures and dating when the ice comes and goes on the adjacent Tornetrask lake, plotting movements of the tree line, examining the bog ecosystems, reconstructing past climates from the growth rings of logs in the lake and investigating the cosmic forces behind the area's spectacular Northern Lights.

So they are on good ground when they say it is getting dramatically warmer here. The lake freezes a month later than it did only a couple of decades ago: in January rather than mid-December. It used to stay frozen till late May, but several times in recent years an early break-up has forced the cancellation of the annual ice-fishing festival on the lake in early May. The average annual temperature here over the past century has been minus 0.7 degrees, but in recent years it has sometimes crept above zero.

Just east of Abisko is the Stordalen mire. This is not a large bog, but it is old, and probably the best-monitored bog in the best-monitored Arctic region in the world. It has withstood numerous periods of natural climate change during the past five thousand years. But suddenly, it seems doomed. For here, as Kirpotin has found across the West Siberian wetland, the evidence of what happens to a bog that finds itself straddling the zero isotherm is obvious at every step. Apart from scientists, the bog's main visitors are birdwatchers. And for them, a couple of years ago, the local authorities built a network of duckboards. But already the boards are capsizing because the mounds of permafrost on which they were built are melting and slumping into newly emerging ponds of water.

Arriving rather spectacularly aboard a helicopter hired to remove some equipment from the site, I found a dry hummock on which to talk to Torben Christensen, a Danish biochemist who heads the research effort here. 'The bog is changing very fast,' he said. Below our feet, the permafrost was still as much as 10 metres deep, but a step away it was gone. We examined a crack in the peat, where another chunk was preparing to slide into the water. 'Of all the places in the world, it is right here on the zero isotherm, on the edge of the permafrost, that you'd expect to see climate change in action. And that is exactly what we are seeing. Of course, they are seeing it on a much bigger scale in the Siberian bogs, but here we are measuring everything.'

Out on the mire, Christensen has some of the most sophisticated equipment for measuring gas emissions in the air to be found anywhere in the world. In one area, individual bog plants grow inside transparent plastic boxes whose lids open and shut as automatic monitoring equipment captures and measures the flux of gases between plant and atmosphere. Pride of place goes to an eddy correlation tower. This logs every tiny wind movement in the air around, vertical as well as horizontal, and uses a laser to measure passing molecules of methane and other gases. Combining the two sets of data, it can produce a constant and extremely accurate read-out of the flux of methane coming off the mire.

There is a regular loss of methane from the bog now, says Christensen. Some of the gas seeps out from the boggy soil, some bubbles up through the pond water and some is brought to the surface by plants. The figures sound small: an average of 6 milligrams of methane is released per square metre of mire per hour. But scaled up, that release packs a greenhouse punch. Combining the flux data with satellite images that show the changing vegetation on the Stordalen mire, Christensen estimates that in the last thirty years methane emissions have risen by 30 per cent and increased this small bog's contribution to global warming by 50 per cent.

There is nothing unusual about Stordalen. It was not chosen to give dramatic results. Monitoring began back when researchers were intent only on monitoring what they believed to be unchanging processes. Other local mires are faring far worse as the zero isotherm comes north. Out in the nearby birch forest, the Katterjokk bog has gone from being an area largely underlain by permafrost to being an ice-free zone in just five years. Stordalen looks, rather, to be typical of bogs across northern Scandinavia and right round the zero isotherm. Individually they are only a pinprick on climate change, but taken together they threaten an eruption.

Back in the warmth of Abisko library, Christensen found a study showing that half the bog permafrost in the north of Finland has disappeared since 1975. The rest will be gone by 2030. Christensen himself has coordinated a study of methane emissions from peatlands at sites right round the Arctic, using temporarily deployed equipment for measuring gas fluxes. North of the zero isotherm, the study shows little change. Little methane bubbles out of the tundra from north-east Greenland, for instance, where the average temperature is still around minus 10 degrees C. But, he says, 'as temperatures rise, methane emissions grow exponentially.' The highest emissions are in western Siberia and Alaska, where big temperature rises are taking place.

What is happening out on these Arctic mires is, at one level, quite subtle. On many of them, temperatures remain cold enough to limit decomposition of vegetable matter, and so carbon is still accumulating as it has done ever since the bogs began to form at the end of the last ice age. But the decomposition rates are rising. And critically, because the melting permafrost is making the bogs ever wetter, more and more of the carbon is released not as carbon dioxide but as methane. That dramatically changes the climate effect of the bogs. Methane being such a powerful greenhouse gas, the warming influence of its release overwhelms the cooling influence of continued absorption of carbon dioxide. Thus, says Christensen, 'mires are generally still a sink for carbon, while at the same time being a cause of global warming. This can be a hard point for people to grasp, but it is absolutely crucial for what is happening right round the Arctic.'

There are still so few good data that it is hard to say for sure how much the Arctic peat bogs are contributing to global warming today. Current emissions of methane are probably still below 50 million tonnes a year. But that is still the warming equivalent of more than a billion tonnes of carbon dioxide. And with lakes forming everywhere and climate models predicting that 90 per cent of the

Arctic permafrost will have melted to a depth of at least 3 metres by 2100, there is 'alarming potential for positive feedback to climate from methane', says Christensen.

Larry Smith estimates that the northern peat bogs of Siberia, Canada, Scandinavia and Alaska could contain 450 billion tonnes of carbon altogether, or one-third of all the carbon in all the world's soils. If all that carbon were released as carbon dioxide it would add something like 3 degrees C to average global temperatures around the world. But if most of it were released as methane instead it could provide a much bigger short-term kick. How big would depend on how fast the methane was released, because after a decade or so methane decomposes to carbon dioxide. If the methane all came out at once it could raise temperatures worldwide by tens of degrees. That might be an unlikely scenario. Even so, the odds must be that melting along the zero isotherm is destined to have a major impact on twenty-first century climate. From Stordalen to Pangody, the Doomsday Device is primed.

15

THE ACID BATH

WHAT CARBON DIOXIDE DOES TO THE OCEANS

The oceans are the ultimate sink for most of the heat from the sun and also for most of the greenhouse gases we are pouring into the atmosphere. The atmosphere may be the place where we live and breathe, but for long-term planetary systems it is just a holding bay. At any one time, the oceans contain fifty times more carbon dioxide dissolved in their waters than there is in the atmosphere. Given time, the oceans can absorb most of what we can throw into the atmosphere. But time is what we do not have, and the oceans' patience with our activities may be limited.

There is a constant movement of carbon dioxide between the oceans' surface and the atmosphere, as the two environments share out the gas. And, because of the ever rising concentrations in the atmosphere, about 2 billion tonnes a year more is currently being absorbed by the oceans than is released. Much of that surplus eventually finds its way to the ocean floor after being absorbed by growing marine organisms – a process often called the biological pump. Sometimes there are so many skeletons falling to the ocean depths that biologists call it marine snow.

Though they are the ultimate sink for most carbon dioxide, the oceans do not simply absorb any spare carbon dioxide left in the atmosphere. The relationship is much more dynamic – and much less reliable. In the long run, carbon dioxide seems to see-saw between the oceans on the one hand and the atmosphere and land vegetation on the other. Plants on land generally prefer things warm, so the carbon 'stock' on the land is greater during warm interglacial eras like our own, and less during ice ages. By contrast, the surface waters of the oceans absorb more carbon dioxide when the waters are cold. This seems to be partly because the plankton that form the basis of life in the oceans prefer cold waters, and partly because when the land is cold and dry, dust storms transport large amounts of minerals that fertilize the oceans.

During the last ice age some 200 billion tonnes of carbon moved from the land and atmosphere to the oceans. This process didn't initiate the ice ages, but it was a very powerful positive feedback driving the cooling. And that is a worry. For if the ice-age pattern holds, future generations can expect the oceans' biological pump to decline as the world warms and large amounts of carbon dioxide are released into the air.

That, at any rate, was the view put forward by Paul Falkowski of Rutgers University in New Brunswick, in a long review of the carbon cycle in *Science*. 'If our current understanding of the ocean carbon cycle is borne out, the sink strength of the ocean will weaken, leaving a larger fraction of anthropogenically produced carbon dioxide in the atmosphere.' With tens of millions of tonnes of carbon being exchanged back and forth between the atmosphere and oceans each year, it would take only a small change to turn the oceans from a carbon sink into a potentially very large carbon source. It might already be happening. In 2003 NASA scientist Watson Gregg published satellite measurements suggesting that the biological productivity of the oceans may have fallen by 6 per cent since the 1980s. It could be part of a natural cycle, he said, but it could also be an early sign that the biological pump is slowing as ocean temperatures rise.

So far, since the beginning of the Industrial Revolution, the oceans have absorbed from the atmosphere something like 120 billion tonnes of carbon resulting from human activities. While much of it has fallen to the sea bed, a considerable amount of it remains dissolved in the ocean waters. With a singular and rather remarkable effect: it is making the oceans more acid.

The carbonic acid produced as carbon dioxide dissolves in sea water is corrosive and especially damaging to organisms that need calcium carbonate for their shells or skeletons. These include coral, sea urchins, starfish, many shellfish and some plankton. Besides eating away at the organisms, the acid also reduces the concentration of carbonate in the water, depriving them of the chemicals they need to grow.

Acidity, measured as the amount of hydrogen ions in the water, is already up by 30 per cent. To put it another way, the pH has dropped by 0.1 points, from 8.2 to about 8.1. If the oceans continue to absorb large amounts of the atmosphere's excess carbon dioxide, then acidification will have more than tripled by the second half of the century, by which time ocean ecosystems could be badly hit. The most vulnerable oceans are probably the remote waters of the Southern Ocean and the Southern Pacific. They are distant from land and so are already short of carbonate, and in particular a form known as aragonite, which seems to be the most critical for growing organisms.

A report from Britain's Royal Society warned that 'corals could be rare on the tropical and sub-tropic reefs such as the Great Barrier Reef by 2050. This will have major ramifications for hundreds of thousands of species that dwell in the reefs and the people that depend on them.' Other species may suffocate or die for want of energy. High-energy marine creatures like squid need lots of oxygen, but the high concentrations of carbon dioxide will make it harder for them to extract oxygen from sea water.

'It is early days,' says Carol Turley of the Plymouth Marine Laboratory, one of the world authorities in this new field of research. 'The experiments are really only getting under way.' But one set of results is already in. James Orr of the Laboratoires des Sciences du Climat et de l'Environnement in France put tiny sea snails called pteropods into an aquarium and exposed them to the kind of ocean chemistry expected later this century. These creatures turn up all round the world and are vital to many ecosystems. They are the most abundant species in some waters around Antarctica, where there can be a thousand individuals in a single cubic metre of sea water. As well as being a major source of food for everything from fish to whales, pteropods are the biggest players in the biological pump there.

THE ACID BATH

Orr found that within hours the acid pitted the pteropods' shells. Within two days, the shell began to peel, exposing the soft flesh beneath. In the real world, predators would break through the weakened shells; 'the snails would not survive,' he concluded. The demise of the pteropods would cause a 'major reduction in the biological pump', the Royal Society agreed. Within a few decades it could leave the oceans more acid than at any time for 300 million years.

Whatever the outcome, we are seeing the start of an unexpected and frightening side effect of rising atmospheric carbon dioxide levels. Perhaps the nearest parallel to the current situation was 55 million years ago. That was the last time a large major slug of carbon was released into the atmosphere in a short period of time . . .

16

THE WIND OF CHANGE

TSUNAMIS, MEGAFARTS AND FOUNTAINS OF THE DEEP

It was the Earth's biggest ever fart. Fifty-five million years ago, more than a trillion tonnes of methane burst from the ocean, sending temperatures soaring by up to 10 degrees C, extinguishing two-thirds of the species in the ocean and causing a major evolutionary shock at the surface. The story, while from long ago, is a reminder that methane is lurking in prodigious quantities in many parts of the planet – not just in frozen bogs – and that one day it could be liberated in catastrophic quantities.

The first whiff of this prehistoric megafart was unearthed in 1991, from a hole drilled 2 kilometres into a submarine ridge just off Antarctica. Examining the different layers of the ancient sediment removed from the hole, geologists James Kennett from the University of California at Santa Barbara and Lowell Stott from the University of Southern California in Los Angeles found evidence of a sudden mass extinction of organisms living on the sea floor 55 million years ago. These species had apparently disappeared from the ocean within a few hundred years, perhaps less. Kennett and Stott soon discovered that other researchers had detected evidence of similar extinctions from the same era in marine sediments in both the Caribbean and Europe. This was clearly a global event – one of the largest extinctions in the history of the planet.

What happened? Looking at the chemistry of fossils in the drilled sediment, the two geologists found some intriguing clues. There was, for instance, a sudden change in the ratio of two types, or isotopes, of oxygen, known as oxygen-18 and oxygen-16. The ratio in the natural environment is very sensitive to temperature and this isotopic 'signature' in sediments and ice cores is a widely used indicator of past temperatures. Kennett and Stott concluded that after rising gradually for several million years ocean temperatures had about 55 million years ago soared much more dramatically. The change happened at the same time as the extinctions.

The sediments also revealed a second isotopic shift, this time between isotopes of carbon. The Earth's organic matter suddenly contained a lot more carbon-12. From somewhere, trillions of tonnes of the stuff had been released into the environment. Clearly a greenhouse gas, either carbon dioxide or methane, had caused both changes. The problem was finding a likely source with sufficient capacity to do the job.

Jerry Dickens, a biochemist at James Cook University in Townsville, Australia, set himself the task of working out where this carbon-12 might have come from. The first suggestion was carbon dioxide in volcanic eruptions, which are a rich source of carbon-12 in the modern atmosphere. But, says Dickens, that required an annual rate of volcanic eruptions a hundred times the average over the past billion years. Fossil fuels like coal, oil and natural gas were possible sources. But they are mostly buried out of harm's way, sealed in rocks. Given that there were no humans digging them up and burning them at the time, that too seemed implausible. Likewise methane from swamps and wetlands like those found today in Borneo and Siberia was ruled out. There were about three times as many of them as today. Even so, they could not have delivered the amount of carbon-12 required. That left one last source: one big enough and accessible enough to unleash a climatic eruption. That, Dickens suggested, had to be the vast stores of methane that geologists have recently been discovering frozen in sediment beneath the oceans: methane clathrates.

Methane clathrates are an enigma. They have until recently escaped the attention of oil and gas prospectors because they don't turn up in the kind of deep and confined geological formations where prospectors traditionally look for fossil fuels. They are generally close to the surface of the ocean floor but frozen – confined not by physical barriers but by high pressures and low temperatures – in a lattice of ice crystals rather like a honeycomb. Scientists still debate exactly how and when they form, but they seem to arise when cold ocean water meets methane created by microbes living beneath the sea bed. Seismic surveys have revealed these structures in the top few hundred metres of sediments beneath tens of thousands of square kilometres of ocean, usually just beyond the edge of continental shelves. Many of these frozen clathrate structures trap even larger stores of gaseous methane beneath, where heat from the Earth's core keeps them from freezing.

Dickens estimates that between 1 and 10 trillion tonnes of methane are tied up today in or beneath clathrates. But their confinement may not be permanent. Release the pressure or raise the temperature and the lattices will shatter, pouring methane up through the sediment into the ocean and finally into the atmosphere. It seems that some such event must have happened 55 million years ago. Moreover, if this was the source of the great release of carbon-12, then it would also explain why the extinctions appeared to be most serious in the ocean depths, where extensive acidification of the ocean would have been almost certain. 'Right now, almost everybody seems to accept that the release of methane clathrates is the only plausible explanation for what happened,' says Dickens.

His chronology goes like this. For several million years the world was warming, probably because of extra-terrestrial influences such as the sun. The warming gradually heated the sediments on the sea bed until it started to shatter the clathrates and release methane. Perhaps it happened in stages, with warming releasing methane that caused further warming that released more methane. But at any rate, over a few centuries or at most a few thousand years, trillions of tonnes of methane were released into the atmosphere – enough to cause the observed global shift in carbon isotopes and a large and long-lasting hike in temperatures.

'The world just went into chaos,' as Dickens puts it. Life on Earth was transformed almost on the scale of the asteroid hit 10 million years before that saw off the dinosaurs. Once the methane releases were over, the planet's ecosystems gradually absorbed the remainder of the great fart, the climate recovered its equilibrium and the oceans settled down again. But the evolutionary consequences of that event long ago have lasted to this day. By the time the climate had recovered, many species on land as well as in the oceans had become extinct, while others had evolved in response to warmer temperatures and flourished.

'At the same time as the great warming, there was a major evolution and dispersal of new kinds of mammals,' says Chris Beard, a palaeontologist at the Carnegie Museum of Natural History in Pittsburgh. It was 'the dawn of the age of mammals'. Among those on the evolutionary move were all kinds of ungulates – including the ancestors of horses, zebras, rhinos, camels and cattle – and primates. And among the new primates evolving in the balmy conditions were the omomyids, the ancestors of simians, who in turn spawned humans.

Could such a cataclysm happen again? Maybe in the twenty-first century? Certainly there is still enough methane buried beneath the oceans. But could current global warming provide the trigger for its release? Some say that is unlikely; modern sea water is still much colder than it was 55 million years ago. But Deborah Thomas of the University of North Carolina, who has analysed the event in detail, is not so sanguine. The oceans may still be cooler, but they are also warming faster than they were 55 million years ago. And the pace of change may be as dangerous as the extent. If so, 'the trigger on the clathrate gun will be a lot touchier than it was 55 million years ago.'

Apparently seaworthy ships can disappear without warning from the ocean for many reasons. They can be hit by giant waves, upturned by submarines, holed by icebergs or dashed onto rocks in storms. Could huge slugs of methane bursting from the ocean depths be another cause? Some say so. Take the strange case of Alan Judd and the Witch Hole.

Judd is a British marine geologist at the University of Newcastle with a long interest in methane clathrates. In the late 1990s, he persuaded a French oil company to fund work in the North Sea to map giant pockmarks on the sea bed. Geologists regard these otherwise inexplicable pockmarks as the aftermath of past methane eruptions from clathrates deep in the sediment. One day, about 150 kilometres off Aberdeen, Judd's remote-controlled probe was exploring a particularly large crater, about 100 metres across and known to mariners as Witch Hole, when it crashed into something. Something large, metal and unidentified, which wrote off the probe.

In the summer of 2000, Judd returned to try to find out what his probe had struck. This time he had money from a television company and a tiny remote submarine equipped with a video camera. He found the culprit. It was the steel hull of a 25-metre-long trawler dating, judging by its design, from the early twentieth century. The ship sat upright on the sea bed, in the middle of the crater, apparently unholed. 'The boat didn't go in either end first; it went down flat,' Judd said later. 'It looks as though it was just swamped.' The ship could have gone down in a storm, but 'for the boat to have randomly landed within Witch Hole would be an amazing coincidence. It is tempting to suggest that it is evidence of a catastrophic gas escape,' he said.

Efforts to identify the ship and find contemporary reports of why it went to the bottom have so far failed. And funds for another survey have failed to materialize. But the story remains an intriguing mystery to set beside other stories of ships that apparently disappeared in calm waters. Some say methane emissions from the depths could explain the mysterious loss of ships in the area of the Atlantic known as the Bermuda Triangle, for instance. Certainly, methane clathrates have been found in the area. So, while there is much mythology and misinformation about the Triangle, this theory could hold some truth. 'When the gas bubbles to the surface, it lowers the density of the water and therefore its buoyancy,' says Judd. 'Any ship caught above would sink as if it were in a lift shaft.' Anybody jumping overboard to save themselves would sink, too. No trace would remain – at the surface.

Meanwhile pockmarks are turning up on the sea bed almost everywhere that there are clathrates: from the tropics to the poles, from the Atlantic and Pacific and Arctic to the Indian and Southern Oceans. Evidence of when methane was released from the ocean floor remains sketchy, but the signs are of major releases. At Blake Ridge off the eastern US, marine geologists have found pockmarks 700 metres wide and up to 30 metres deep, like huge moon craters. And drilling studies suggest that the ridge may still have around 15 billion tonnes of frozen methane hidden beneath the craters, and at least as much again trapped as free gas in warmer sediments beneath the frozen zone. European researchers have found pockmarks just as big in the Barents Sea south-east of Svalbard. The widely quoted estimate that between 1 and 10 trillion tonnes of methane is trapped down there remains a bit of a stab in the dark, but the scale sounds right.

The lattice structures that hold methane clathrates survive only at low temperatures and high pressures, so sightings are rare. Fishing nets catch lumps from time to time as occasionally they survive briefly at the ocean surface. They fizz away on the ship's deck, releasing their methane. Alarmed fishermen usually throw them back fast. Researchers have found white clathrate chunks 'the size of radishes' sitting in the mud on the bottom of the Barents Sea, and sometimes track small plumes of methane rising from the sea bed to the surface. Russian researchers have reported clathrates bursting out of the Caspian Sea and igniting 'like a huge blowtorch, producing flames that rise several hundred metres high'. But these events are mild curiosities compared with the evidence being pieced together of major catastrophic events caused by methane releases from beneath the ocean. And these events occurred much more recently than 55 million years ago.

On the east coast of Scotland, cliff faces often show a mysterious layer of grey silt about 10 centimetres thick sandwiched between layers of peat. The silt seems unremarkable, except that it extends right up the coast for hundreds of kilometres, and is full of the remains of tiny marine organisms that are normally found only on the ocean floor. The silt was deposited about 8,000 years ago by a tsunami that surged across the North Sea after the collapse of an underwater cliff on the edge of the continental shelf west of Norway. This was a huge event. The 400-kilometre-long cliff slumped more than 3 kilometres vertically down the slope onto the floor of the deep ocean, taking with it a staggering 1,700 cubic kilometres of the sediment. It spread across an area of sea bed almost the size of Scotland.

The scars left by this huge submarine slide were first spotted in 1979 by Norman Cherkis of the Naval Research Laboratory in Washington, DC. Cherkis was using sonar equipment to scour the ocean bed for hiding places for military submarines. He assumed at first that the slide had been caused by an underwater earthquake, though there was little seismological evidence for this. That presumption was shaken by a Norwegian marine geologist, Juergen Mienert from the University of Tromso, who saw that the area of sea bed that had slumped, known as Storegga, also contained large numbers of pockmarks associated with clathrate bursts.

Mienert noted that the slide coincided with a rise of 6 degrees C in ocean temperatures off Norway, as currents carrying the warm tropical waters of the Gulf Stream became much stronger in the aftermath of the last ice age. The strong wash of warm water over a previously cold sea bed would have been enough, he said, to melt clathrates. Since a single cubic metre of clathrate contains enough methane to produce 160 cubic metres of gas at normal atmospheric pressure, the releases would have had explosive force, stirring up the sea-bed sediments over a huge area, and creating more releases and a cataclysmic slide.

Mienert estimated that this undersea eruption released between 4 and 8 billion tonnes of methane – enough to heat the global atmosphere by several degrees. His theory gained dramatic support when analysis of Greenland ice cores showed a big rise in methane concentrations in the air at that time. Some argue that the methane surge came from tropical wetlands that grew as the world warmed and became wetter. Mienert disagrees, but the argument has yet to be resolved.

The tsunami certainly had a huge impact. A 12-metre-high wave crashed into the Norwegian coast and deposited silt 6 metres above the shoreline in Scotland. The Shetland Islands took the brunt, receiving at least two waves that left a slimy trace 20 metres above the then sea level. In the hours after Storegga slipped, many Stone Age people must have died on the shores of Europe. And it wasn't an isolated event. There appear to have been several earlier slips at Storegga, and the fear must be that it could happen again here. 'There is still a lot of methane on the north side of the Storegga slide,' Mienert says.

Since the discovery of the Storegga slip, the remains of a number of other similar slips have been discovered in areas of the ocean known to harbour methane clathrates. They have turned up off British Columbia in Canada, off both the east and west coasts of the US and at the mouths of great rivers like the Amazon and the Congo, where huge offshore fans of sediment contain methane generated by rotting vegetation from the rainforests upstream. Their timing is not yet certain, but Mienert believes that the thermal shock caused by Storegga may have had a domino effect, releasing other clathrate stocks already made vulnerable by the warming postglacial oceans.

Some researchers postulate a 'clathrate gun' theory of climate change, in which at the end of the ice ages, and perhaps at other times, successive releases of methane instigated a worldwide warming. They see the catastrophic event 55 million years ago as just the biggest of a whole family of methane-related climate disasters.

When I met Juergen Mienert in his lab on a hill overlooking a fjord on the edge of Tromso – suitably raised, we joked, in case of a tsunami – he was planning a major new European research project to find more remains of slides and clathrate blowouts. The Euromargins project, which he chairs, 'will be targeting areas where there are both pockmarks, indicating past clathrate releases, and warm ocean currents, indicating a risk of destabilization', he said.

He is already on the trail of an ancient slip high in the Arctic, off the north coast of Spitzbergen. This area is currently warming fast and is bathed periodically in warm waters from the Gulf Stream breaking through the Fram Strait into the Arctic. 'Some of the world's richest methane deposits lie right below that current,' he said. He showed me new survey images of the sea bed there, taken on a cruise two months before in an area known as Malene Bay. They reveal another huge event. 'Look at this,' he enthused. 'Look at the height of the cliff that fell. It was 1,400 metres high, seven times the height of the Storegga collapse.'

The prognosis, Mienert says, is worrying. Current conditions are disturbingly similar to those in which the great methane releases of the past happened – fast-rising sea temperatures penetrating the sediment and defrosting the frozen methane. Global warming, he believes, 'will cause more blowouts and more craters and more releases'. The risk of a giant tsunami blasting into Europe, the most densely populated continent on Earth, at the same time that a huge outburst of methane pushes climate change into overdrive is disturbing to say the least.

Some argue that such concerns are exaggerated. It would take decades or even centuries for a warming pulse from the ocean to penetrate sediment zones where methane clathrates generally occur. But Mienert counters that clathrates are being found ever closer to the surface, particularly in the Arctic. In any event, there is a second and much faster route downwards for the heat. US naval researcher Warren Wood has discovered that sea-bed sediments often contain cracks that extend into the frozen clathrate zone. Warm water takes no time to penetrate the cracks and can quickly unleash the methane. As Richard Alley said of the crevasses inside ice caps, 'cracks change everything.'

Methane is only the third most important greenhouse gas, after water vapour and carbon dioxide. But, says Euan Nisbet, 'arguably it is the most likely to cause catastrophic change.' This is 'because the amount needed to change climate is smaller than for carbon dioxide, and because the amount of the gas available, in soils and especially methane clathrates, is so large'. Methane has clearly had catastrophic effects in the past. In the dangerous world of sudden, abrupt and unstoppable climate change, methane is the gunslinger.

PART FOUR

REFLECTING ON WARMING

17

WHAT'S WATTS?

PLANET EARTH'S ENERGY IMBALANCE

Jim Hansen knows about the atmosphere from top to bottom. He began his career as an atmospheric physicist, studying under James van Allen, after whom the van Allen belts of the upper atmosphere are named. He published papers on the Venusian atmosphere before he moved on to our own. So when Hansen stops talking about degrees of temperature and starts counting how many watts of energy reach the Earth's atmosphere and how many leave it, I recognize that we are getting down to the nitty-gritty of what sets the Earth's thermostat.

I know about watts. I have a 60-watt bulb in the lamp over my desk. At school almost forty years ago, my physics teacher had a stock line for any lesson on electricity. 'It's the watts what kill,' he said, meaning that they are what matters. When Hansen says the sunlight reaching the surface of the Earth in recent centuries has been about 240 watts for every square metre, I can visualize that. It is four 60-watt bulbs shining on my desk.

That figure only ever changes slightly, because the sun itself is largely unchanging. If the sun were to grow stronger, more radiation would reach the Earth and we would warm up. But only so much. A warmed surface also releases more energy, so eventually a new equilibrium would be reached. Similarly, as additional greenhouse gases trap more solar energy, the Earth warms until a new equilibrium is reached, with as much energy leaving as arriving. Put another way, the Earth's temperature is whatever is required to send back to space the same amount of energy that the planet absorbs.

So what is happening today? Thanks to our addition of greenhouse gases to the atmosphere, the planet is suffering what Hansen calls 'a large and growing energy imbalance' which 'has no known precedent'. The planet is warming, but it has not yet reached a new equilibrium.

The net warming effect of man-made pollutants at present is about 1.8 watts per square metre. Most of this goes into heating either the lower atmosphere or the oceans. The ocean surface and the atmosphere share heat fairly freely, constantly exchanging energy. Because the oceans have a greater heat capacity than the atmosphere, they take the lion's share of the extra energy. But there are time lags in this exchange system. It takes some time to heat the oceans to their full depth. The warming of recent decades has created a pulse of heat that has so far descended around 750 metres into the oceans in places. As this pulse progresses, the oceans are draining more heat out of the atmosphere than they will once the oceans and atmosphere return to a long-term balance. It is rather like using a central heating system to warm a house. We have to heat all the water in all the radiators before the full effect of heating air in the house gets going. Likewise, on planet Earth, the full impact of global warming will be felt in the atmosphere only after the oceans have been warmed.

The best guess is that about 0.6 degrees C – representing about 0.8 watts per square metre – is currently lopped off the warming of the atmosphere by the task of warming the oceans. That is warming 'in the pipeline', says Hansen. Whenever we manage to stabilize greenhouse gases in the atmosphere, there will still be that extra 0.6 degrees to come. Half of it, Hansen reckons, will take place within thirty to forty years of stabilization, and the rest over subsequent decades or perhaps centuries.

While most of the extra heat being trapped by greenhouse gases is currently going into heating the oceans and atmosphere, there is a third outlet – the energy required to melt ice. At present no more than 2 per cent is involved in this task. But Hansen believes that that percentage is likely to rise substantially. Recent surging glaciers and disintegrating ice shelves in Greenland and Antarctica suggest that it may already be increasing. Melting could in future become 'explosively rapid', Hansen says, especially as icebergs begin to crash into the oceans in ever greater numbers.

There would be a short-term trade-off. Extra energy going into ice melting would raise sea levels faster but leave less energy for raising temperatures. But in the longer run, that would be of no help. For, as more ice melts, it will be replaced by ocean water, tundra or forest. Those darker surfaces will be able to absorb more solar energy than the ice they replace. So we may get accelerated ice melting *and* more warming.

The critical term here is albedo, the measure of the

reflectivity of the planet's surface. Anything that changes the Earth's albedo – whether melting ice or more clouds or pollution itself – will impact on the ability of the Earth to hold on to solar energy just as surely as changes in greenhouse gases. On average the planet's albedo is 30 per cent – which means that 30 per cent of the sunlight reaching the surface is reflected back into space and 70 per cent is absorbed. But that is just an average. In the Arctic, the albedo can rise above 90 per cent, while over cloudless oceans, it can be less than 20 per cent.

During the last ice age, when ice sheets covered a third of the northern hemisphere, the vast expanses of white were enough to increase the planet's albedo from 30 to 33 per cent. That was enough to reduce solar heating of the Earth's surface by an average of 4 watts per square metre. It was responsible for two-thirds of the cooling that created the glaciation itself. And just as more ice raised planetary albedo and cooled the planet back then, so less ice will lower albedo and warm the planet today.

According to albedo expert Veerabhadran Ramanathan of the Scripps Institution of Oceanography at San Diego in California, 'If the planet's albedo dropped by just a tenth from today's level, to 27 per cent, the effect would be comparable to a fivefold increase in atmospheric concentrations of carbon dioxide.' To underline the importance of the issue, Ramanathan is organizing a Global Albedo Project to probe the planet's changing albedo. Lightweight robotic aircraft began flying from the Maldives in the Indian Ocean in early 2006. The project could prove as important as Charles Keeling's measurements of carbon dioxide in the air.

The prognosis for albedo cannot be good. We have already seen how the exposure of oceans in the Arctic is triggering runaway local warming and ice loss that can only amplify global warming. The same is also happening on land. Right around the Arctic, spring is coming earlier. And such is the power of the warming feedbacks that it is coming with ever greater speed. As lakes crack open, rivers reawaken and the ice and snow disappear, the landscape is suddenly able to absorb heat. The 'cold trap' of reflective white ice is sprung, and temperatures can rise by 10 degrees C in a single day. No sooner have the snowsuits come off than travellers are sweltering in shirtsleeves.

Stuart Chapin of the Institute of Arctic Biology in Fairbanks says that the extra ice-free days of a typical Alaskan summer have so far been enough to add 3 watts per square metre to the annual average warming there. As a result, he says, the Arctic is already absorbing three times as much extra heat as most of the rest of the planet. And there are other positive feedbacks at work in the Arctic tundra. In many places, trees and shrubs are advancing north, taking advantage of warmer air and less icy soils. Trees are darker again than tundra plants. And because snow usually falls swiftly off their branches, they provide a dark surface to the sun earlier than the tree-less tundra. Chapin estimates that where trees replace tundra they absorb and transfer to the atmosphere about an extra 5 watts per square metre.

This, incidentally, creates a surprising problem for policymakers trying to combat climate change. Under the Kyoto Protocol, there are incentives for countries to plant trees to soak up carbon dioxide from the atmosphere. They can earn 'carbon credits' equivalent to the carbon taken up as the trees grow, and offset these credits against their emissions in power stations, car exhausts and the like. The idea is to promote cost-effective ways to remove greenhouse gases from the atmosphere, the presumption being that that will cool the planet. But in Arctic regions, the effect will usually be the reverse, because while new trees will indeed absorb carbon dioxide they will also warm the planet by absorbing more solar radiation than the tundra they replace.

Clearly there is a balance between the cooling and warming. But Richard Betts at Britain's Hadley Centre says that in most places in the Arctic the warming will win. In northern Canada, he estimates that the warming effect of a darker landscape will be more than twice the cooling effect from the absorption of carbon dioxide. And in the frozen wastes of eastern Siberia, where trees grow even more slowly, the warming effect will be five times greater. Every tree planted will hasten the spring, hasten the Arctic thaw and hasten global warming.

18

CLOUDS FROM BOTH SIDES
UNCOVERING FLAWS IN THE CLIMATE MODELS

The graph flashed up on the screen for only a few seconds, but it set alarm bells ringing. Had I read it right? The occasion was a workshop on climate change at Britain's Hadley Centre for Climate Prediction, held in Exeter in mid-2004. The room was packed with climate modellers from around the world. Even they raised a collective eyebrow when the graph sank in. If carbon dioxide in the atmosphere doubled from its pre-industrial level, the graph suggested, global warming would rise far above the widely accepted prediction of between 1.5 and 4.5 degrees C. The real warming could be 10 degrees C, or even higher. Surely some mistake? Too much wine at lunch? No. This was for real.

Till now, climate modellers have drawn their graphs of the likely effect of doubling carbon dioxide levels in the form of what is known in the trade as a bell graph. It has a bell shape, with the best estimate of about 3 degrees in the middle and probabilities falling symmetrically either side. So the chance of the real warming being 4.5 degrees, for instance, is the same as of it being 1.5 degrees. But the graph of likely warming that James Murphy of the Hadley Centre was displaying on an overhead screen that morning looked very different. The middle point of the prediction was much the same as everybody else's. But instead of the graph either side being symmetrical and bell shaped, it was highly skewed and had a long 'tail' at the top end of the temperature range. It showed a very real chance of warming from a doubling of carbon dioxide reaching 6, 8, 10 or even 12 degrees C.

Carbon dioxide is widely expected to reach double its pre-industrial levels within a century if we carry on burning coal and oil in what economists call a business-as-usual scenario. But nobody has seriously tried to work out what 10 degrees of extra warming would mean for the planet or for human civilization. It would certainly be cataclysmic.

Let's be clear. Murphy was not making a firm prediction of climatic Armageddon. But nor was this a Hollywood movie. The high temperatures on the display, he said, 'may not be the most likely, but they cannot be discounted'. Nor was Murphy alone with his skewed tail. The meeting also saw a projection by David Stainforth from Oxford University that suggested a plausible warming of 12 degrees C. Six months later, this new generation of scarily skewed distributions started turning up in the scientific journals. Unless the editors take fright, these figures will probably become part of the official wisdom, incorporated into the next report of the IPCC.

So what is going on? For one thing, modellers have for the first time been systematically checking their models for the full range of uncertainties about the sensitivity of the climate system to feedbacks that might be triggered by greenhouse gases. Assessing those efforts for the IPCC was the main task of the Exeter meeting. And what has emerged very strongly is that clouds, which have always been seen as one of the weakest links in the models, are even more of a wild card than anyone had imagined. The old presumption that clouds would not change too much as the world warms is being turned on its head. There may be more clouds. Or fewer. And their climatic impact could alter. It is far from clear if more clouds would damp down the greenhouse effect, as previously thought, or intensify it. Being mostly of an age to remember 1970s Joni Mitchell songs, the climate scientists in Exeter mused over coffee how they had 'looked at clouds from both sides now'. And they didn't like what they saw.

An assessment of the sensitivity of global temperatures to outside forcing – whether changes in sunlight or the addition of greenhouse gases – has been central to climate modelling ever since Svante Arrhenius began his calculations back in the 1890s. This assessment mostly revolves around disentangling the main feedbacks.

Ever since the days of Arrhenius, the three biggest feedbacks in the climate models have been ice, water vapour and clouds. The feedback effect of melting ice on the reflectivity of the planet's surface we have already looked at. It explains why the Arctic is warming faster than elsewhere and giving an extra push to global warming. Water vapour, like carbon dioxide, is a potent greenhouse gas, without which our planet would freeze. The story of what will happen to water vapour is a little less clear-cut. A warmer world will certainly evaporate more water from soils and oceans. This process is already increasing the amount of water vapour in the atmosphere, amplifying warming. In the standard climate models, extra water vapour in the air at least doubles the direct warming effect of carbon dioxide. But it's when we come to clouds that the calculations get sticky.

A lot of water vapour in the air eventually forms clouds. On a first guess, you would say that clouds would have the opposite effect from water vapour, shading us from the sun's rays and keeping air temperatures down. They do that on a summer's day, of course. But at night they generally keep us warm, acting like a blanket that traps heat. Globally, these two effects – or rather their absence – are most pronounced in deserts. Where there are no clouds, the days are boiling, but the nights can get extremely cold, even in the tropics.

The influence of clouds on temperatures turns out also to depend on the nature of the clouds. Attributes such as their height, depth, colour and density can be vital, because different clouds have different optical properties. The wispy cirrus clouds that form in the upper atmosphere heat the atmosphere beneath because they are good at absorbing the sun's rays and re-radiating heat into the air below, whereas the low, flat stratus clouds of a dreary summer's day are good at keeping the world below cool.

Researchers still know surprisingly little about how many and what sort of clouds are above our heads. It only recently emerged that there may be many more cirrus clouds than anyone had thought, for instance. Many are almost invisible to the naked eye, but seem nonetheless highly effective at trapping heat. Some studies suggest that, taken globally, the cooling and warming effects of clouds currently largely cancel each other out, with perhaps a slight overall cooling effect. But nobody is sure.

And even small changes in cloudiness could affect planetary albedo substantially. If a warmer world tipped clouds into causing greater warming, the effects could be considerable.

So what is the prognosis? Again, a first guess is that extra evaporation will make more clouds because a lot of the water vapour will eventually turn into cloud droplets. But even that may not be so simple. Evaporation doesn't just lift water vapour into the air to create more clouds: it also burns off clouds, leaving behind blue skies. And greater evaporation can also make clouds form faster, so that they fill with moisture faster, make raindrops faster and dissipate faster. So, in a greenhouse world, fluffy cumulus clouds that we are used to seeing scudding across the sky all day could instead boil up into dark cumulo-nimbus clouds and rain out, leaving behind more blue skies.

Bruce Wielicki has been trying to figure out the answer to such questions during more than twenty years of cloud-watching at NASA's Langley Research Center in Hampton, Virginia. He says satellite data suggest that clouds still probably have an overall cooling effect on the planet; but, especially in the tropics, there is a trend to clearer skies. Since the mid-1980s, the great tropical convection processes that cause air to rise where the sun is at its fiercest have intensified. As a result, storm clouds are forming and growing more quickly in those areas where the air is rising. This may be increasing the intensity of hurricanes across the tropics. Less obvious is his discovery that the storm clouds not only form more quickly but also rain out more quickly. That leaves the tropics, taken as a whole, drier and less cloudy.

Many researchers see this discovery of clearer tropical skies as strong evidence of an unexpected positive feedback to global warming. But Wielicki is cautious. We need to know, because the tropics are where an estimated two-thirds of the moisture in the atmosphere evaporates – an important element in the planet's thermostat. 'Since clouds are thought to be the weakest link in predicting future climate change, these new results are unsettling – the models may be more uncertain than we had thought,' says Wielicki. His own first guess is that clouds may be between two and four times more important in controlling global temperatures than previously thought.

And that takes us back to the graphs on display in Exeter. To make his graph, Murphy took a standard climate model and tweaked it to reflect the new range of uncertainties for cloud cover, lifetime and thickness. His model responded by delivering much higher probabilities of greater-than-expected warming. 'Variations in cloud feedback played a major role in the predictions of higher temperatures,' he said. Susan Solomon, who as chair of the IPCC's science working group will be the final arbiter on what goes into its next assessment of climate change in 2007, concurs. The biggest difference between models that give high estimates of global warming and those that offer lower predictions, she says, is how they handle cloud feedbacks.

Who is right? Are the fears about a strong positive feedback from clouds correct or not? One way of finding out is to test how the different models reflect the real world today. The IPCC is currently using this approach more widely to help weed out poor models from its analysis. Murphy is in no doubt what the outcome will be. He says that the models that predict low warming 'have a lot of unrealistic representations of clouds. The weeding process suggests higher temperatures.' That is not proof, but it is worrying.

* * *

Clouds are not the only way in which the reflectivity of the Earth's atmosphere is being changed. Planet Earth is becoming hazier; the wild blue yonder is not so blue. The problem is pollution spreading across the northern hemisphere and much of Asia, blotting out the sun. The issue is not just aesthetic. Nor just medical, though millions of people die from the toxic effects of this pollution every year. It is also climatic. While some parts of the world are seeing soaring temperatures, some of the world's most densely populated countries have seen temperatures go into reverse. Climatologists who have spent many years warning about global warming are reaching the conclusion that we may also need to be at least as concerned about the effects of this localized cooling.

The pollutants of concern here are normally lumped together under the name 'aerosols', but they are of many types and come from many sources. The culprits range from operators of power stations in Europe to farmers burning crop stubble in Africa and trees in the Amazon; and from the steel manufacturers of India to millions of women cooking dinner over millions of open cooking stoves across the tropics. Most of these activities produce greenhouse gases, but they also produce aerosols in the form of smoke, soot, dust, smuts of half-burnt vegetation and much tinier but highly reflective sulphate particles. Depending on their characteristics, these aerosols reflect or absorb solar radiation. In fact, most do both in varying quantities. But with one important exception that we shall return to, the dominant effect is cooling. The result is that some parts of the planet, from central Europe to the plains of India and the Amazon jungle to eastern China, have missed out on global warming either permanently or at certain times of the year.

A global cooling to counteract global warming might seem a good idea. Sadly things are not so simple. The competing forces are pulling the climate system in two different directions that may not so much counteract as inflame each other. Certainly they introduce a new element of uncertainty in atmospheric processes. But while, for excellent public health reasons, many countries are trying to reduce their emissions of smog-making aerosols, the clean-up will lift the 'parasol of pollution' over those countries. The likely result will be an instant burst of warming that could happen within days of the pollution clearing.

We can see evidence of this already in central Europe. Fifteen years ago, countries like Poland, Czechoslovakia and East Germany reeked with the smell of burning fossil fuels from the old Soviet-style heavy industries. Chimneys belched and smogs were endemic. The region where the three countries met became known as the 'black triangle'. The pollution was having a local cooling effect more than twice as great as the warming effect of greenhouse gases. Since the fall of the Berlin Wall, the old polluting industries have mostly shut down and the air has cleared. More sun penetrates the smog-filled landscape and central Europe has warmed correspondingly. In the past fifteen years, temperatures here have risen at three times the global average rate.

This real-world experiment shows clearly the power of aerosols to cool the Earth's surface. And it raises another question for the future: how much warming is being stored up globally by aerosols? 'We are dealing with a coiled spring, with temperatures being held back by aerosols,' says Susan Solomon, chief scientist for the IPCC. 'If you shut off aerosols today, temperatures would increase rapidly, but we don't yet know exactly how much because we don't know how coiled the spring is.' The best guess until recently was that aerosols were holding back a quarter of the warming, or about 0.2 degrees C. In other words, a greenhouse warming of 0.8 degrees since pre-industrial times has been reduced by aerosols to a current warming of 0.6 degrees. But critics say this calculation is little more than a guess, and the first efforts at more direct measurement of radiation changes caused by aerosols suggest that the spring may be much more tightly coiled.

I was present at one of the first meetings where these ideas were discussed in detail. The occasion was a workshop of climate scientists held at Dahlem, a quiet suburb of Berlin, in 2003. The meeting was discussing 'earth system analysis', and the man who brought the issue to the table was the distinguished Dutch atmospheric chemist Paul Crutzen, a brilliant and creative mind who first divined many of the secrets of the chemicals behind the destruction of the ozone layer. Back in the 1980s, Crutzen had stumbled on the notion that during a nuclear war, so many fires would be produced that the smoke would darken the day 'and temperatures would crash'. The effect was termed 'nuclear winter'. That insight has led to continued analysis of the role of smoke and other aerosols in climate and Crutzen's conclusion, argued in Dahlem, that aerosols could be disguising not a quarter but anything between a half and three-quarters of the present greenhouse effect. 'They are giving us a false sense of security,' he said. Past calculations of the cooling effect of aerosols, he said, had been inferred by comparing the warming predicted by climate models with actual warming. The aerosol cooling effect was reckoned as the warming that had 'gone missing'. But as modeller Stephen Schwartz of the Brookhaven National Laboratory put it on another occasion, 'that approach assumes that we know that the climate model is accurate, which of course is what needs to be tested.'

After dinner – over a few Heinekens, as I remember – Peter Cox, a hard-thinking, hard-drinking climate modeller then at the Met Office in England, did some back-of-the-bar-mat calculations about what Crutzen's conjecture might mean for future climate. He became rather absorbed. A couple of bottles later he had come to the conclusion that, if Crutzen was right, the true warming effect of doubling carbon dioxide could be more than twice as high as existing estimates, at between 7 and 10 degrees C. The following morning his more sober colleagues registered agreement. I went home and wrote a story for *New Scientist*, quoting Cox's numbers and the workshop's conclusion that the findings had 'dramatic consequences for estimates of future climate change'. I was rather excited by it, but the story singularly failed to interest the rest of the world.

Later Cox, his Hadley Centre colleague Chris Jones, and Meinrat Andreae of the Max Planck Institute for Chemistry in Mainz tested the guesses in more detail, and reached the same conclusions as Cox had on his bar mat. They did it by running climate models that assumed either a low greenhouse warming moderated by a small cooling from aerosols or a bigger greenhouse warming held back by a bigger aerosol cooling. They reported in *Nature* that the 'best fit' involved a warming from doubling greenhouse gases that, without the moderating effect of aerosols, would be 'in excess of 6 degrees' and 'may be as high as 10 degrees'.

'Such an enormous increase in temperatures would be greater than the temperature changes from the previous ice age to the present,' said Andreae. 'It is so far outside the range covered by our experience and scientific understanding that we cannot with any confidence predict the consequences for the Earth.'

Still the world didn't take much notice. I asked Andreae about this strange indifference. 'It's always amazing,' he e-mailed me, 'how many people don't see how important this issue is for the future development of the climate system.' The discussion at the Dahlem meeting had rather changed his world view, he said. 'Before the Dahlem meeting, I was becoming a kind of climate complacent, in the sense that I was convinced of coming global warming, but felt that it was going to be a couple of degrees and we could deal with that. Also, I felt that the aerosols were doing us a favour in slowing and reducing warming. But after it I came to realize that the aerosols brake will come off global warming, and also that the aerosol cooling introduces a great uncertainty about climate sensitivity. I'm now in a situation where as a human being I hope that I'm wrong as a scientist. If we are right with our current assessment, there are really dire times ahead.'

Models are only models, of course. But whatever the precise scale of the current aerosol effect, it would be quite wrong to imagine that it can carry on protecting us from the worst as global warming gathers pace. That is because aerosols and greenhouse gases have very different lifespans in the atmosphere. Aerosols stay for only a few days before they are washed to the ground in rain. By contrast, carbon dioxide has a lifespan of a century or more. If, for the sake of argument, we stuck with current emission levels of both aerosols and carbon dioxide, the aerosol levels in the air would stay the same. There would be no accumulation and no increase in the cooling effect. But carbon dioxide levels would carry on rising and bring with them ever greater warming.

Probably. The trouble is that scientific knowledge about aerosols is, if anything, even poorer than it is about the effects of clouds. Says Stephen Schwartz: 'There are many different kinds of aerosols, lots of interactions among them and unknown issues of cloud microphysics – all of which need to be better understood. This is hard science which I am afraid nobody has come to grips with yet.' There is no dispute that some aerosols, such as sulphate particles from coal-fired power stations, predominantly scatter sunlight and reflect it back into space. They increase albedo and cool the planet for sure. But others have some scattering effect but also absorb solar radiation and then re-radiate it, warming the atmosphere around. And with them it is harder to be sure where the balance between the two effects lies.

Here the biggest concern is soot, the black carbon produced from the incomplete burning of coal, biomass or diesel. Scientific understanding of the role of soot is, to be frank, all over the place, as a quick scan of the major scientific journals makes clear. In March 2000, a paper in *Science* said soot was 'masking global warming'; eleven months later another in its chief rival *Nature* said soot was 'generating global warming'. Ten months later presentations at a big US conference of the American Geophysical Union called it variously a 'cooling agent' and 'the biggest cause of global warming after carbon dioxide'.

The truth seems to be this. A cloud of soot – whether from a forest fire, a cooking stove or an industrial boiler – shields the Earth from the sun's rays, thus cooling the ground beneath. But it also absorbs some of that radiation and converts it to heat, which it radiates into the surrounding air. So soot cools the ground but warms the air. The ground doesn't move but the air does, so the cooling effect, while intense, is mostly located near the pollution source, while the warming effect, though less intense, extends much further.

There is still great uncertainty about the precise role of soot in global climate. Jim Hansen suggests that it could be responsible for up to a quarter of warming over parts of the northern hemisphere. He believes that soot may be the third most important man-made contributor to the greenhouse effect, behind carbon dioxide and methane, and that controlling it offers one of the cheapest, most effective and quickest ways of curbing global warming. Even so, in those parts of the world where it is produced in large quantities it is undoubtedly cooling the land. Those parts of the world are mainly in Asia. And now there is a new concern. Could aerosol emissions in India and China turn off the Asian monsoon?

19

A BILLION FIRES

HOW BROWN HAZE COULD TURN OFF THE MONSOON

I have been travelling to India for twenty years now. Not regularly, but often enough to notice that every time I go, the air seems to be dirtier and more choked with black smoke and fumes. In the cities, much of this comes from the exhaust pipes of the millions of ill-maintained diesel-burning buses and two-stroke rickshaws that ply the gridlocked streets. The haze also contains natural sea salt and mineral dust, a fair amount of fly ash and sulphur dioxide from India's coal-burning power stations, and huge amounts of organic material and soot from the countryside. For in India's million villages, where most of its billion-strong population still live, the air is often scarcely better than it is in the cities, with smoke billowing from a hundred million cooking stoves, all burning wood, dried cow dung and crop residues.

This smoke is becoming a major climatic phenomenon. It is merging into one giant cloud that climate researchers call India's 'brown haze'. Its heart is over the north Indian plain, one of the world's most densely populated areas, which suffers near-constant smogs during the winter months. They are a giant version of the old pea-souper smogs that used to hit London in the days when the city was heated by coal fires. As I complete this chapter, Delhi fogs are reportedly worse than ever, with thick fog preventing flights from its airport. But the haze spreads more widely, shrouding the whole of India and beyond.

The term 'brown haze' was coined by scientists during the first investigation of the phenomenon. In 1999, some two hundred scientists taking part in the Indian Ocean Experiment (INDOEX) assembled in the Maldives for a three-month blitz measuring the air over India and the Indian Ocean from aircraft and ships. The results were a surprise, even to those who had planned the project. Every winter, from November to April, a pall of smog more than 2 kilometres thick occupied a huge area south of the Himalayas, stretching from Nepal through India and Pakistan, out over the Arabian Sea and the Bay of Bengal, and even south of the equator as far as the Seychelles and the Chagos Islands. It covered 10 million square kilometres, an area seven times the size of India.

'To find thick brown smog 4,000 metres up in the Himalayas, and over the coral islands of the Maldives, was a shock,' says Paul Crutzen, one of the masterminds of the project. Crutzen, who predicted a dramatic thinning of the ozone layer fifteen years before it happened, said the haze had a similar potential to cause 'unpleasant environmental surprise' in India and beyond. The haze could, he said, have 'very major consequences' for the atmosphere.

The INDOEX findings proved controversial in India, which appeared to be singled out for criticism. Why pick on us? locals asked. Indian government scientists issued a detailed and largely spurious 'rebuttal'. The INDOEX scientists quickly switched from talking about an Indian brown haze to discussing the 'Asian brown haze' – and quite rightly, for the haze is an Asia-wide phenomenon. But when I used that term at a meeting in India in mid-2005, I was hissed. Even mentioning an Asian haze is considered politically incorrect today. Why single out Asia? they ask. In fact antagonism has got so great that many Indian scientists now refuse to discuss the subject with foreigners like me, for fear of getting into political hot water.

India has been the focus of attention because its aerosol pollution is of genuinely global importance. Dorothy Koch of Columbia University in New York estimates that a third of the soot reaching the Arctic, sending pollution meters soaring from Mount Zeppelin in Svalbard to northern Canada, comes from South Asia. The soot is falling out onto the snow and ice, making the white surface darker and so triggering melting. When her findings were published in April 2005, one headline read: 'Home fires in India help to melt the Arctic icecap half a world away'. No wonder the Indians are twitchy. Suddenly a country with one of the lowest per-capita emissions of greenhouse gases in the world was being fingered as a prime cause of climate change.

But, wary though they may be in public, India's scientists have been at work finding out where the pollution all comes from. At first, they assumed that most must be the product of India's fast-growing and un-doubtedly polluting industries. But at the Indian Institute of Technology in Mumbai, they have been busy in the lab mocking up Indian rural kitchens to check emissions from cooking stoves of the kind found right across the Indian countryside. They fuelled the fires with wood, crop waste and dried cattle manure; and on the stoves, they boiled kettles and even cooked lunch. They concluded that smoke emissions from Indian domestic cooking fires produce between 1 and 2 million tonnes of aerosols a year, including a quarter of a million tonnes of soot. That makes them responsible for some 40 per cent of India's aerosol emissions.

Discussion about the climatic impact of the Asian brown haze has become a statistical minefield. The 'head-line figure', widely quoted, is that the haze reduces the amount of solar radiation reaching the Earth's surface over India in winter by an average of about 22 watts per square metre. That is a reduction of about a tenth, and would be enough to cause massive cooling. The statistic is literally true, but only part of the story. For only about 7 watts of that radiation is lost entirely, 'backscattered' into space. The other 15 watts is absorbed by the soot in the aerosols and re-radiated, heating the atmosphere. Thus, though the radiation budget is much altered, the cooling effect is much less than it might otherwise be. Even so, in winter it is sufficient both to counteract global warming and to cool the air across much of India by an average of about 0.5 degrees C. In summer, when the pollution is rained out in the monsoon and the skies are clearer, temperatures have risen in recent decades by about 0.5 degrees C, in line with the global average.

The consequences don't end there, says Veerabhadran Ramanathan, the Indian scientist who, with Crutzen, masterminded INDOEX from the Scripps Institution of Oceanography at San Diego in California. In particular, the cooling impact of the haze over the Indian land surface delays the heating of the land that stimulates the monsoon winds. It thus threatens the lifeblood of India: the monsoon rains.

There seems to be some confusion among scientists about the Indian monsoon. Scientists investigating the brown haze all claim that the monsoon has weakened in recent decades, and they see this as a likely effect of the haze. But researchers investigating global warming are equally certain that it has increased in intensity. What undisputed evidence there is suggests that the monsoon rains have become more intense in the traditionally wetter south of India, where the haze is less strong, but they have diminished in the north, where the haze is thickest. How those trends develop is obviously of vast importance for a country entirely dependent on just a hundred days of monsoon rains to water the crops that feed a billion people. A collapse of the monsoon in South Asia would be a global calamity of immense proportions.

And South Asia may not be alone. East Asia could be in the same boat – a situation that would threaten food production for the world's most populous nation, China. North of the Himalayas, there is a similar intense winter brown haze, though it is composed less of the smoke from burning cow dung and more from the sulphur dioxide and other fumes from burning Chinese coal. And it is interrupting the sun. When Yun Qian and Dale Kaiser from the US government's Northwest National Laboratory in Richmond, Washington, studied the records of Chinese meteorological sunshine recorders over the past fifty years, they found a recent decline in sunshine in the most polluted south and east of the country of 5–6 per cent since 1980.

This decline is lowering temperatures. While global

warming is evident across much of China, daytime temperatures in the most polluted regions have fallen by about 0.6 degrees C. That in turn seems to be altering rainfall patterns. In the south of the country, the monsoon rains are becoming stronger, with flooding in the great southern river, the Yangtze; whereas further north, in the catchment of the Yellow River, there is now less rainfall. Chinese records, which are among the most meticulous in the world, suggest that this shift is the biggest alteration to the country's rainfall patterns in a thousand years. To some extent the links between the rainfall trends and the increasing brown haze are conjecture. But when climate models are programmed to include a strong Asian brown haze many of them produce extra rainfall in southern China, coupled with near-permanent droughts in the north. So, if the models are right, while the haze lingers these major calamities are set to continue.

Meinrat Andreae estimates that about 7 billion tonnes of biomass is burned in the tropics each year – about 1 tonne for every inhabitant on the Earth. All of it produces aerosols that billow into the air.

Asian countries, with their huge populations, have the worst smogs. But parts of Africa and the Brazilian Amazon are also shrouded when farmers clear land for crops by burning grasslands and forests. In the Brazilian Amazon, hundreds of thousands of fires burn each year, covering the area with billowing dense smoke. During the weeks of burning, the amount of sunshine reaching the ground drops by a typical 16 per cent. In Zambia, studies have found a 22 per cent drop in sunlight as the savannah is burned.

The changes are 'causing all sorts of havoc with the

atmospheric circulation', says Dale Kaiser, who is the author of the Amazon study. Over the Amazon, he says, the smoke causes cooling and suppresses the formation of raindrops. That both reduces rainfall and keeps the aerosols in the air for longer. Meanwhile, the build-up of water vapour results in the upper atmosphere becoming wetter, according to Daniel Rosenfeld of the Hebrew University, who flew research planes through the smoke over the Amazon. It eventually forms a few extremely intense thunderstorms, known in the trade as 'hot towers', that cause hail storms. Hail only falls in the Amazon when fires have been burning.

Some of these changes could have impacts far beyond the regions where the smoke forms. Condensation in the Amazon 'hot towers' releases very large amounts of heat into the upper atmosphere, influencing jet streams and other wind patterns across the tropics and beyond. And more water vapour may reach the stratosphere, where it could increase ozone destruction. Meanwhile, modelling studies supervised by Jim Hansen suggest that soot emissions over India and China may trigger drought in the African Sahel and even warming in western Canada – though exactly how remains unclear.

These impacts are, of course, only the predictions of climate models. It is hard to prove whether they reflect events in the real world. But the models are based on real physical processes in the atmosphere. So at the least, they suggest the potential for a worldwide climatic effect from aerosol emissions in the tropics. Cooking stoves in India, it seems, could have global consequences.

20

HYDROXYL HOLIDAY

THE DAY THE PLANET'S CLEANER DIDN'T SHOW FOR WORK

It could be the doomsday that creeps up on us unawares: the collapse of the atmosphere's cleansing service. For one of the most disturbing secrets of our planet's metabolism is that just one chemical is responsible for cleaning most of the pollution out of the atmosphere. If it took a day off, we would be in serious trouble, with smogs spreading unchecked across the planet.

The chemical in question is called hydroxyl. Its molecules are made up of one atom of oxygen and one atom of hydrogen. It is created when ultraviolet radiation bombards common gases such as ozone and water vapour. But it is the most ephemeral of chemicals. Almost as soon as it is created, it reacts with some other molecule, mostly some polluting substance, and is gone again. It has an average lifetime of about a second. Because it comes and goes so fast, it is also rather rare, with an average concentration in the atmosphere of less than one part per trillion. You could pack every last molecule of the stuff into the Great Pyramid in Egypt and still have room for two more atmosphere's worth.

Yet it is crucial to life on Earth. For hydroxyl is, more or less literally, the atmosphere's detergent. It transforms all manner of gaseous pollutants so that they become soluble in water and wash away in the rain. The process is called oxidation. So, to take one example, it converts sulphur dioxide, which would otherwise clog up the air for months, to acid rain, which soon falls to the ground. Much the same happens to carbon monoxide and methane – both of which are oxidized to carbon dioxide – to nitrogen oxide and many others. The one major pollutant it doesn't neutralize is carbon dioxide, which, partly as a result, has a much longer lifetime in the atmosphere than most other pollutants.

Concentrations of hydroxyl are generally much higher in the warm air over the tropics, where the ultraviolet radiation is most intense, but are close to non-existent in the Arctic, where, despite ozone holes, there is usually little ultraviolet around to make more hydroxyl. As a result, 'toxic chemicals that might survive for only a few days in the tropics will last for a year or more in Arctic air,' says Frank Wania of the University of Toronto. That is one reason, he says, why pollutants like acid hazes and pesticides accumulate in the Arctic, poisoning polar bears and much else.

Hydroxyl has a hard life keeping up with our polluting gases, especially since it is destroyed in the process of oxidizing them. Fears that the atmosphere's janitor could be overworked and in trouble go back a few years. But because the chemical is so transient and rare, it is virtually impossible to measure hydroxyl concentrations directly. All the estimates are indirect, based on measuring chemicals with which it reacts. So when Joel Levine, a NASA chemist, suggested back in the 1980s that there could have been a 25 per cent decline in hydroxyl in the air in the previous thirty years, his argument didn't make much headway because he couldn't prove it. There was no chance of his producing something definitive like the Keeling curve on carbon dioxide.

Much the same fate befell a brief forecast in the 2001 IPCC report of a possible 20 per cent decline in hydroxyl by the year 2100 because of excess demands placed on it by a rising tide of pollution, and a report the same year by Ronald Prinn, a leading atmospheric chemist from the Massachusetts Institute of Technology, of a possible decline in global hydroxyl levels during the 1990s. But we should be concerned.

Hydroxyl spends more time oxidizing one chemical than any other. That chemical is carbon monoxide. Emitted mostly from forest fires, fossil fuel burning and small domestic stoves, it has for many years been the Cinderella pollutant. Dangerous to humans in confined spaces, it has been largely ignored as an environmental pollutant. The biggest concern has been that it oxidizes to carbon dioxide. But its concentration in the air tripled worldwide during the twentieth century. That suggests a bottleneck that could be the prelude to a wider break-down of the cleansing service.

In the absence of good data on hydroxyl and its works, probably the best hope of identifying a problem ahead of time is through modelling. Sasha Madronich of the National Center for Atmospheric Research in Boulder, Colorado, is one of the few researchers to attempt to model how hydroxyl might respond to changing pollution levels. He says that the atmospheric cleansing service could have a breaking point. 'Under high pollution, the chemistry of the atmosphere becomes chaotic and extremely unpredictable. Beyond certain threshold values, hydroxyl can decrease catastrophically,' he says. Many urban areas, he says, 'are already sufficiently polluted that hydroxyl levels are locally suppressed'. This is partly because the sheer volume of pollution consumes all the available hydroxyl, but also because the smog itself prevents ultraviolet radiation from penetrating into the air to create more.

'The oxidation processes that should clean the air virtually shut down in smog-bound cities like Athens and Mexico City,' he says. It takes a breath of fresh air from the countryside to revive them. 'If, in future, large parts of the atmosphere are as polluted as these cities are today, then we could anticipate the collapse of hydroxyl on a global scale.' With large areas of Asia becoming sub-merged beneath a cloud of 'brown haze' every year, it may be that the atmosphere is approaching just such a crisis. Nobody knows.

But the doomsday scenario may require another element. If the clean-up chemical is under pressure from too much dirt, the worst thing to happen would be a decline in supply of the chemical. So the critical question may be: what might reduce the amount of hydroxyl pro-duced by the atmosphere? Clearly smogs are a problem because they reduce ultraviolet radiation in the lower atmosphere. But a thicker ozone layer, nature's protective filter against ultraviolet, could have the same effect. And the world is currently working quite hard to repair the damaged ozone layer and make it thicker. This creates an unpleaseant double-bind.

The worry is that over the past thirty or so years, we have

been living on borrowed time with hydroxyl. We have thinned the ozone layer, and so let more ultraviolet radiation into the lower atmosphere. And while that is bad for marine ecosystems and probably causing more skin cancers, it has ensured a beefed-up supply of hydroxyl to cleanse the air of many pollutants. Arguably, it has helped the planetary cleansing service keep on top of a rising tide of pollution. Over the next half-century, we should succeed in healing the ozone layer once again. There are good ecological, human health and even climatic reasons for doing this. But it could have a downside.

So here is the doomsday scenario. If we repair the ozone layer, we will reduce hydroxyl production back to levels in the mid-twentieth century. But we will be doing it at a time when the demands on hydroxyl's services are considerably higher than they were in the mid-twentieth century. That could be the moment when Madronich's threshold is crossed and oxidation processes in the atmosphere go into sharp decline. I have no data, no models and no peer-reviewed papers to justify this scenario. It is just that: a scenario and not a prediction. But it is plausible speculation. It could conceivably happen.

PART FIVE

ICE AGES AND SOLAR PULSES

21
GOLDILOCKS AND THE THREE PLANETS

WHY THE EARTH IS 'JUST RIGHT' FOR LIFE

Our sun has an inner ring of planets, starting with Mercury and moving out to Venus, the Earth and Mars. Right from their births 5 billion years ago as cosmic debris, these planets have been more than lumps of rock. For one thing, they are hot, with a thin solid crust hiding a large molten core. Turbulent chemistry in the depths releases gases through the crusts. While Mercury was too small and had too weak a gravity to capture these gases, the other three have held on to at least some of these gases, creating atmospheres. Those atmospheres contain greenhouse gases such as carbon dioxide, water vapour and methane that trap solar heat and create climates.

The three atmospheres of the three planets were initially probably rather similar, but they have evolved in very different ways. Today, Venus has a thick atmosphere with enough greenhouse gases to hold temperatures at around 450 degrees C. Mars appears once to have had a considerable atmosphere and a climate that supported rainfall. It may have had life as well. But somewhere along the way, it lost much of its atmosphere and dried up, and any life is now presumed dead. The demise of this life-support system on Mars is a conundrum, because the planet has plenty of carbon at its surface. That carbon was probably once floating in the atmosphere in the form of carbon dioxide, where it would have formed a blanket sufficiently warm for liquid water and for life. But most of that carbon has ended up in rocks.

The Earth, by contrast, has a rich and chemically very active atmosphere, and a sufficiency of greenhouse gases to maintain equable temperatures and lots of liquid water – and it is very much alive. Some planetary scientists have dubbed the Earth the 'Goldilocks planet'. When in the children's story Goldilocks tasted porridge at the house of the three bears she found one bowl (Venus) too hot, one (Mars) too cold, but one (Earth) just right. At first sight, this seems the purest chance. Earth must have been just the right distance from the sun. And yet, since in the early days the three planets had very similar atmospheres, the theory has developed that their different fates had as much to do with the fates of those atmospheres as with their distance from the sun.

The Earth's atmosphere has certainly endured, and proved a congenial place for the development of myriad life forms. Things were often difficult in the early days, it is true. At various points, the planet seems to have been entirely covered in ice and snow, with life surviving only in warm crevasses beneath the frozen exterior. The fate of Mars beckoned. 'It was a close call,' says Joe Kirschvink of the Californian Institute of Technology in Pasadena, who first coined the term Snowball Earth to describe this condition, which last occurred some 600 million years ago. He believes that the planet only escaped a fate similar to that of Mars because carbon dioxide was emitted from volcanoes beneath the ice. 'If the Earth had been a bit further from the Sun, the temperature at the poles could have dropped enough to freeze the carbon dioxide, robbing us of this greenhouse escape from Snowball Earth.'

Despite such difficulties, the Earth came through and, for the last half-billion years at least, has maintained a surprisingly constant temperature. Not, as we shall see, completely constant, but surprisingly constant given the cosmic forces being played out around it. In particular there was the sun. It is the main source of most of the energy and warmth at the Earth's surface, of course. By comparison, the contribution of the heat from the Earth's core is minute. But the sun has changed a great deal over the lifetime of the Earth. Back in the early days – for about the first billion years of the Earth's existence – it was a weak beast. It emitted about a third less energy than it does today. Even 500 million years ago, it was as much as 10 per cent weaker than today. Yet, with Snowball Earth a distant memory, the world seems to have been warmer then than it is now, and ice free. This was because the atmosphere was rich in methane, carbon dioxide and water vapour, all forming a thick blanket keeping the planet and its growing armies of primitive life warm. Volcanic activity was still strong, so new releases of carbon dioxide topped up any leakage from the atmosphere, keeping concentrations around twenty times higher than today.

But as the planet has aged, the emissions from volcanoes have reduced and carbon dioxide has gradually started to disappear from the atmosphere. Its decline may at various times have threatened a return of Snowball

Earth, and a Martian relapse into a cold, lifeless world. But the decline may ultimately have saved the planet from a similar fate to that of Venus. This raises an interesting question. Did this happy Goldilocks outcome happen entirely by chance? Or could the planet have developed some kind of crude thermostat? The surprising answer is that it seems to have done just that.

Carbon dioxide, then as now, was removed from the atmosphere of the Earth by being dissolved in rain to form dilute carbonic acid. That acid ate away at rocks on the ground, which were made primarily of calcium silicate, creating calcium carbonate, which ended up as sediment on the floor of the oceans. This process has a temperature control built in, because the amount of rain depends on the temperature. So erosion rates rise when it is warm. But faster erosion removes more carbon dioxide from the air and lowers temperatures again. If the thermostat over-shoots and it gets too cold, then the rate of weathering slows and temperatures recover. This is a negative feed-back operating through the carbon cycle. It won't save us today, because it takes millions of years to have a serious impact. But over geological timescales, it was probably rather good at moderating temperature and keeping the planet at temperatures convenient for life.

Very convenient. Suspiciously so, thought the charismatic British chemist and inventor Jim Lovelock back in the 1980s. Lovelock wondered if life itself might be controlling this process; and soon afterwards two of his acolytes, Tyler Volk and David Schwartzman, suggested that he was right by demonstrating that basalt rocks erode a thousand times faster in the presence of organisms such as bacteria. This introduces a new and extremely dynamic negative feedback. More bacteria will keep the planet cool. But if the air gets too cool, the planet becomes covered in ice, the bacteria die, the erosion slows and the atmosphere warms again. This process is potentially an extremely powerful thermostat for planet Earth and is one of the foundation stones of Lovelock's grand vision of the Earth as a self-regulating system called Gaia. It might also explain why the carbon cycle feedback did not save Mars: perhaps, at some critical moment, the red planet did not have enough life to make it work properly.

Lovelock is a controversial character. Now in his eighties, he first devised his idea of Gaia while working for NASA and trying to think of ways to discover if other planets had life. He figured that the best way was to look for signs of gases that could only be made or maintained in the air by life forms. And he began to realize that life could evolve quite naturally in ways that would maintain an environment that suited it. He argues that, since the early days, life on Earth has evolved sophisticated strategies for stabilizing climate over long timescales. For him, the temperature of life on Earth was 'just right' because life made it so by taking control of key planetary life-support systems like the carbon cycle.

For many years, Lovelock was virtually cast out of the scientific community. Gaia was seen by many as quasi-religious mumbo-jumbo. Major journals like *Nature* and *Science* would not publish his work. He made his living as a freelance inventor of scientific devices. But his idea of the Earth as, metaphorically at least, a single living organism has made him the spiritual father of a whole generation of Earth system scientists. Whether or not you buy the notion of a living Earth, his way of thinking about the Earth as a single system with its own feedbacks has been extremely influential.

* * *

The thermostat, whether run by life or geology, is pretty crude. For some 400 million years, planet Earth has been getting cooler. Some see this as a refutation of Gaian ideas. But others, like Greg Retallack, a soil scientist at the University of Oregon, argue that the cooling happened because life, or at any rate large parts of it, wanted it that way. Plants in particular, he says, like it cool. And plants have proved extremely efficient at capturing carbon dioxide and burying it permanently where it cannot return to the atmosphere. Some 7 trillion tonnes of old vegetable carbon have been stored for tens of millions of years beneath the Earth's surface in the form of fossil fuels. In addition, probably as much methane is captured in frozen clathrates beneath the ocean bed. That is a lot of warming stored away, as we are currently in danger of discovering the hard way. .

The cooling of the Earth has been a long, slow and fitful process. Around 55 million years ago, as we saw earlier, Earth experienced the 'biggest fart in history', a vast surge of methane into the atmosphere from the undersea clathrate store that pushed air temperatures up by around 5 degrees C. That was clearly no part of a Gaian grand plan. But Gaians would argue that life-mediated feedbacks resumed control. The methane eventually decayed to carbon dioxide, which was in turn absorbed back into the oceans. But even after normal services had been resumed, levels of carbon dioxide in the atmosphere were still about five times higher than they are today – at around 2,000 parts per million. Within a million years or so, however, those concentrations began to fall sharply. (Sharply, that is, on geological timescales, for the average pace of decline was less than one-ten-thousandth of the rate of increase in recent decades.) By 40 million years ago, they had subsided to 700 ppm. And by around 24 million years ago, they were below 500 ppm, probably for the first time since the planet's earliest days.

It was around then that an ice sheet spread across Antarctica – the first permanent ice to form on the planet for hundreds of millions of years. And by about 3 million years ago, another surge of cooling had begun, resulting in ice sheets forming in the northern hemisphere, too. Explanations for this general cooling range from continental drift in the western Pacific to another turn of the Gaian thermostat. But we can leave that to one side. Because the ice ages themselves – the geologically brief but extremely vicious cold snaps within the general cooling trend – happened on timescales of much more interest in our current climatic predicament. Unravelling the causes of the ice ages may, many climate scientists believe, provide vital clues to our own fate in the coming decades.

22

THE BIG FREEZE

HOW A WOBBLE IN OUR ORBIT TRIGGERED
THE ICE AGES

The discovery that the world had once been plunged into
an ice age was one of the great scientific revelations of the
nineteenth century. It was to Earth sciences what Charles
Darwin's theories on evolution were to life sciences. It
changed everything. The story emerged gradually, but the
first man to perceive the scale of the glaciation that had
overtaken so much of the northern hemisphere was a
Swiss naturalist called Louis Agassiz. While Agassiz was
summering in the Alps in 1836, his host pointed out giant
scratch marks on the mountainsides that showed, he said,
how glaciers must once have extended much further down
their valleys.

Agassiz pondered the significance of this. He realized
that he had seen similar marks in the landscape in many
parts of Europe that were distant from present-day
glaciers. He heard similar reports of glacial scratch marks
from across North America. And he read newspaper
stories of perfectly preserved mammoths being dug from

the snow in Siberia, their meat so fresh that it was fed to local dogs and scavenged by polar bears. The only explanation, he concluded, was that much of the northern hemisphere must once have been ice covered and that the event happened very suddenly, in a vast ice apocalypse. 'The land of Europe, previously covered with tropical vegetation and inhabited by herds of great elephants, enormous hippopotami and gigantic carnivore, was suddenly buried under a vast expanse of ice,' he wrote. 'The movement of a powerful creation was supplanted by the silence of death.'

His vision was like a creation myth in reverse. Advances in geology soon revealed that there was not one ice age but a whole series of glaciations, occurring at intervals of roughly every 100,000 years and separated by warm periods like our own. But his picture has otherwise survived remarkably intact. Indeed recent evidence has revived his original idea that the onset of the last ice age must have been rather fast, with temperatures crashing in at most a couple of hundred years and very probably much less.

We now know that two main ice sheets formed. One stretched from the British Isles, across the North Sea and Scandinavia, and then east through Russia and western Siberia and north across the Barents Sea as far as Svalbard. A second, even larger, sheet covered the whole of Canada and southern Alaska with a spur extending over Greenland. Another smaller sheet sat over Iceland, and the seas around were covered in thick floating sea ice. Strangely, northern Alaska and eastern Siberia, though deep frozen, were never covered in ice. But, combined with the older ice covering Antarctica, these sheets contained three times more ice than is present on the Earth today – enough to keep sea levels worldwide some 120 metres lower than today – and covered 30 per cent of the Earth's land surface. The ice sheets were high as well as broad, rising up to 4 kilometres above the land surface. They chilled the air above and acted as a barricade against the prevailing westerly winds, which were forced south, skirting round the ice sheets. This perpetuated the ice sheets, since the winds would have been the most obvious source of warmth to melt them.

Temperatures fell by around 5 degrees C as a global average, but were 20 degrees lower than they are today in parts of Greenland, while just 3 degrees lower in the western Pacific Ocean. The world beyond the ice sheets became dry and cold. Deserts covered the American Midwest, France and the wide lands of Europe and Asia between Germany and the modern-day Gobi desert in Mongolia. Further south, the Sahara desert expanded, the Asian monsoon was largely extinguished and the tropical rainforests of Africa and South America contracted to a few refuges, surrounded by grasslands. At the low point around 70,000 years ago, even the grasslands were largely extinguished, leaving huge expanses of desert, from where winds whipped up huge dust storms. Humans lived by hunting on the plains and hunkering down in the small areas where lush vegetation persisted despite the cold and arid conditions.

It was clear to Agassiz and his fellow researchers from the start that something drastic must have triggered all this. Astronomical forces were suggested early on: in particular, the idea that the gravitational pull of other planets in the solar system such as Jupiter could influence the steady ebb and flow of the seasons, and in that way cause glaciers and ice sheets to grow. Many scientists of the day played with this idea. But the first man to subject it to detailed analysis was a Scottish son of a crofter with virtually no formal learning but a passion for self-education and an extraordinary streak of diligence. James Croll was a shy, large-framed man with big ambitions. He stumbled on the idea of an astronomical cause for the ice age while reading in libraries and, transfixed, spent most of the 1860s and 1870s pursuing the idea. He took numerous jobs, from insurance salesman to school caretaker to carpenter, in order to finance his passion.

The astronomical forces, he discovered, have three principal effects on the Earth, all of which slightly alter the distribution of the solar radiation reaching the Earth. The effects are greatest in polar regions, where they can alter the amount of sunlight by as much as 10 per cent. First, they change the shape of the Earth's annual orbit round the sun. The orbit is not circular but slightly elliptical, and the shape of this ellipse changes according to the gravitational pull on the Earth of the other orbiting planets. This variation in the 'eccentricity' of the Earth's orbit has a cycle that repeats itself about every 100,000 years.

As well as orbiting the sun once every year, the Earth spins, making one revolution every day. But the axis round which it spins is not quite at right angles to the direction of the orbit around the sun. So looked at from space, the Earth appears to be spinning on a slight tilt. The interaction between the orbit around the sun and the tilt of the axis of the Earth is what gives us our seasons, because it means that at certain times of the year the northern and southern hemispheres see more or less of the sun. But this situation is not static. The astronomical forces also gradually alter the tilt of the axis. This change in the Earth's 'inclination' causes a difference in the intensity of the seasons. It has a 41,000-year cycle.

Finally, there is a further wobble in the axis around which the Earth rotates, called the precession. This is exactly like the wobble that affects a spinning top. It influences the time of year when the different hemispheres are furthest from or nearest to the sun. It is complicated by its relationship with the other two effects, but repeats on a cycle of between 19,000 and 23,000 years. Currently the northern hemisphere has its summer and the southern hemisphere has its winter when the Earth is farthest from the sun; 10,000 years ago, it was the other way round.

It turns out that the 'eccentricity' of the Earth's orbit around the sun drives the 100,000-year cycles into and out of ice ages. Meanwhile the other two effects, especially the precession, seem to trigger the short warm episodes that punctuate each ice age.

Croll realized that, averaged over a year, these changes made little difference to the amount of solar radiation reaching the Earth. The overall effect was probably less than 0.2 watts per square metre. But the changes did alter where and when the sun hit. Croll calculated in great detail how these influences waxed and waned over tens of thousands of years. And he established, at any rate to his own satisfaction, that they coincided with what geologists were then discovering about the timing of the Earth's progress into and out of ice ages.

Taken together, the changing orbital shape, planetary tilt and rotational wobble alter the strength of seasonality, making summers and winters more or less intense. And it was this that triggered the growth of ice sheets on land in the northern hemisphere, he said. Ice sheets would grow when northern winters were coldest. That would be when the Earth was furthest from the sun, and when changing tilt ensured it received the least sunlight. Once ice sheets started to grow, they would reflect ever more sunlight back into space and intensify the cooling. He realized too that there was much less room for ice sheets to spread in the southern hemisphere because they were confined to the continent of Antarctica. So the northern hemisphere would dominate events, driving the overall heat budget of the planet. Also, he suggested, other feedbacks, such as changes to winds and ocean currents, could help drive the world further into an ice age.

In fact it turned out that Croll was wrong in assuming that it was cold winters that were critical. Later research proved that it was cold summers that gave the world a bigger kick into ice ages, by giving winter accumulations of snow little chance to melt. Nonetheless, Croll's work was a breathtaking piece of sustained cogent analysis that opened up a new field – much as Arrhenius did later with his examination of the impact of changing carbon dioxide levels on climate.

Croll's theory won him a few medals. But, being of low birth and of a taciturn disposition, he never fitted into the scientific salons of the day. They quickly tired of him and his ideas. Croll spent the last decade of his working life as the resident surveyor and clerk at the Scottish Geological Survey in Edinburgh. To the last, he had to do his research in his own time. By the end of the nineteenth century, Croll and his ideas were largely forgotten. Even Arrhenius, who might have been expected to understand the importance of his work, dismissed it as an unwelcome rival to his own ideas, though in fact, as we shall see, it complemented them.

Today, the idea of astronomical forces influencing the formation of ice sheets is back in vogue and probably here to stay. Proof of its worth finally came in the 1970s. The British geophysicist Nick Shackleton carried out painstaking isotopic analysis of sediment on the ocean floor and in the process finally dated the glacial cycles sufficiently accurately to make clear their association with astronomical events. But, even as the textbooks have been rewritten, Croll has been largely lost from the story. The orbital changes that he analysed so painstakingly are known universally as the Milankovitch wobbles, after Milutin Milankovitch, a balding, monocled mathematician from Serbia who revived and elaborated Croll's ideas in the early twentieth century.

While Croll and Milankovitch have established to most people's satisfaction that orbital changes are the pacemaker of the ice ages, they did not by any means clear up the processes involved. How did a small change in the distribution of solar heating get amplified into a global freeze on a scale probably not seen since the Snowball Earth thawed 600 million years before? And why, among a series of different wobbles, was it just one, with a return period of 100,000 years, that had much the greatest impact on global climate? A wobble, moreover, with an apparently weaker effect on solar radiation reaching the Earth than the others. It seems, in the words of Dan Schrag, a geochemist at Harvard University in Massachusetts, that the Earth system contains 'powerful embedded amplifiers that can make it highly sensitive to relatively small forcings'. Or, as Richard Alley would put it, we have a drunk on our hands. Identifying those amplifiers is important, not least because it should help

212

answer how the Earth's climate system might respond today to our own interference in its actions.

Croll believed strongly in the power of growing ice itself to amplify cooling, and there is plenty of evidence to support the strength of this ice-albedo feedback. Once snow began to accumulate on the Canadian highlands around Hudson Bay, the ice sheet tended to grow of its own accord by cooling the area around it. Jim Hansen calculates that at the height of the last glaciation ice reduced the amount of heat absorbed by the planet's surface by some 4 watts per square metre. What has troubled researchers rather more is exactly what limited it. Why, after reaching their greatest extent about 21,000 years ago, did the ice sheets begin to retreat?

Given the power of the ice-albedo feedback, it is far from clear why the ice sheets did not continue to grow until they had covered the entire planet and created a comeback for Snowball Earth. Even a change in the wobble to end the change in seasonality that started the ice growth might not have been enough. And certainly no change in the wobble can explain the extremely fast collapse of the ice sheets at the end of the last glaciation.

Some fast feedback must have taken hold. One suggestion is that the sheer size of the ice sheets shut down further growth and eventually caused their rapid destruction. The main theory is that ice sheets are vulnerable to attack by heat coming up from the interior of the planet. This underfloor heating is tiny compared with the sun's. But, trapped beneath the ice, it would have become of increasing importance as the sheets grew. Eventually, the theory goes, some threshold was passed and the ice sheets melted from their base, creating a giant continent-wide version of one of Hansen's 'slippery slopes' with great chunks of ice sheet skating to the ocean.

The second feedback that converted a planetary wobble into an ice age was greenhouse gases. Anyone who doubts the role of carbon dioxide in warming and cooling the Earth should look at the graphs of atmospheric temperature and carbon dioxide levels in ice cores taken from the Greenland and Antarctic ice sheets. They cover the last half-million years, a period that includes several glaciations. Throughout, the two graphs are in lockstep. As carbon dioxide levels fall, so do temperatures, and vice versa. That does not determine which leads, but it clearly shows that they are engaged in a very intimate dance, in which carbon dioxide must amplify temperature changes even where it does not initiate them.

As temperatures fell at the start of each glaciation, around 200 billion tonnes of carbon left the atmosphere. The same amount returned during the brief interglacial periods. Its disappearance was enough to reduce directly the Earth's uptake of solar energy by about 2 watts per square metre. But what triggered this big shift in the planet's carbon cycle, and where did the carbon go? It certainly did not end up in vegetation on land, since that was shrinking as the world cooled. The obvious answer is the oceans. There are today about 40 trillion tonnes of carbon dissolved in the oceans – fifty times as much as in the atmosphere. So a minor uptake of carbon by the oceans could have had a huge effect on the atmosphere.

How might this have happened? Physics will help. Colder water (as long as it has not frozen) dissolves carbon dioxide better than warmer water. But most researchers believe that there must be some more dynamic feedback involved as well. To take a cue from Gaia, life is the obvious force here. One idea is that the initial cooling made the oceans more biologically productive. Plankton, the meadows of the oceans, do like colder temperatures. That is why the Southern Ocean around Antarctica is today one of the most productive stretches of ocean on the planet. As the plankton grew, they drew more carbon dioxide out of the atmosphere. This strengthening of the biological pump would probably have been encouraged by enhanced dust storms created by stronger winds and spreading deserts, which would have distributed mineral dust across the oceans. Even today, minerals like iron are the limiting factor on the fertility of much of the ocean food chain.

There may have been other feedbacks at work to push the planet into ice ages and drag it back out again. Methane may have been important. Its atmospheric concentration is in a lockstep with temperature apparently as fixed as that of carbon dioxide. One likely explanation is that the arid ice ages dried up wetlands and reduced their emissions of methane. Likewise a colder atmosphere would have contained less water vapour – which would also have amplified the cooling.

A final amplifier may have been the ocean circulation system, with its huge ability to move heat round the planet. There is good evidence that the circulation system slows down during ice ages, and may have shut down entirely at the coldest point in the last glaciation. This is the province of one of the legends of the climate debate, Wally Broecker, and we will return to it in the next chapter.

The study of the ice ages suggests that the natural climate system has had two conditions to which it constantly returns. One is glaciated; the other is interglacial. The former has an atmosphere containing around 400 billion tonnes of carbon dioxide; the latter has an atmosphere containing about 600 billion tonnes. The planet oscillates between the two states regularly, repeatedly and rapidly. But it doesn't hang around in any in-between states.

The evidence, says Berrien Moore III, director of the Institute for the Study of the Earth, Oceans and Space at the University of New Hampshire, 'suggests a tightly governed control system with firm stops'. There must be negative feedbacks that push any small perturbation back to the previous position. But there must also be strong positive feedbacks. Once things go too far, and the system crosses a hidden threshold, those positive feedbacks kick it to the other stable state. Each time, the guiding feedback seems to have moved about 200 billion tonnes of carbon rapidly between the atmosphere and the ocean.

That appears to have been the story for about the past 2 million years. Until now. For the first time in a very long time, the system is currently being pushed outside this range. In the past century or so, human activity has moved another 200 billion tonnes of carbon into the atmosphere on top of the high concentrations of the inter-glacial state. The atmosphere now contains about 800 billion tonnes of carbon dioxide – twice as much carbon as it did during the last ice age and a third more than in recent interglacial eras, including the most recent. And we are adding several billion tonnes more each year. This extra carbon released into the atmosphere has not been part of recent natural cycles. It comes mainly from fossilized carbon fuels, the remains of swamps and forests that grew tens of millions of years ago.

We are in uncharted territory. And the big question is: how will the system respond to this vast injection? Where will the carbon end up? There seem to be three possibilities. First, as some optimists hope, the system may deploy negative feedbacks to suppress change. Perhaps an accelerating biological pump in the ocean might remove the carbon from the atmosphere. It is possible. But the oceans generally like it cold. And there is no sign of such negative feedbacks kicking in yet, nor any obvious reason why they might. This is 'new carbon', of which the system has no experience.

The second possibility is broadly the one embraced by most climate models and the scientific consensus of the IPCC. It is that the system will carry on operating as normal, gradually accumulating the carbon and raising temperatures gradually. There will be no abrupt thresholds that launch the climate system to a new state. This is moderately comforting, and fits the standard computer models, but is contrary to evidence of how the planet has functioned over the past 2 million years.

And that raises a third possibility. Many Earth system scientists think that their climate modelling colleagues have not yet got the measure of the Earth system. They fear that we may be close to a threshold beyond which strong positive feedbacks take hold, as they do when the Earth begins to move between glacial and interglacial eras. The feedbacks may flip the system to a new as-yet-unknown state. Most likely it would be one with much higher atmospheric concentrations of carbon dioxide and methane – more like the early days on planet Earth. Getting there might see an era of huge carbon releases from the soil, or massive methane farts from the ocean floor, or wholesale changes to the ocean circulation system, or the runaway melting of the ice caps. That is conjecture. We simply don't know. But hold on to your hat: we could be in for a bumpy ride.

23

THE OCEAN CONVEYOR

THE REAL DAY AFTER TOMORROW

Wally Broecker is a maverick – a prodigious and fearless generator of ideas and one of the most influential figures in climate science for half a century. Sometimes he can be more. Amid the admiration for his science, you hear some harsh words about him in the science community. A bully, some say, especially to young scientists; a man who will use his influence to suppress ideas with which he disagrees. For a man in his seventies, he certainly comes on strong and relishes conflicts. Here are his unprompted on-the-record remarks to me on one of the US's leading climate modellers, who incurred the wrath of some Republican senators: 'I think the senators were well out of line, but if anyone deserves to get hit it was him. The goddam guy is a slick talker and super-confident. He won't listen to anyone else. I don't trust people like that. A lot of the data sets he uses are shitty, you know. They are just not up to what he is trying to do.'

Broecker is not a man to cross lightly. And to be honest

I thought a bit before writing the above. Much as I like his vigour, I'd hate to be caught in his cross wires. Some think he has earned the right to sound off about young colleagues he thinks don't pass muster. Some worry that Broecker seems to save his invective for people who resemble him in his younger years. But he is a man in a hurry. When I met him late in 2005 at the Lamont-Doherty Earth Observatory of Columbia University in New York, his distinguished friend and collaborator Gerard Bond, a man a decade younger than Broecker, had recently died.

Broecker is a geochemist with an unimpeachable track record in pioneering the use of isotopic analysis to plot ocean circulation. He has been writing and thinking for more than three decades about what he calls the ocean conveyor, which more traditional scientists call the meridional overturning circulation or the thermohaline circulation. Whatever you call it, it is the granddaddy of all ocean currents, a thousand-year circulation with 'a flow equal to that of a hundred Amazon rivers', as he puts it.

The conveyor begins with the strong northward flow of the Gulf Stream pouring warm, salty water from the South Atlantic across the tropics and into the far North Atlantic. In the North Atlantic, the water is cooled, particularly in winter, by the bitter winds blowing off Canada and Greenland. This cooling increases the density of the water, a process amplified by the formation of ice, which takes only the fresh water and leaves behind increasingly saline and dense water. Eventually the dense water sinks to the bottom of the ocean, generally in two spots: one to the west of Greenland in the Labrador Sea and the other to the east, down Wadhams' vertical chimney. From there the water begins a journey south along the sea bed of the far South Atlantic, where a tributary, formed from cold, saline water plunging to the ocean bed around Antarctica, joins up. The conveyor then heads east through the Indian and Pacific Oceans before resurfacing roughly a thousand years later in the South Atlantic and flowing north again as the Gulf Stream to the far North Atlantic, where it goes to the bottom once more.

The circulation has many roles, distributing warm water from the tropics to the polar regions, mixing the oceans, and aiding the exchange of carbon dioxide between the atmosphere and the oceans. In Richard Alley's words, it 'allows Europeans to grow roses farther north than Canadians meet polar bears'. On the face of it, the circulation is self-sustaining. The plunging of surface water to the ocean floor around Greenland draws Gulf Stream water north, which provides more water for the drop. But it is also temperamental, prone to switching on and off abruptly. That switch, says Broecker, is a vital component of the entire global climate system. Not everyone agrees on the nature of the switch and how much it matters, but he makes a persuasive case.

Broecker's picture of the ocean conveyor is disarmingly simple. Too simple, some say. He admits it had its origins in a rough sketch. Asked by *Natural History* magazine to produce a diagram to illustrate a complicated argument about ocean water movement, he drew a map with a few arrows suggesting likely 'rivers' of intense flow within the circulation. 'They sent it to an artist; he drew something and I made a couple of corrections. I didn't realize it was going to be that important, but it was a popular magazine and

Warm shallow current
Cold and salty deep current

A 'logo for climate change': Broecker's diagram of the ocean conveyor, which takes surface water from the Arctic on a thousand-year submarine odyssey, ending in the Atlantic Gulf Stream that warms Europe. The conveyor appears to switch abruptly on and off, and in the process may dictate the planet's climate.

221

suddenly the diagram became a kind of logo for climate change.'

Broecker is quite candid about the crudeness of the sketch. But while some scientists might have disowned it, he recognizes its power and has embraced it. Its origins lie in Broecker's pioneering work using chemical tracers to identify movements of water in the oceans. He noticed how water in the Pacific and Indian Oceans appeared to be a mixture of water that plunged to the depths in the North Atlantic and, to a lesser extent, around Antarctica. He could also see that the North Atlantic deep water comprised water that had recently made its way north as the Gulf Stream. To some extent, he filled in the rest. 'The conveyor is clearly real,' he insists. 'But of course it's not as highly organized as it appears in the diagram.' It is more a trend than a current, 'a combination of random motions'. And yet his rough sketch has proved to be one of the most important concepts to have emerged from climate science in the past quarter-century.

He chose the term 'conveyor' because, he says, 'I think names are very powerful, and that was much better than the proper scientific term. Some scientists say it is stupid, but lay people can imagine a conveyor belt much more easily.' He certainly has a way with words. Broecker was the first scientist to use the term global warming, in a paper in the 1970s.

I first discovered the conveyor back in the late 1980s, when researching a book on environmental change. I was fascinated by the simplicity of the idea; by the fact that the conveyor might have two natural states, on and off; and by the scary possibility that climate change might shut the conveyor down if the waters off Greenland became so flooded with fresh water that the dynamics of dense saline water formation around the chimneys broke down. For me the idea was the first real inkling that climate change might not be as it was in the mainstream models; that the greenhouse effect might unleash something altogether nastier.

Early on, Broecker was often ambivalent about the potential for truly disastrous events. But by 1995, he felt confident enough to title a lecture on the conveyor to a big science conference 'Abrupt Climate Change: Is One Hiding in the Greenhouse?' In it he outlined how evidence from sea-floor and lake sediments, ice cores, coral and glacier records 'demonstrates unequivocally' that an on-off switch on the global conveyor operated at the beginning and end of the last ice age. The suggestion was that the conveyor had shut down and single-handedly started the ice ages, lowering temperatures by '4 degrees C or more . . . often within the lifespan of a generation' – a claim he inflated soon afterwards, in the pages of *Scientific American*, to '10 degrees C over the course of as little as a decade'.

Broecker's picture, then, is of a powerful but fickle ocean conveyor with an on-off switch functioning in the far North Atlantic. Switched on, it warms the world, especially the northern hemisphere, and is typical of periods between ice ages. Switched off, it cools the northern hemisphere and is typical of glaciations. But the system flickers at other times, too, he says. It triggered warm episodes that punctuated the depths of the last ice age, and perhaps drove more recent events like Europe's medieval warm period and the little ice age. Often, Broecker accepts, the ultimate forcing for these dramatic changes may lie in a celestial event like the slow movements of the Milankovitch cycles. But when a threshold is crossed and sudden climate change occurs, it is the conveyor that throws the switch.

These remain extremely controversial claims. Most would accept that Broecker is right that the conveyor slowed during the ice ages and probably shut down at various points. But most researchers believe that it was a consequence and not a cause of the glaciation. The big forces behind the cooling, they say, were the shift of carbon dioxide into the oceans and the spread of ice. And how important the ocean conveyor was in those processes has yet to be demonstrated. While it may have intensified cooling in the North Atlantic region, where the Gulf Stream is an acknowledged important feature keeping the region warm, it is far less clear whether its global effects are anything like as big as Broecker claims.

But Broecker has rarely got bogged down in detail. Two years after making his claims for the ocean conveyor and the ice ages – and just a week before the world met in Japan to agree the Kyoto Protocol – he was warning that climate change could trigger a future shutdown of the conveyor. 'There is surely a possibility that the ongoing build-up of greenhouse gases might trigger yet another of those ocean reorganizations,' he said. If it did, 'Dublin would acquire the climate of Spitzbergen in ten years or less ... the consequences would be devastating.' He called the conveyor the 'Achilles' heel of the climate system'.

Broecker was also, I think, making a wider point. He wants to generate a change in the way we think about the planet. Climate systems work, he suggests, rather as Stephen Jay Gould said evolution worked: not gradually through constant incremental change but in sudden bursts. Gould's phrase 'punctuated equilibrium' sounds right for Wally's world of climate, too. And his new paradigm fits the science of chaos theory, too, in which his ocean conveyor is an 'emergent property' in the wider Earth system.

But the crux of the public debate on Broecker's ocean conveyor remains the very simple question: could global warming shut down the conveyor? Broecker seems rarely to have doubted it. And the claim has in recent years seemed almost to have a life of its own. This struck me most strongly at a conference on 'dangerous' climate change held at Britain's Hadley Centre for Climate Prediction in Exeter in 2005. There I met Michael Schlesinger of the University of Illinois at Urbana-Champaign. He is a sharp-suited guy sporting a pastiche of 1950s Teddy-boy clothes and hair style. But if there were serious doubts in Exeter about whether his style sense would ever come back into fashion, there was no doubt that his ideas about climate change had found their moment.

For more than a decade, Schlesinger has been making Broecker's case that a shutdown of the ocean conveyor could be closer than the mainstream climate modellers think. Some critics felt that he just did not know when to give up and move on. But he stuck with it, criticizing the IPCC and its models for systematically eliminating a range of quite possible 'doomsday scenarios' from consideration. 'The trouble with trying to reach a consensus is that all the interesting ideas get eliminated,' he said. Science by committee ends up throwing away the good stuff – like the idea of the shutting down of the conveyor. But in Exeter, Schlesinger was back in vogue. He had been invited to present his model findings that a global warming of just 2 degrees C would melt the Greenland ice sheet fast enough to swamp the ocean with fresh water and shut down the conveyor. The risk, he said, was 'unacceptably large'.

Although he had been saying much the same for a decade, he was now considered mainstream enough to be invited across the Atlantic to expound his ideas at a conference organized by the British government. And he was no longer alone. Later in the day, Peter Challenor of the British National Oceanography Centre in Southampton said he had shortened his own odds about the likelihood of a conveyor shutdown from one in thirty to one in three. He guessed that a 3-degree warming of Greenland would do it. Given how fast Greenland is currently warming, that seems a racing certainty.

But all this is models. What evidence is there, in the ocean, for the state of the conveyor? The truth is that dangerous change is already afoot in the North Atlantic. And, whatever the scepticism about some of Broecker's grander claims, the conveyor may already be in deep trouble. Since the mid-1960s, says Ruth Curry of the Woods Hole Oceanographic Institution in Massachusetts, the waters of the far North Atlantic off Greenland, where Wadhams' lone chimney delivers water to the ocean floor and maintains Broecker's conveyor, have become decidedly fresher.

In fact much of the change happened back in the 1960s, when some 10,000 cubic kilometres of fresh water gushed out of the Arctic through the Fram Strait. Oceanographers called the event the Great Salinity Anomaly. To this day nobody is quite sure why it happened. It could have been ice breaking off the great Greenland ice sheet, or sea ice caught up in unusual circulation patterns, or increased flow from the great Siberian rivers like the Ob and the Yenisei. Luckily, most of the fresh water did not hang around too long, and rapidly headed south into the North Atlantic proper. Only 4,000 cubic kilometres remained. Curry's studies of the phenomenon, published in *Science* in June 2005, concluded that 9,000 cubic kilometres would have been enough to 'substantially reduce' the conveyor and double that 'could essentially shut it down'. So it was a close call.

With the region's water still substantially fresher than it was at the start of the 1960s, the conveyor remains on the critical list. Another single slug of fresh water any time soon could be disastrous. In the coming decades, some combination of increased rainfall, increased run-off from the land surrounding the Arctic or faster rates of ice melting could turn off the conveyor. And there would be no turning back, because models suggest that once off, it would not easily switch back on. As Broecker's colleague Peter deMenocal puts it, 'a shift in the ocean conveyor, once initiated, is essentially irreversible over a time period of many decades to centuries. It would permanently alter the climatic norms for some of the most densely populated and highly developed regions of the world.'

As I prepared to submit this book to the publisher, new research dramatically underlined the risks and fears for the conveyor. Harry Bryden of the National Oceanography Centre in Southampton had deployed measuring buoys in a line across the Atlantic, from the Canary Islands to the Bahamas, and found that the flow of water north from the Gulf Stream into the North Atlantic had faltered by 30 per cent since the mid 1990s. There was less warm water going north at the surface and less cold water coming back south along the ocean floor.

It was, so far as anyone knew, an unprecedented event.

Analysing the water in more detail, Bryden found that the 'deep water' from the Labrador Sea west of Greenland still seemed to be flowing south. But the volume of deep water coming south from the Greenland Sea, the site of Wadhams' chimney, had collapsed to half its former level. The implication was clear: the disappearance of the chimneys that Wadhams had watched with such despair was indeed hobbling the ocean circulation.

None of this demonstrated that Broecker's bleaker predictions for what would happen if the conveyor shut down were about to come true. That 'London would experience the winter cold that now grips Irkutsk in Siberia.' Something 'more like the little ice age' was the worst that most climate modellers feared. But there does seem to be a real possibility that many of Broecker's ideas are about to be put rather dramatically to the test.

24

AN ARCTIC FLOWER
CLUES TO A CLIMATE SWITCHBACK

It must have felt like the springtime of the world. Anybody living on the Earth 13,000 years ago could only have felt elation. Some 80,000 years of ice age were coming to an end. Temperatures were rising; ice was melting; rivers were in flood; and permafrost was giving way to trees and meadows across Europe and North America. In the Atlantic Ocean, the Gulf Stream was pushing north again, bringing warm tropical water and re-establishing an ocean circulation system that had shut down entirely in the depths of the ice age. Westerly winds blowing across the ocean were picking up the heat and distributing it across the continent and deep into Asia.

Meanwhile, in the tropics, the deserts were in retreat, the rainforests were expanding again from their ice-age refuges and the Asian monsoon was kicking back in. Most spectacularly, the Sahara was bursting with life, covered in vegetation and huge lakes. This was the dawn of the age of *Homo sapiens*, who had supplanted the last of the

Neanderthals during the long glaciation. If there had been a Charles Keeling among them, he would have measured rising levels of carbon dioxide and methane in the air that were amplifying the thaw. He might even have invented the term global warming to describe it.

Then the unthinkable happened: the whole thing went into reverse again. Almost overnight, the thaw halted. Temperatures became as cold as they were in the depths of the ice age. The forests returning to northern climes were wiped out; the permafrost extended; and ice sheets and glaciers started to regain their former terrain.

The Stone Age optimists of the day should have known better, of course. If they had been able to look back over the previous 5,000 years, they would have known that the climate had been on a switchback. For 18,000 years before the present, there was still a full-on ice age. By 16,000 years ago, the world was warming strongly. But by 15,000 years ago it was cold again, with ice sheets reforming. At 14,500 years ago, it became so warm that within 400 years the ice caps melted sufficiently to raise sea levels worldwide by 20 metres. But at the end, the cold gained the upper hand once more, only to give way to the pronounced warming of 13,000 years ago that crashed again 12,800 years ago.

Today we can see this extraordinary climatic history recorded in ice cores extracted from the ice of Greenland and Antarctica. Graphs of the temperatures back then look like seismic readings during a big earthquake – or cardiac read-outs during a heart attack. They show a climate system in a protracted series of spasms. Looking back, we recognize the death throes of the ice age. But that is with hindsight. At the time, there was little evidence that the climate system had any sense of direction at all. It lurched between its glacial and inter-glacial modes. The one thing it wasn't doing was settling for a happy medium.

The last great cold snap of the ice age, 12,800 years ago, is known today as the Younger Dryas era. The dryas is a white Arctic rose with a yellow centre that suddenly re-appeared in European sedimentary remains as the old cold reasserted itself. The era is called the Younger Dryas to distinguish it from the Older Dryas, the previous climate reversal a thousand years before, and the Oldest Dryas, which came before that. The Younger Dryas, like the others, was swift and dramatic. Within about a gener-ation, temperatures fell across the northern hemisphere. Perhaps by as little as 2–3 degrees C in the tropics, but by an average of as much as 16 degrees further north. And, according to ice cores analysed by George Denton of the University of Maine, by 30 degrees in winter at Scoresby Sound in eastern Greenland.

It wasn't just temperatures that crashed. Records of Chinese dust and African lakes and tropical trade winds and South American river flows and New Zealand glaciers all reveal dramatic changes happening in step 12,800 years ago. The world was much more dry, windy and dusty. And in the southern hemisphere, temperatures may have gone in the opposite direction. Marine sediment cores show dramatic warming in the southern Atlantic and the Indian Ocean – as do temperature records in most Antarctic ice cores.

The Younger Dryas freeze lasted for fifty or so gener-ations, 1,300 years. One can imagine tribes of *Homo sapiens* desperately relearning the crafts that got their ancestors through the ice ages. But it may also have triggered innovation. Some believe that dry conditions in the Middle East at the time may have encouraged the first experiments with crop cultivation and the domestication of animals. And then the freeze ended, temperatures returning to their former levels even faster than they had fallen. Analysts of the Greenland ice-core chronology say publicly that the warming must have happened within a decade. But that is the minimum certain resolution of their ice cores. Richard Alley, who was there handling the ice cores, says: 'Most of that change looks like it happened in a single year. It could have been less, perhaps even a single season. It was a weird time indeed.' Like *The Day After Tomorrow*, only in reverse.

All this is doubly strange because the Younger Dryas cooling went against the grain of all the long-term trends for the planet. The orbital changes that had triggered the glaciation had faded by now; astronomical forces were pushing the planet towards the next interglacial era. Of course the real work was being done by feedbacks like melting ice, the return of greenhouse gases like carbon dioxide and methane into the atmosphere, and the revival of the ocean conveyor. These feedbacks would have turned a smooth progression into a series of jumps. But they would not easily have changed the direction of change. So why the backward flip? What made climate plunge back into the icy abyss when all the forcings and all the feedbacks should have been kicking the world into warmer times?

Chaos theory may help here. Alley says that it is the very time when conditions are changing fastest that the chances are greatest for seemingly random, unexpected and abrupt change in any direction. The system is stirred up and vulnerable. The drunk is on the rampage. And there is a reasonable chance that some of the abrupt changes will be in the opposite direction to that expected. This is what, in the clever subtitle to his 2001 report on abrupt climate change, Alley called 'inevitable surprise'. What is equally clear is that at the time the entire planetary climate system had just two possible states: glacial and interglacial. It knew no third way. And so, during the several thousand years when it was on the cusp between the two, it flickered between them.

On the ground, one element was a sudden switch in Broecker's ocean conveyor. Having switched on during the warm period beforehand, it switched off during the Younger Dryas. It would be going too far to say that this proves that the global conveyor is the great climate switch that Broecker claims. But it makes a compelling case that events in the far North Atlantic can, without any help from astronomical or any other forces, sometimes have dramatic and long-lasting effects on global climate.

The unexpected switch of the ocean conveyor was almost certainly triggered by melting ice. In the final millennia of the ice age, as melting of the ice sheets made fitful but sometimes dramatic progress, a very large amount of liquid water was produced. Often it did not pour directly into the oceans but formed giant lakes. The largest of these lakes is called Lake Agassiz, after the discoverer of the ice ages. It stretched for more than a thousand kilometres across a wide area of the American Midwest, from Saskatchewan to Ontario in Canada and the Dakotas to Minnesota in the US, generally moving with the advancing front of warming.

In the early stages of the deglaciation, the lake drained south, down the Mississippi River into the Gulf of Mexico.

But about 12,800 years ago, it seems that something stopped this. Perhaps the route south was blocked by land gradually rising after removal of the weight of the ice. Perhaps the lake simply passed over a natural watershed as it moved north with the ice sheet. But at any rate the lake was forced to drain east and there was eventually a huge breakout of fresh water from the heart of North America into the basin now occupied by the Great Lakes and on into the North Atlantic.

The vast rush of cold, fresh water would have drastically cooled and freshened the ocean. High salinity was critical for sustaining the newly revived, and perhaps still precarious, ocean conveyor. So the fresh water shut down the conveyor once more. The warm Gulf Stream was no longer drawn north. Temperatures crashed across the North Atlantic region, and probably most of all around Greenland. The entire global climate system would have been shaken, and may have lurched back from its interglacial to its glacial mode.

Little of this narrative is cut and dried. The evidence is patchy. Some doubt whether even a vast eruption of fresh water down the St Lawrence Seaway would have had much influence on ocean salinity on the other side of Greenland. And others, hard-line opponents of the Broecker hypothesis, wonder exactly how important the ocean conveyor is to global climate. Even Broecker admits that parts of the story are 'a puzzle'.

But new evidence is emerging all the time. One compelling rewrite of the Broecker narrative has come from John Chiang at Berkeley in California. His modelling studies of the North Atlantic suggest that the most critical event at the start of the Younger Dryas may have been not the shutdown of the ocean conveyor itself but the impact of the invasion of fresh water on the formation of sea ice in the North Atlantic. He says that an invasion diluting the flow of warm water from the Gulf Stream would have rapidly frozen the ocean surface. The freeze itself would have flipped a climate switch, preventing further deep-water formation, sealing out the Gulf Stream and, through the ice-albedo feedback, dramatically chilling the entire region.

Broecker has adopted this idea as an elaboration of his conveyor scenario. Some others see it as a replacement or even a refutation. Alley says: 'It looks like this is the real switch in the North Atlantic. In the winter, does the water sink before it freezes, or freeze before it sinks? Sink or freeze. There are only two possible answers. That's the switch.' Fresher, colder water will freeze; warmer, more saline water will sink. If the water sinks, the conveyor remains in place and the northern hemisphere stays warm. If it freezes, the circulation halts and the westerly winds crossing the ocean towards Europe and Asia stop being warmed by the Gulf Stream and instead are chilled by thousands of kilometres of sea ice. 'The difference between the two is the difference in places between temperatures at zero degrees Celsius and at minus 30 degrees,' says Alley.

And that switch flipped, Alley argues, at the start and finish of the Younger Dryas. At the start, fresh water invaded the North Atlantic; the ocean froze and within a decade 'there were ice floes in the North Sea and permafrost in the Netherlands.' The westerly winds would have picked up the cold of the Atlantic ice and blown it right across Europe and into Asia. They would have cooled the heart of the Eurasian land mass, preventing it from warming sufficiently to generate the onshore winds that bring the monsoon rains to Asia. This revised narrative also explains the concurrent warming in the southern hemisphere. If the Gulf Stream was not flowing north, the heat that it once took across the equator stayed in the South Atlantic. So as the north of the planet froze, the south warmed. A fresh-water release in northern Canada had become a global climatic cataclysm. One, moreover, that went against all the long-term trends of the time.

It took about 1,300 years before the North Atlantic water switched back to sinking rather than freezing in winter. There is no consensus on what finally flipped the switch. But when it happened it was at least as fast as the original freeze. The North Atlantic no longer froze; instead the water was salty and dense enough to sink. The ocean warmed; the winds warmed; temperatures were restored in a year; nature returned to reclaim the tundra; and deglaciation got back on track.

For some this story is encouraging. If it takes huge volumes of cold water flowing out of a lake to switch off the ocean conveyor, we should be safe, they say. There are no unstable lakes around of the kind created by the melting of the ice sheets. In any case, the world is warmer today than it was even at the start of the Younger Dryas. It may be, says Alley, that the world climate system is much more stable in warm times than cold times. But equally it may not. For one thing, the superwarm world we are creating may have quite different perils. For another, even the old perils may not have been neutralized as much as optimists think.

There is a cautionary tale here that happened 8,200 years ago. Despite large amounts of warming after the demise of the Younger Dryas cold event, the ice had one last hoorah. Again there was a large intrusion of cold fresh water into the North Atlantic. Again there was a big fresh-water release, again the ocean covered in ice, and again there seems to have been a disruption to the global conveyor. This was a lesser event than the Younger Dryas, probably only regional in its impact on climate and lasting for only about 350 years. But it was nonetheless one of the biggest climate shifts of the past 10,000 years. And perhaps most significantly for us today, says Alley, it happened in a world markedly more like our own than that of the Younger Dryas. Temperatures were generally rather close to those of today and the ice sheets were quite similar to today's. The event suggests, if nothing else, that if sufficient fresh water were to invade the North Atlantic today, it could have a similar impact.

As we have seen, there have in recent decades been large slugs of fresh water pouring into the far North Atlantic. They may have come close to triggering a shutdown of the ocean conveyor. And this trend is unlikely to end. As the climate warms and the permafrost melts in Siberia, river flows from there into the Arctic Ocean are rising strongly. And there is always the prospect of future catastrophic melting of the Greenland ice sheet, where glaciers are accelerating and lakes are forming.

Gavin Schmidt, one of Hansen's climate modellers at NASA's Goddard Institute for Space Studies in New York, says that the event 8,200 years ago is a critical test for today's climate models. 'If we are to make credible predictions about the risks we run today of catastrophic climate change, those models need to be able to reproduce what happened 8,200 years ago,' he says. 'If we could do that, it would be really good. It could tell us a lot about processes highly relevant for the climate of the twenty-first century.'

25

THE PULSE

HOW THE SUN MAKES CLIMATE CHANGE

The Arctic pack ice extended so far south that Eskimo fishing boats landed on the north coast of Scotland. They didn't meet much opposition, because the hungry Highlanders had abandoned their crofts after grain harvests had failed for seven straight years and gone raiding for food in the lowlands to the south. In the 1690s temperatures in Scotland were more than 2 degrees C below normal; snow lay on the ground long into the summer. Those who stayed behind in the hills were reduced to eating nettles and making bread from tree bark. The political repercussions of this Scottish turmoil are still with us today. The highland rulers became so worried by fears of insurrection that they shipped off angry clansmen and their starving families to set up Presbyterian colonies in Catholic northern Ireland. And eventually, after widespread famine in the 1690s brought despair about the future for the Scots as a nation, they forged a union with England.

This was the little ice age, a climatic affair that began early in the fourteenth century and flickered on and off before peaking in the late seventeenth century and finally releasing its grip some 150 years ago. Like a mild echo of the ice ages, it spread its icy fingers from the north across Europe, pushing Alpine glaciers down valleys, creating spectacular skating scenes for the Dutch painters Breugel and van der Neer, and allowing Londoners to enjoy the frolics of regular frost fairs on the frozen River Thames. On one occasion Henry VIII travelled by sleigh down the river to Greenwich, and on another an elephant was led across the ice near Blackfriars Bridge.

There were some warm periods amid the cold. In the 1420s, an armada of Chinese explorers is reputed to have sailed round the north coast of Greenland, a journey that would be impossible even in today's reduced Arctic ice. Between about 1440 and 1540, England was mild enough for cherries to be cultivated in the Durham hills of the north-east. Much of Europe was exceptionally warm in the 1730s. But at the height of the little ice age, the Baltic Sea froze over and there was widespread famine across northern Europe. Some suggest that half the populations of Norway and Sweden perished. Iceland was cut off by sea ice for years on end and its shoals of cod abandoned the seas for warmer climes. Some say the cold was the hidden hand behind the famine, rising grain prices and bread riots that triggered the French Revolution of 1789.

In North America, tribes banded together into the League of the Iroquois to share scarce food supplies. The Cree gave up farming corn and went back to hunting bison. But the era was symbolized most poignantly by the collapse of a Viking settlement founded in the balmy days of the eleventh century by Leif Erikson. The Viking king had an estate agent's flair for coining a good name to attract settlers to the place he called Greenland. The settlement on the southern tip of the Arctic island thrived for four hundred years, but by the mid-fifteenth century crops were failing and sea ice cut off any chance of food aid from Europe.

If the Viking settlers had followed the ways of their Eskimo neighbours and turned to hunting seals and polar bears, they might have survived. But instead, they stuck to their hens and sheep and grain crops, and built ever bigger churches in the hope that God would save them. He did not. When relief finally arrived, there was nobody left alive in the settlement. Creeping starvation had cut the average height of a Greenland Viking from a sturdy 1.78 metres to a stunted 1.57 metres. The last women were so deformed that they were probably incapable of bearing a new generation. We know all this because their buried corpses were preserved in the spreading permafrost.

The little ice age, first documented in the 1960s by the British climate historian Hubert Lamb, is now an established part of Europe's history. It has often been seen as just a historical curiosity, a nasty but local blip in a balmy world of European climatic certainty. But it is increasingly clear that what Europe termed the little ice age was close to a global climatic convulsion, which took different forms in different places.

Because it came and went over several centuries, the task of attributing different climate events round the world to the influence of the little ice age is fraught with difficulties. But reasonable cases have been made that it blanketed parts of Ethiopia in snow, destroyed crops and precipitated the collapse of the Ming dynasty in seventeenth-century China, and spread ice across Lake Superior in North America. In the tropics, temperatures were probably largely unchanged, but rainfall patterns altered substantially. In the Amazon basin, the centuries of Europe's little ice age were so dry that fires ravaged tinderbox rainforests. In the Sahara, which often seems to experience opposite climate trends to those in the Amazon, repeated floods in the early seventeenth century washed away the great desert city of Timbuktu.

The little ice age is not the only climate anomaly in recorded history. Another, known because of its influence on European climate as the medieval warm period, ran from perhaps AD 800 to 1300, ending right as the little ice age began. Being rather more distant than the little ice age, its history and nature are rather less clear. Certainly at various times grains grew further north in Norway than they do today, and vineyards flourished on the Pennines in England. Warmth brought Europe wealth. There was an orgy of construction of magnificent Gothic cathedrals. The Vikings, as we have seen, set up in Greenland at a time when parts of it could certainly be described as green. Some claim that the medieval warm period may have been warmer even than it is in the early twenty-first century. But most researchers are much more cautious.

Existing reconstructions of past temperature come mainly from analysing the thickness of the annual growth rings of old trees. There are exceptions, but generally the wider the rings the stronger the annual growth and the warmer the summer. Keith Briffa, a British specialist in extracting climate information from tree rings, says: 'The seventeenth century was undoubtedly cold. The evidence that the period 1570 to 1850 was also cold seems pretty robust. But the medieval warm period is still massively uncertain. There is not much data and so much spatial bias in the data. We think there was a warm period around AD 900, certainly at high northern latitudes in summer, where we have the tree ring evidence. But we have virtually nothing else.' It looks likely that much of Europe was between 1 and 2 degrees C warmer in the medieval warm period than it was in the early twentieth century, while the little ice age was a similar amount cooler in Europe. But any global trends were almost certainly much smaller.

In any case, to talk about a medieval warm period at all is, in the view of many, a very Eurocentric view. Tree rings from the southern hemisphere show no sign of anything similar there. Indeed, away from the North Atlantic, those centuries were characterized if anything by long super-droughts that caused the collapse of several major civilizations. In Central America, the Mayans had thrived for 2,000 years and built one of the world's most advanced and long-lasting civilizations. Theirs was a sophisticated, urbanized and scientific and technologically advanced society of around 10 million people, with prolific artistic activities and strong trade links with its neighbours and seemingly every resource necessary to carry on thriving – strikingly like our own in many respects. Yet faced with three decades-long droughts between AD 800 and 950, which may have been the worst in the region since the end of the ice age, the entire society crumbled, leaving its remains in the jungle. A few hundred kilometres north, a series of advanced native North American societies collapsed under the impact of sustained droughts through the American West. Best documented are the Anasazi people, ancestors of the modern Pueblo Indians. They had built elaborate apartment complexes in the canyons of New Mexico and developed sophisticated irrigation systems for growing crops, but were forced to flee into the wilderness after a long drought that peaked in the 1280s.

The little ice age and the medieval warm period appear to have been recent, natural examples of climate change. Though the warming and cooling implied in their names may have been restricted largely to the North Atlantic region, they seem to have left a signature in glaciers and megadroughts across the planet. So what caused them? And does it have anything to tell us about our own future climate?

There have been many theories about what caused these climate changes. The pendulum moves too fast for any orbital cycles. Some have suggested a role for volcanic eruptions, which shroud the planet with aerosols that can cool it. It is true that at certain times during the little ice age, there were major eruptions. The year after the eruption of Tambora in Indonesia in 1815, crops failed from India to Europe and North America. It became known as 'the year without a summer'. But volcanic dust clouds only cool temperatures for a few years at most. They may from time to time have exacerbated the cooling, but they were not sufficiently frequent or unusual to explain a long cold era lasting on and off for almost half a millennium.

Most climatologists believe that the sun should get the blame. The coldest part of the little ice age, in the mid- to late-seventeenth century, is known as the Maunder Minimum. The popularizing of the telescope by Galileo a few decades before meant that astronomers of the day were able to note the virtual disappearance of the by-then-familiar spots on the surface of the sun between 1645 and 1715. This is now recognized as a good indicator of a reduced output of solar energy. The best guess is that solar radiation reaching the Earth's surface during the Maunder Minimum fell by perhaps half a watt per square metre, or around 0.2 per cent. But climatologists find it perplexing that such a major effect could result from such a modest change.

Enter an idiosyncratic, larger-than-life researcher working at the Lamont-Doherty Earth Observatory of Columbia University, just down the corridor from Wally Broecker. His name was Bond, Gerard Bond. Like Broecker, he hated getting bogged down in detail and liked seeing the big picture. Like Broecker, he was willing to fly a kite, trusted his intuition and had the confidence to propose an idea in public just to see if anyone could shoot it down. And, again like his compatriot, he had the intellectual reputation to get his kite-flying published in the often conservative scientific literature.

Bond argued forcefully until his death in 2005 that the little ice age and the medieval warm period were the most recent signs of a pervasive pulse in the world's climatic system. This pulse, he said, had a cycle that recurred once every 1,500 years or so. It was a pulse, moreover, that seemed largely unaffected by other apparently bigger influences on global climate, like the Milankovitch orbital cycles that triggered the major glaciations. Ice age or no ice age, he argued, the pulse just kept on going. Bond didn't invent the pulse out of thin air. Other researchers had unwittingly been on its trail for years. But, like his friend down the corridor, Bond was the man who had the confidence to compose a big picture out of the scattered fragments of evidence.

*   *   *

In the early 1980s, a graduate student in Germany made the first breakthrough. While at the University of Göttingen, Hartmut Heinrich was examining cores of sediment drilled from the bed of the North Atlantic. He found a number of curious layers of rock fragments that showed up in cores drilled as far apart as the east coast of Canada, the waters west of the British Isles and around Bermuda. Radiocarbon dating revealed that these rock fragments were laid down in at least six bands over the last 60,000 years until the end of the last glaciation, at intervals of roughly every 8,000 years.

I looked at some of these rock fragments in the marine sediment store at Bond's old laboratory in New York. They are enormously distinctive. A browse among the other trays of sediment reveals generally fairly subtle differences between the different cores: a change of colour here, a slightly different consistency of dust there. Almost everything in these sediments has gone through the mill of being eroded from the Earth's surface, discharged down rivers and dumped in tiny bits on the sea bed. But then there are Heinrich's layers. These are a mass of stones the size of gravel or pebbles, but sharp-edged and clearly untouched by the normal processes of erosion and deposition. Researchers soon gave the events that produced them their own name: Heinrich events. There was nothing else like them in the sediment record.

Apart from their size and shape, there was something else odd about these rock fragments. Though they had been found way out in the middle of the Atlantic Ocean, geologists swiftly established that they came from far away, from the Hudson Bay area of northern Canada. How could they have got so far offshore and so far south?

What took them there? The only logical explanation, given that all the Heinrich events took place during the last glaciation, was that they had been ripped from the bedrock by great glaciers and carried south on the underside of icebergs. They travelled a long way because the North Atlantic was extremely cold and were eventually dumped on to the ocean floor as the icebergs melted. That begged other questions. What climatic events would send vast armadas of icebergs sailing south into the tropics? And why the apparent 8,000-year cycle?

The next clue came a few years later, in the early 1990s, when a distinguished Danish glaciologist, Willi Dansgaard from the University of Copenhagen, discovered in the Greenland ice-core record a series of large and sudden temperature changes that again punctuated the last glaciation. Several times, temperatures leapt up by between 2 and 10 degrees C within a decade or so, before falling again after a few hundred years. So far more than twenty of these warm phases have been identified in the ice-core record. During many of them, temperatures in Europe at least may have been as warm as today.

These warming events seemed too to have some kind of periodicity or pulse. Temperatures moved from cold to warm and back to cold again repeatedly, with a cycle ranging between 1,300 and 1,800 years. It was recognizably a pulse, just as a human pulse that races and then slows is recognizable, and seemed to complete a full cycle on average roughly every 1,500 years. This pulse also swiftly got a name, the rather cumbersome Dansgaard-Oeschger cycle, after Dansgaard and his Swiss colleague, Hans Oeschger.

The connection between the Heinrich events and the

Dansgaard-Oeschger cycle wasn't recognized immediately. Understandably enough. One marked cool events, the other warm events; they had different time signatures; and one was revealed in the sediments of the mid-Atlantic while the other emerged from the Greenland ice cores. Both in any case seemed at first to be minor local curiosities confined to the last glaciation, and therefore of no relevance to modern climate. But Bond had a hunch that the two were linked in some way, and that they had a global significance. Both, he noted, appeared to coincide with other climate changes such as the advances and retreat of glaciers in Europe and North America. Like the Younger Dryas event and the climate flip 8,200 years ago, they seemed either to push the world into a different climate mode or to be part of such a process. Down the corridor, Bond's buddy Broecker was on hand to suggest a possible link to the ocean conveyor. The story began to take on a life of its own. But first the pair needed evidence to back up the hunch.

Bond began to re-examine trays of sediment cores from the bed of the North Atlantic that were assembled in his New York archive. Some were old cores, taken years before by the Lamont-Doherty research vessel *Vema* from beneath the waters off Ireland and the channel between Greenland and Iceland. Others were new, drilled under Bond's supervision off Newfoundland.

As expected, Bond found further evidence of Heinrich's rock fragments roughly every 8,000 years or so through the last glaciation. But the marine sediment cores also revealed lesser layers of materials normally alien to the sea bed of the North Atlantic. Most excitingly of all, these lesser layers occurred roughly every 1,500 years and appeared to form a cold phase of the Dansgaard-Oeschger cycle in the Greenland ice cores. This was pay dirt. Doubly so when it became clear that the iceberg armadas of the Heinrich events occurred during unusually cold phases of the Dansgaard-Oeschger cycles. The pattern seemed to involve a large Heinrich event followed by five less and less severe 1,500-year Dansgaard-Oeschger cycles, until the next big Heinrich event kicked in.

Most remarkably of all perhaps, Bond found that, while there have been no major Heinrich events during the 10,000 years since the end of the last ice age – the last was 15,000 years ago – the marine imprint of the 1,500-year pulse has not missed a beat. 'The oscillations carry on no matter what the state of the climate,' he said.

Bond died in 2005, at the age of sixty-five. His long-time colleague Peter deMenocal has continued his work, looking for more signs of the pulse. Examining sea-bed sediments off Africa's west coast, he has found that every 1,500 years or so there were huge increases in dust particles in the sediments, suggesting big dust storms on land. The sediments also revealed dramatic increases in the remains of temperature-sensitive marine plankton, suggesting a temperature switchback in tropical Africa of as much as 5 degrees C. 'The transitions were sharp. Climate changes that we thought should take thousands of years to happen occurred within a generation or two,' deMenocal says.

Bond's final claim that the pulse can be seen in recurrent climatic events right through to the present seems to be vindicated, especially by temperatures in Europe and North America. There was an especially strong cooling event in the northern hemisphere that ended around 2,000 years ago to be replaced by the medieval warm period that reached its height perhaps 1,100 years ago and then by another cold era that bottomed out around 350 years ago, during the Maunder Minimum – when temperatures fell by up to 2 degrees C in northern Europe and the Eskimos reached Scotland in their kayaks.

Bond's study was an extraordinary piece of detective work. But it raises more questions than it answers. Two stand out. What, if any, is the relationship between these cycles and other parts of the climate system such as Broecker's ocean conveyor? And, of course, what causes the mysterious pulse?

By 2001, Bond believed he had confirmed the answer that many suspected all along. He went back to the Greenland ice cores to look for evidence of solar cycles. There is no known direct marker for solar cycles in the cores. But other researchers had discovered that isotopic traces of cosmic rays bombarding the atmosphere were left in the ice cores. And that when solar radiation is at its most intense, cosmic rays are literally blown away from the solar system. Thus there are fewer 'cosmogenic' isotopes like carbon-14 and beryllium-10 left in the ice cores during periods of strong solar radiation.

Bond came up trumps again. The evidence tallied. Over the past 12,000 years, the fluctuations in detritus from the iceberg armadas in the Atlantic coincided with changes in cosmogenic isotopes in the ice cores. There was thus a solar pulse that translated into a pulse in icebergs, global temperatures and recurrent climatic events found through both the glacial and the post-glacial eras.

Bond was convinced before his death that most climate change over the past 10,000 years had been driven by his solar pulse, amplified through feedbacks such as ice formation and the changing intensity of the ocean conveyor.

He worried that people might interpret this as showing that global warming was natural. 'But that would be a misuse of the data,' he told me in an interview shortly before his death. Rather, he said, the most important lesson from his research is what it shows about the sensitivity of the system itself. 'The Earth's climate system is highly sensitive to extremely weak perturbations in the sun's energy output.' And if it is sensitive to weak changes in solar forcing, it is likely to be sensitive also 'to other forcings such as those caused by human additions of greenhouse gases to the atmosphere'.

What exactly drives the amplifications of the solar pulse is another matter, however. For years, as Bond worked on his ideas, Broecker had declared that the Dansgaard-Oeschger temperature cycle in Greenland was linked to fluctuations in his ocean conveyor. Certainly the geography seemed right. Both appeared to originate in the far North Atlantic, though the precise linking mechanisms were fuzzy. It seemed clear, too, that during the periods when ice armadas were floating south in the Atlantic, temperatures in the North Atlantic were cold and the amount of deep water being formed around Greenland declined. In extreme cases – perhaps during full-scale Heinrich events – the conveyor probably shut down. Perhaps a reduction in solar radiation triggered the entire sequence. But the evidence of what caused what was largely circumstantial. And as we will see later, there is another explanation, producing a large amplification from another quarter entirely.

But whatever the amplifier, the pulse is real and extremely pervasive. Perhaps only in the past fifty years has something come along with greater power to disrupt climate.

PART SIX

TROPICAL HEAT

26

THE FALL

THE END OF AFRICA'S GOLDEN AGE

If there was a golden age for humans on the Earth – a Garden of Eden that flowed with milk and honey – then it was the high point of the Holocene, the era that followed the end of the last ice age. From around 8,000 to 5,500 years ago, the world was as warm as it is today, but there appear to have been few strong hurricanes and few disruptive El Niños; and it was certainly a world in which the regions occupied today by great deserts in Asia, the Americas and especially Africa were much wetter than they are now. Optimists suggest that such conditions might be what await us in a greenhouse world. As we shall see, there are celestial reasons why that probably won't happen. But that era, and its abrupt ending, may still offer important lessons about our future climate.

No place on Earth exemplifies the fall from this climatically blessed state better than the Sahara. The world's largest desert was not always so arid. Where seas of sand now shimmer in the sun, there were once vast lakes, swamps and rivers. Lake Chad, which today covers a paltry few hundred square kilometres, was then a vast inland sea, dubbed by scientists Lake Megachad. It was the size of France, Spain, Germany and the UK put together. Today the lake evaporates in the desert sun, but then it overflowed its inland basin and, at different times, drained south via Nigeria into the Atlantic Ocean or east down a vast wadi to the Nile.

The difference is that back then the Sahara had assured rains. The whole of North Africa was watered by a monsoon system rather like the one that keeps much of Asia wet today. Rain-bearing winds penetrated deep into the interior. From Senegal on the shores of the Atlantic to the Horn of Africa in the east, and from the beaches of the Mediterranean in the north to the threshold of the central African rainforest, vast rivers flowed for thousands of kilometres. Along their banks were swamps, forests and verdant bush.

Beneath the Algerian desert, archaeologists have recently found the sand-choked remains of wadis that once drained 1,000 kilometres from the Ahaggar Mountains into the Mediterranean. And in southern Libya, a region so waterless that even camel trains avoid it, archaeologists are finding the bones of crocodiles and hippos, elephants and antelope. If there was a vestige of true desert at the heart of North Africa, then it was very much smaller than the desert is today. And of course there were people: shepherds and fishers and hunters, and some of the earliest known fields of grains like sorghum and millet. Archaeologists digging in the sands of northern Chad, currently the dustiest place on Earth, have found human settlements around the lost shore of the ancient Lake Megachad. Paintings in caves deep in the desert depict the lives of the inhabitants of the verdant Sahara of the Holocene.

There are other, more useful remains of this time. Rocks beneath the Sahara contain the largest underground reservoir of fresh water in the world. They were mostly filled from leaking wadis in the early Holocene. Some desert settlements today tap these waters at oases. Colonel Gadaffi has constructed pumps and a huge pipeline network to take this water from beneath southern Libya to his coastal farmers. He calls the network his Great Man-made River, though it is a feeble imitation of the real rivers that once ran here.

The wet Sahara and the era known more generally as the African Humid Period began around 13,000 years ago as the ice age abated and, except for the Younger Dryas hiatus, lasted right through to the end of the 'golden age'. It coincided with a time when the Earth's tilt known as the precession ensured that the sun was blazing down on the Sahara with full intensity in summer. The land cooked and convective air currents were strong. As the warm air rose, wet air was drawn in from over the Atlantic to replace it. The process was the same one that creates today's monsoon rain system in Asia. Meanwhile, the monsoon rains were recycled by the rich vegetation across North Africa. Rather as in the Amazon today, the rain nurtured lush vegetation that ensured that much of it evaporated back into the air. The continually moistened winds took rain to the heart of the Sahara.

But the African Humid Period came to an end very suddenly. In the space of perhaps a century, the rivers of the Sahara emptied, the swamps dried up, the bush died and the monsoon rain clouds were replaced by clouds of wind-blown sand. The climate system had crossed a threshold that triggered massive change. What happened? The first answer is that the sun moved. Or rather, the precession of the Earth's orbit around the sun continued its stately progress and gradually took away the extremely favourable conditions for Saharan rains. And as summer solar heating lessened due to these changes in the Earth's orbit, the warm air rose a little less and the monsoon winds from the ocean penetrated a little less far inland some years. The process was gradual and went on without any appreciable effect on rainfall in most of the Sahara for more than 3,000 years. The vegetation feedback ensured that, most years at least, the rain kept falling. If Lake Megachad was retreating, we have no evidence of it.

But at some point, the feedback began to falter. Perhaps there was a chance variation in rainfall that dried out the bush for a year or two. The sun was no longer strong enough to make good and revive the rains. Suddenly, what had been a feedback that kept the Sahara watered became a feedback that dried it out. While the orbital changes were very slow, the response of the monsoon climate system was very fast once it had passed a critical threshold, and it never recovered. The green Sahara had become a brown Sahara. The North African monsoon rains had died.

Not everybody agrees that the vegetation feedback was the only trigger for the drying of the Sahara. There may have been some influence from one of Gerard Bond's solar pulses. But both archaeological evidence and climate models suggest that in all probability this flip in the Saharan climate was extremely sudden. Martin Claussen at the Potsdam Institute for Climate Impact Research in Germany has played out this tragedy in detail in his model. He turns time forwards and backwards, recreates the subtle orbital changes and fine tunes the vegetation feedbacks. More or less whatever he does to mimic the conditions of 5,500 years ago, the result is the same. The system flips abruptly, turning bush to desert and seas of water to seas of sand.

Other researchers have replicated his findings. Peter deMenocal at Lamont-Doherty calculates that the system flipped when solar radiation in the Sahara crossed a threshold of 470 watts per square metre. Jon Foley of the University of Wisconsin found that a reduction in Holocene summer sun sufficient to reduce temperatures by just 0.4 degrees C would have cut rainfall across the Sahara by a quarter, and by much more in the furthest interior of the continent. He says that once a region such as the Sahara becomes dry and brown it requires exceptional rains to trigger a regreening. Beyond a certain point – such as that reached 5,500 years ago – virtually no amount of extra rain is likely to be enough. The lack of vegetation 'acts to lock in and reinforce the drought'.

Back then, the people of the Sahara couldn't have known if the droughts that suddenly afflicted them were permanent or not. But as the desert asserted control across the region, and the lakes and waterways dried up, they had no alternative but to leave. As part of the exodus, lakeside settlements near the Sudanese border in Egypt were all abandoned at about the same time. One was Nabta, famous now as the site of the world's earliest known stone structures with an astronomical purpose. They predate Stonehenge in England by about 1,000 years. The key stones point to where the sun would have set at the summer solstice 6,000 years ago. Beneath some of the stones are burial sites for the cattle that the people tended. Nobody can be sure what the structures' precise purpose was, but it is intriguing to suppose that they were used in an attempt to track the celestial changes that were disrupting the rains and turning their pastures to desert.

It may have been from such places that the myths and legends of past golden ages, and of the Garden of Eden, first emerged. The people who departed from the Sahara to set up new homes on the Nile or even further afield would have taken their memories of a golden past. It is interesting that biblical scholars have calculated mankind's expulsion from the Garden of Eden at around 6,000 years ago, when kingdoms across the Sahara would have been collapsing. It was, in their language, 'the Fall'. But the Garden of Eden need not have been in the Sahara, because similar stories were played out elsewhere. Arabia dried out at the same time, leaving behind a huge underground reservoir of water not much smaller than that beneath the Sahara. Claussen calculates that the desertification of Arabia could have been caused by the same combination of gradual orbital change and a dramatic vegetation feedback.

The evidence is as yet sketchy, but the dramatic drying of the Sahara and Arabia appears to coincide with other climate changes round the world. In the Pacific Ocean, El Niño switched into a more active mode at around this time. There were cold periods from the Andes to the European Alps. In both cases, glaciers advanced strongly down their valleys; often they are only returning to their former positions today. In the Austrian Tyrol, one victim of the advance was the 'ice man' named Otzi, whose freeze-dried remains emerged from melting ice in 1991. In Ireland, a 7,000-year temperature record held in tree rings shows cold times that included the coldest summer in the entire record.

All this is particularly intriguing because, unlike previous great climatic events of the era of the ice ages, there is little evidence that the primary action had much to do with the polar regions. It seems to have been an abrupt climate change formed in the tropics and with its major impacts there, and only ripples beyond. One in the eye for Wally Broecker, some of its investigators have been heard to say – a point to which we will return.

But what does this say about the future of the Sahara? Could warming in the twenty-first century trigger a greener, wetter Sahara? It is an intriguing idea, with plenty of adherents. Reindert Haarsma, a climate modeller at the Royal Netherlands Meteorological Institute, says the Sahara could be destined for a 50 per cent increase in rainfall – enough to trigger a return to the 'golden age', in which crocodiles float through swamps in places where today locusts swarm. Claussen, whose model first stimulated the idea, is more sceptical. He points out that the orbital situation today is very different, so summer solar radiation is not great enough to create a revived African monsoon. DeMenocal says solar radiation is currently 4 per cent lower in the Sahara than it was when 'the Fall' occurred. But on the other hand, he admits, much higher levels of carbon dioxide in the air might compensate for this by stimulating an earlier recovery of Saharan vegetation.

Optimists point out that on a very modest scale there is currently something of a revival going on in Saharan rains and vegetation – albeit from the depths of the droughts that afflicted the region in the 1970s and 1980s. It hasn't happened everywhere, and some places have since slipped back. But, according to Chris Reij of the Free University in Amsterdam, improved farming methods, such as digging terraces and holding water on the land, may have encouraged a modest greening of parts of the Sahara, and the resulting vegetation feedback could be one reason for the revived rains. But it would be a big step from that to predicting a reversion to the 'Garden of Eden' days.

While some in the Sahara may conceivably be able to look forward to greener, wetter times, the prognosis for many other arid regions round the world is not so good. The big fear from the American West to northern China and southern Africa to the Mediterranean is of a twenty-first century dominated by longer and fiercer droughts.

Again, history is the first guide. DeMenocal has been looking at the history of droughts and civilization in the Americas, and finds strong evidence of periods of drought much longer than any known in modern times. 'There is good scientific evidence that vast regions of North America witnessed several such periods during the last millennium, with devastating cultural consequences,' he says. 'These megadroughts can persist for a century or more.'

The six-year dust bowl of the 1930s, which caused mass migrations westwards, was 'pale by comparison' with its predecessors. Droughts in the nineteenth century devastated many Native Americans as well as their bison. At the end of the sixteenth century, a twenty-two-year drought destroyed an early English colony at Roanoke in Virginia. It became known as the Lost Colony after all its inhabitants disappeared between their arrival in 1587 and the return of a supply ship four years later. Going back earlier, tree rings show there was near permanent drought from AD 900 to 1300 west of the Mississippi and through Central America. Drought that destroyed the Mayan and Anasazi civilizations. DeMenocal concludes that complex, organized societies can get by in short droughts. They have stocks of food and water and know how to trade their way out of trouble in the short term. But few of them can deal with megadroughts. If hunger doesn't get them, then the strife and turmoil caused by trying to survive does.

And the signs are that worsening droughts are again becoming the norm in regions that have suffered megadroughts in the past. In the American West, the biggest river, the Colorado, is a shadow of its former self. Early in the twentieth century, the average flow was 16 cubic kilometres a year. From 1999 to 2003, the average sank to 8.7 cubic kilometres – worse even than the dust-bowl years of the mid-1930s. In 2002, it fell to just 3.7 cubic kilometres. In 2005, the drought was continuing. In Central Asia, the Afghan war of 2002 was fought against a backdrop of drought as debilitating as any Taliban tyranny. The Hamoun wetland covering 4,000 square kilometres on the remote border between Afghanistan and Iran has for millennia been a place of refuge for people from both countries in times of trouble. But that year it dried out and turned to salt flats. Southern Europe is increasingly beset by forest fires, desiccated crops and drought orders.

Richard Seager at Lamont-Doherty says that there is a long-standing correlation between droughts in the western US, South America, parts of Europe and Central Asia. And that is a pattern we see reasserting itself in the twenty-first century as the Arizona desert creeps north, southern Europe increasingly resembles North Africa and

Central Asia takes on the appearance of Iraq or the Arabian peninsula. Kevin Trenberth of the National Center for Atmospheric Research in Boulder, Colorado, reports that the percentage of the Earth's land area stricken by serious drought has more than doubled in thirty years from 15 per cent to 30 per cent. 'The climate models predict increased drying over most land areas. Our analyses suggest that this may already have begun,' he says.

That seems to be a common view. Mark Cane, a specialist in Pacific weather at Lamont-Doherty, says scarily: 'The medieval warm period a thousand years ago was a very small forcing compared to what is going on with global warming now. But it was still strong enough to cause a 300- to 400-year drought in the western US. That could be an analogue for what will happen under anthropogenic warming. If the mechanisms we think work hold true, then we'll get big droughts in the West again.' The Garden of Eden it is not.

Many believe that El Niño and the pattern of ocean temperatures in the Pacific are heavily implicated in the historic megadroughts, perhaps as part of a global re-organization of climate systems linked to Gerard Bond's pulses. And this should set modern alarm bells ringing, says Ed Cook, a leading tree-ring expert from Lamont-Doherty. 'If warming over the tropical Pacific promotes drought over the western US ... any trend towards warmer temperatures could lead to a serious long-term increase in aridity over western North America.' Martin Hoerling of the National Oceanic and Atmospheric Administration in Boulder, Colorado, thinks that such a process is already under way. He blames the increasing droughtiness of the tropics on a persistent ocean warming in the Pacific that, he says, is 'unsurpassed during the twentieth century'. The pattern of dryness is beginning to look less like a local, short-term aberration and more like a long-term trend, he says, and predicts that global warming 'may be a harbinger of future severe and extensive droughts'.

It won't happen everywhere, of course. Climate models predict that a warmer world will, on average, have more moisture in the atmosphere and that, in general, the wet places will get wetter and the dry places will get drier. They predict that areas of uplift, where rising air will trigger storm clouds and abundant rain, will see the uplift become more intense. But the areas of sinking air, which are the traditional desert lands of the world, will see more intense sinking and drying. In many parts of the world, this 'hyperweather' is likely to set competing forces against each other. Stronger storms will blow off the oceans and, in places, monsoon-type rains may begin to restart. But the rain-bearing winds will often be confronted by intensifying arid zones of descending air in the continental interiors. It is not obvious which force will win and where.

Will the Sahara desert expand and intensify, as the drought theorists argue? Or will North Africa be reclaimed by a revived African monsoon? Megadrought or Garden of Eden? Nobody can answer that question yet. Perhaps the greatest likelihood is that in many places, from the Sahara to the American West and Arabia, there will be more and longer droughts, interspersed with brief but devastating outbreaks of intense storms and floods.

27

SEE-SAW ACROSS THE OCEAN
HOW SAHARAN DESERT GREENS THE AMAZON

Two of the world's largest and most fragile ecosystems face each other across the Atlantic. On one side is the Amazon rainforest; on the other the Sahara. They seem to be unconnected and ecological opposites. The Sahara is rainless and largely empty of vegetation. The Amazon is one of the wettest places on Earth, and certainly the most biologically diverse, with perhaps half of the world's species beneath its canopy. But these two opposites are not so far apart. For one thing, the physical gap is surprisingly small. The Atlantic is narrow near the equator and the two worlds are less than half as far apart as London and New York. And secondly, many believe they have a surprising symbiosis. Their fates may be inter-twined in a rather unexpected way – and one that could have important consequences in the coming decades.

The key to the symbiosis lies in the remote heart of the Sahara, a region called Bodélé in northern Chad. Few people go here. It is littered with unexploded bombs and land mines left behind during Libya's invasion of Chad during the 1980s. And it is by some way the dustiest place on Earth. Satellite images show year-round dust storms raging across Bodélé and entering the atmospheric circulation. According to Richard Washington of Oxford University, two-fifths of the dust in the atmosphere comes from the Sahara, and of that half comes from Bodélé.

Some of this dust stays local. But much of it is carried on the prevailing winds west, crossing the desert wastes of Niger, Mali and Mauritania before heading out across the Atlantic. The red dust clouds can grow 3 kilometres high as they approach America. They cause spectacular sunrises over Miami, before the dust falls in the rains of the Caribbean and the Amazon. And there have been a lot of good sunrises in recent decades. The amount of dust crossing the Atlantic grew fivefold between the wet 1960s and the dry 1980s.

The Saharan dust has a series of unexpected effects on the Americas. According to hurricane forecasters in Florida, during dry, dusty years in the Sahara there are fewer hurricanes on the other side of the Atlantic. It seems that dust in the air interrupts the critical updraughts of warm, moist air that fuel the storms. Equally surprisingly, desert bacteria caught up in the winds are being blamed for bringing new diseases to Caribbean coral reefs and even triggering asthma among Caribbean children.

And there is a third important link. Saharan dust storms carry huge amounts of minerals, iron and organic matter that enriches soils widely in the Americas. Bodélé dust seems especially valuable. Its dunes are the dried-out remains of the bed of the vast Lake Megachad, which covered central Sahara until its abrupt demise as the region turned to desert 5,500 years ago. Most of the dunes are not made of sand or broken rock. They are the remains of trillions of diatomites, microscopic fresh-water creatures that once lived in huge numbers in the lake. These fragments are light enough to blow freely in the wind. That's why they make such plentiful dust storms. And they also make great fertilizer. If Bodélé had any rain, the diatomites would have rich farmland. Instead, Chad's loss is the Americas' gain, says Hans Joachim Schellnhuber, a German physicist turned Earth system scientist, who as director of Britain's Tyndall Climate Centre in Norwich has made a study of the unlikely connection. 'Bizarre as it may seem, the arid, barren Sahara fertilizes the Amazon rainforest. This process has been going on for thousands of years, and is one reason why the Amazon basin teems with life.'

The two unique habitats are on a kind of see-saw, he says. When the Sahara is dry, as it has been for much of the past quarter-century, its dust crosses the Atlantic in huge quantities and fertilizes the Amazon, making it superabundant. When the Sahara is wet, the dust storms subside and the Amazon goes hungry. That the Sahara seems to have only two basic modes, wet and dry, suggests that there may be two distinct modes in the Amazon, too. The last big change in the Sahara came 5,500 years ago when the region lurched from wet to dry, probably within a few decades. As yet we know little about how the Amazon changed at that time. But if Schellnhuber is right, the Sahara's loss may have been the Amazon's gain. There may have been a major change for the better in the rainforests.

In the twenty-first century, the see-saw could be on the move again. There are hints that the Sahara may become wetter, says Schellnhuber. And if the wetting turns to greening, and the vegetation feedback kicks in, the whole of North Africa could change dramatically. That would be good news for the Sahara, of course. But perhaps bad news for the Amazon, which already seems to be close to its own tipping point as the climate dries and rainforests give up their carbon. Could a wetter Sahara be the final nail in the Amazon coffin? Schellnhuber believes it could be so.

28

TROPICAL HIGH

WHY AN ICE MAN IS REWRITING CLIMATE HISTORY

There are two special things about Lonnie Thompson. First, doctors reckon that he has spent more time on mountains above 6,000 metres than any other lowlander on the planet. And second, in his deep freeze back home in Columbus, Ohio, he has probably the most detailed physical record anywhere of the climate of planet Earth over the past 20,000 years. Not bad for the sixty-year-old son of a hick from Gassaway, a tiny railroad town in West Virginia.

Make that three things. Because Thompson is, in a mild-mannered but determined way, a revolutionary in the world of glaciology. For four decades now, climate scientists have been drilling ice cores into the polar regions to find the secrets of climates past. They have found a lot, and they have developed some impressive theories about how the world's climate system is driven from these cold wastelands. But thirty years ago Thompson, then still a graduate student in the geology of coal with a temporary post drilling ice cores in Antarctica, set out to prove them wrong about the origins of climate.

With his early mentor, the legendary British glaciologist John Mercer, Thompson ignored the poles and began drilling ice cores in glaciers high in the Andes, the Himalayas and other mountain regions of the tropics. This was unheard of at the time. Finding funding was hard, because nobody had a budget for such work. But he has uncovered a new, entirely unexpected world of tropical climate change. And now, after fifty expeditions to five continents, and with 6,000 metres of ice cores stored in his freezer, he believes he is on the path to proving that the true triggers and drivers and Achilles' heels and thresholds and tipping points for the world's climate lie in the tropics.

For men like Broecker, men of the polar school, this is sacrilege. But while his case is not yet proven, he has found some unexpected fans. Richard Alley, a career member of the polar school, is an admirer of the senior from Gassaway. He told me with a smile: 'Lonnie is a legend, and he may well turn out to be right.' Whether he is right or not, Thompson's ice cores and the data he has painstakingly extracted from them are the lifeblood of an emerging debate between the polar and tropical schools – a debate that might not be happening at all without him.

Thompson is a loner. He has always avoided the big organizations and funding bodies that dominate so much climate science. Sometimes that has been out of necessity; now he sees it as a virtue. It has given him the freedom to do and think things his way. With his researcher wife, Ellen Mosley-Thompson, he set up a small team at the Byrd Polar Research Institute, part of the Ohio State

University. 'We started small and we try to be self-contained,' he says. 'That makes us flexible. We don't have to stand in line for analysis of cores, or for supplies. And we have our own workshops to make everything.'

Team Thompson build their own lightweight drills and photovoltaic generators, because the only means of getting the right kit onto the high slopes of the world's tallest mountains is horseback. And they have their own four automatic mass spectrometers, working 24 hours a day 365 days a year to analyse the samples brought back from around the world. Thompson doesn't even trust the big science institutions to look after his ice cores after he has gone. With the prize money that has come his way in recent years, he has created a trust fund to keep the freezers going in perpetuity.

Being independent means he can pack his bags and head round the world on a whim if he thinks there is an ice core to be had. Back in 1997, he took advantage of a brief thaw in diplomatic relations between Moscow and Washington to fly to Franz Josef Land in the Siberian Arctic. There he extracted 315 metres of ice from near an old Russian nuclear bomber base, and persuaded the bomber pilots to fly it back to Moscow for him. More recently, after years of stonewalling by the Tanzanian authorities, he took his drilling kit on to a tourist flight to Dar es Salaam and smooth-talked his way up Kilimanjaro to extract vital evidence of the demise of its ice cap.

Thompson has spent half a lifetime taking his ice pick, crampons and drilling gear to the Andes and the Himalayas, Tibet and the Russian Arctic, Alaska and East Africa. Back in Columbus, he has interrogated the ice and the bubbles of air trapped inside for signs of dust, metals, salts and isotopes of oxygen and carbon that in turn will reveal not just temperatures and rainfall but the comings and goings of El Niño events, forest fires, droughts and monsoons.

His first love, he says, is Quelccaya, the first ice cap he scaled in Peru with John Mercer. It is the one he keeps going back to. He can see the whole world evolve there, he says, from the revival of El Niños in the Pacific around 5,500 years ago to the decades of drought that finished off the pre-Colombian Moche empire; from the first record in the tropics of the little ice age to the recent isotopic signature of global warming. Here and elsewhere across the tropics he has also found a dust 'spike' in the ice that shows that dust storms were sweeping across the tropics 4,200 years ago – evidence, it seems, of a sudden near-global megadrought.

Most intriguingly for glaciologists, Thompson's worldwide collection of ice cores has revealed a previously unknown pattern in the formation of glaciers across the tropics. It seems to be independent of the great glaciations waxing and waning in the polar regions. It seems instead to follow latitude, starting in the southern hemisphere close to the Tropic of Capricorn, where he has found evidence that glaciers began to form in Bolivia 25,000 years ago. Then, as if by clockwork, other glaciers began to form and grow further north. One by one, they started through Peru and Ecuador. Then, 12,000 years ago, a continent to the east but following the same northward trajectory, an ice cap began to form at the summit of Kilimanjaro on the equator. Skipping north again to the Himalayas, only around 8,000 years ago glaciers started to grow near the Tropic of Cancer. Across three continents, glacier formation was oblivious to longitude or the equator or anything else. Latitude ruled.

How come? Thompson has tied this extraordinary progression to the wobble in the Earth's orbit known as the precession, which gradually alters the line of latitude where the most intense solar heating occurs. This is the same slow wobble that sustained the African monsoon over the Sahara when the sun was overhead there in the early Holocene, but snuffed out the rains as the sun moved on. In the mountains of the tropics, Thompson says, glaciers generally started where the sun was fiercest. The sun was most intense over the Tropic of Capricorn at the start of this era and moved north, ending by being most intense over the Tropic of Cancer. It appeared to trigger the formation of glaciers all the way.

On the face of it, this seems odd. Why would the harshest sun and hottest temperatures create glaciers? Thompson has a simple explanation. The zone of maximum sun in the tropics is also the zone of maximum rainfall, which in the highest mountains means the zone of maximum snow. Up there, he says, it has always been cold enough for glaciers to form. So temperature is not an issue. What the high valleys have often lacked is moisture to feed the growth of glaciers. The sun brought the moisture and with it the snow and the glaciers.

What should we make of all this? Many would argue that all the natural variability in the tropical climate that Thompson is uncovering offers a soothing reminder that the planet and human society are no strangers to climate change. Not Lonnie. His analysis is uncovering invisible thresholds in the climate system, he says. Cross them and the whole system goes into a spin, with dramatic cooling or warming, great droughts and El Niño turned full on or full off for centuries at a time. 'Should we not be just as concerned that carbon dioxide might send us above a threshold?' If that happens, he says, 'we won't get gradual climate change as projected, we will instead get abrupt change.'

Thompson is tracking with concern the progress of modern climate change in melting his glaciers. Back in 1976, he took a core of the ice at the summit of Quelccaya. It showed layers of ice laid down annually for 1,500 years. In 1991, when he returned to update the record, he found that the annual accumulation had stopped and the top 20 metres of the ice had melted away – dramatic evidence of a recent and sudden shift in an ancient ice cap's fortunes. In the valley below, Quelccaya's largest glacier, the Qori Kalis, is retreating by 150 metres a year and has lost a fifth of its area since 1963. Across Peru, a quarter of the ice surface has disappeared in thirty years. Elsewhere in the Andes, Bolivia's Chacaltaya glacier lost two-thirds of its ice in the 1990s, and Venezuela has lost four of its six glaciers since 1975.

In Africa, 80 per cent of the ice on Mount Kilimanjaro has melted away in ninety years; Mount Kenya has lost seven of its eighteen glaciers since 1900; and most of the ice on the Rwenzori Mountains between Uganda and Congo has gone, too. Across the Indian Ocean on New Guinea, the West Meren glacier vanished altogether in the late 1990s, and its neighbour Carstensz has shrunk by 80 per cent in sixty years. Thompson has seen the same trends in the Himalayas and Tibet. Glacial retreat, he says, 'is happening at virtually all the tropical glaciers'. In some places there may be local factors. Occasionally declining snowfall will do the damage. But he insists that while snowfall in high altitudes may be critical to getting a glacier started, it is rarely critical in its demise, which starts lower down the slopes. Globally, he says, there can be no other explanation for the universal disappearance of glaciers than global warming.

Thompson believes that he has only begun to explore the potential of his ice cores to answer questions about the tropics. He wants to take cores from ice still attached to the Nevado del Ruiz volcano in northern Colombia. The mountain exploded in 1985, engulfing 20,000 people in a landslide of ash. 'I think we could get a record of how often that volcano erupts,' he says, apparently oblivious to the risk for researchers in such an expedition. He believes that the ice of Quelccaya can offer a history of fires and drought in the nearby Amazon. And he is looking at dust from China that has collected in ice in Alaska. It is already providing a history of pesticide use in China and may eventually reveal whether dust out of Asia, as well as that from the Sahara, could have fertilized the soils of the Americas.

By uncovering the secret climate history of the tropics Thompson is helping to strip climatology of an unhealthy fixation with what happens close to the homes of the researchers – in the North Atlantic. 'An important reason why we think that Greenland and those places are so important to the global climate is because so much research has been done there – and that is mainly because it is more convenient than going to Tibet or Patagonia.' He believes that this fixation with the familiar is diverting researchers from where the real climatic action is – in the tropics, in the world of El Niño and the Asian monsoon and megadroughts and the dramatic feedbacks that dried up the Sahara. All of which he sees as being 'at least as important as anything

Wally Broecker has cooked up on the North Atlantic'.

To Thompson, it has always seemed obvious that 'the global climate is driven from the tropics.' Most of the surface of the Earth is in the tropics, he says. 'It is where the majority of the heat reaches the Earth and from where it is distributed round the globe. It is where the great climate systems like the monsoon and El Niño are based.' He argues that truly global climatic events can start only where heat and moisture can be delivered both north and south round the globe. There may be feedbacks operating in the North Atlantic or around Antarctica. But the big drivers must be in the tropics.

Thompson has his own heroes. Mercer is one. Another is James Croll, the lowly Victorian Scot who worked his way through life as a waiter, school caretaker and carpenter so that he could research the astronomical forces behind the ice ages. And Thompson has simple advice for young scientists: plough your own furrow. 'Go somewhere or do something that nobody else has even thought about working on.' Some academics from the wrong side of the tracks would have settled quietly into faculty life, thankful for their social advance. Not Lonnie. He does research the hard way. 'On one trip we were up on Quelccaya for three months. We had to cut the ice cores by hand into 6,000 samples, take them downhill on our backs and then melt them and put the water in bottles sealed with wax.' On another occasion, he found himself in New Zealand dangling on a rope above 600 metres of empty space.

A student with Thompson years ago died of the after-effects of altitude sickness. His father sued. That still hurts. Thompson would be the last professor on Earth to send his students somewhere he wasn't prepared to go himself. He is still prepared to live for months under canvas in freezing cold and lung-achingly thin air. Just turning sixty when we met, he was recently back from his biennial trip to the Andes, and his diary included upcoming trips up Kilimanjaro and central Africa's 'mountains of the moon'. He had tentative plans for expeditions to the last glaciers on New Guinea and a Siberian island near where the last mastodon died of the cold 5,000 years ago.

He told me he reckoned his techniques could one day help uncover the remains of life in the ice caps of Mars. And I swear his eyes lit up when I suggested he might be on the first flight to the red planet.

29

THE CURSE OF AKKAD

THE STRANGE REVIVAL OF ENVIRONMENTAL DETERMINISM

Around 4,200 years ago, the world's top empire was run by Sargon, the despotic but otherwise unexceptional ruler of the Akkadian empire. Some have called this the first true empire in the world. Certainly it seemed to be a new form of society, created out of a number of previously autonomous city states on the flood plains of the Tigris and Euphrates rivers in Mesopotamia, modern-day Iraq. Its rule extended all the way from the headwaters of the two rivers in Turkey, across much of Syria and as far south as the Persian Gulf. But Sargon's empire had been in business for only a century or so when it suddenly collapsed. Archaeologists initially put this down to an invasion of barbarian hordes from the surrounding mountains. But an energetic field archaeologist called Harvey Weiss from Yale changed that rather lazy assumption – and with it changed much else about our perceptions of the rise and fall of past civilizations.

In the late 1970s, while working in Syria, Weiss discovered a 'lost city' beneath the desert sands, close to the Iraqi border. Over more than a decade he excavated the remains of the settlement, named Tell Leilan. He pieced together the story of a highly organized city that had grown over several thousand years from a small village to a prosperous outpost of the Akkadian empire. But there was a mystery. It appeared that for some three hundred years, the city had been abandoned and its streets had filled with wind-blown dust.

He tied the events at Tell Leilan to a contemporary cuneiform text entitled 'The Curse of Akkad', which recorded a great drought in which the fields of most of northern Mesopotamia were abruptly abandoned. The granaries emptied, the fruit trees died in the orchards and even the fish departed as the great rivers dried up. Refugees flooded south, and the people of southern Mesopotamia built a wall 180 kilometres long to keep them out. Archaeologists had previously dismissed 'The Curse of Akkad' as mythology. The idea that climatic and other environment change determined the progress of societies had been hugely out of fashion. The prevailing view was that politics, economics, wars and dynasties made and broke empires, and that climate was just a more or less benign backdrop.

But Weiss was convinced that only a massive shift in climate could explain a 300-year collapse, before the climate apparently recovered enough for the northern plains to be settled once more. When he published his findings, they provoked consternation in the archaeological community but huge interest among climate scientists. Not least Peter deMenocal at Lamont-Doherty. 'After Weiss's publication environmental determinism had a huge revival,' he says. Especially after it emerged that the dust storms of Mesopotamia were part of a wider process of aridification right across the Middle East and beyond that had seen off other societies, too.

In New York, deMenocal was working with a student, Heidi Cullen, on analysing a core of marine sediment drilled from beneath the Gulf of Oman, 2,500 kilometres to the south of Tell Leilan. They decided to look for evidence of dust storms in the core. 'We thought the dust might be visible there and Heidi started to go through it. It was very painstaking work and, to be honest, she was about to give up. Then boom. One day she found it. The 300-year layer of dust, dated at 4,200 years ago, and much of it clearly derived from Mesopotamia. We sent it to Harvey and he was ecstatic.'

The news spread. Lonnie Thompson and his team went back to their tropical ice cores and found similar layers of black dust. When I asked him about this, his eyes lit up. 'It was a huge global dust spike,' he said. In the ice on the summit of Kilimanjaro in East Africa, there is only one dust 'spike' in the 12,000-year record. And it occurs right at 4,200 years ago, he said. On the other side of the planet from Syria, at Quelccaya in Peru, the same period pro-duced 'the biggest dust event in the ice core in a 17,000 year record'. Fallout of dust onto the glacier was at a hundred times normal levels. 'And it shows up in the Asian monsoon region of the Himalayas, too,' says Thompson's dust analyst Mary Davis.

In lakes from Lake Van in eastern Turkey to the Dead Sea in Palestine and in Africa from Kenya to Morocco, water levels fell by tens or even hundreds of metres 4,200 years ago. Civilizations were ending everywhere. In Egypt, those years produced a collapse of order that marked the break between the old and middle kingdoms. 'On the tombs of the Pharaohs, their histories talk of expansion until 4,200 years before the present, when there were droughts and mass migrations and sand dunes crossing the Nile,' says Thompson. In Palestine the situation was even worse, according to Arie Issar, an Israeli hydrologist and author of a detailed study of climate change and civilization in the region. The level of the Dead Sea dropped 100 metres. 'All the urban centres were abandoned and the cities, which had existed for several hundred years, remained only as large heaps of ruins. They were not resettled until nearly half a millennium later.' Further east in the Indus Valley of modern-day Pakistan, the urban centres of the Harappan civilization collapsed at the same time.

What caused all this? Nobody is sure. Jeffrey Severinghaus of the Scripps Institution of Oceanography in California has found tantalizing evidence of a dust signal in the Greenland ice cores 4,200 years ago. But rather than finding more dust than before, he found less. There was also a decline in sea ice in the North Atlantic. This has been interpreted as evidence of a change in the ocean conveyor. Did Broecker's conveyor drive things once again? On the face of it, that interpretation looks unlikely. For on this occasion, rather as during the previous great climatic disruption 5,500 years ago, events in the north look like mere ripples flowing out from much bigger events in the tropics.

Peter deMenocal sees this as more evidence that climate switches may lurk in the tropics at least as much as at the poles. A triumph for the tropical school? Maybe. But Richard Alley again reaches for the common ground. Perhaps, he says, the Arctic feedbacks were at their height during and immediately after the ice ages but lost their influence once most of the ice had gone. During the height of the Holocene, at least, perhaps the tropics ruled. But if so, what is driving the feedbacks in the tropics? Where are the tropical equivalents of Broecker's conveyor, Alley's 'sink or freeze' switch and Juergen Mienert's clathrate gun?

30

A CHUNK OF CORAL

PROBING THE HIDDEN LIFE OF EL NIÑO

Some researchers have a way of combining business with pleasure. Not for Dan Schrag the arduous journeys into the thin, cold air on tropical glaciers. Back in 1997, he was on his fourth trip to the paradise islands of the East Indies in search of ancient coral. One day he was sauntering along a beach on Bunaken Island, a speck of old atoll off the Indonesian island of Sulawesi. 'We had had a glorious dive, during which we saw a huge school of barracuda,' he remembers. 'We stopped for lunch and I took a walk down the beach, behind the mangrove swamp. It was the last day of the trip. We had failed to find anything useful, and I was preparing to go home. Then I saw this massive coral head on the beach, incredibly well preserved.' He chiselled a piece out and headed for the plane.

Back in the lab at Harvard, Schrag discovered that this fossilized piece of coral was 125,000 years old and contained annual growth rings covering a sixty-five-year period at that date, which gave a brief 'window' on the climate of the western Pacific back before the last ice age. It was, he said, a 'fantastic discovery. I guess I got really, really lucky.' The coral he had found was the first piece ever located that was large enough and well enough preserved to give a good snapshot of ancient El Niños. What's more, says Schrag, it came from a region that is in the 'bull's-eye' of El Niño, in the heart of Indonesia. His pre-prandial discovery is helping transform our understanding of El Niño's place in the climate system.

Until recently, climatologists looked on El Niño as a minor aberration in the tropical Pacific, of only passing interest to the wider world. But in the past two decades it has become the fifth horseman of the Apocalypse, a bringer of devastating floods, fires and famine from Ethiopia to Indonesia to Ecuador, and a sender of weird weather round the world. It has been appearing more frequently, and with effects that are much more violent and last longer. Its current level of activity is unparalleled in the historical record. Yet the historical record doesn't go back far, so nobody is sure if this is a perfectly normal upturn or an alarming consequence of global climate change. Schrag's coral is helping provide some answers. It makes a strong case that global warming is already having a profound effect on what climatologists are coming to regard as the flywheel of the world's climate.

El Niño is a periodic reversal of ocean currents, winds and weather systems that stretches across the equatorial Pacific Ocean, halfway round the planet at its widest girth. It is a redistributor of heat and energy in the hottest part of the world's oceans that kicks in when the regular circulation systems can no longer cope. In normal times, the winds and surface waters of the tropical Pacific, driven by the Earth's rotation, flow from the Americas in the east to Indonesia in the west. In the tropical heat, the water warms as it goes. The result is the gradual accumulation of a pool of hot water on the ocean surface around Indonesia. This pool can be up to 8 degrees C warmer than the water on the other side of the ocean, and can contain more heat energy than the entire atmosphere. All that heat generates storm clouds that keep the rainforests of South East Asia wet.

But the constant flow to the west also piles up water. Trapped against the Indonesian archipelago, the warm pool can rise as much as 40 centimetres above sea levels further east. Clearly this state of affairs cannot last. And, every few years, usually when the winds slacken, this raised pool of warm water breaks out and flows back across the surface of the ocean, right along the equator. As the warm water moves east, the wind and weather systems that it creates follow. That is El Niño.

Deprived of their storm-generating weather systems, Indonesia and a wide area of the western Pacific, including much of Australia, dry out. There are forest and bush fires, and crops shrivel in the fields. Meanwhile, the displaced wet and stormy rainforest climate drenches normally arid Pacific islands, and often reaches the coastal deserts of the Americas. Ripples from this vast movement of heat and moisture spread round the globe. They move west through the Indian Ocean, disrupting the Indian monsoon and causing rains or drought in Africa, depending on the season. They move east. Beyond the flooding on the Pacific shores of the Americas, El Niño brings drought in the Amazon rainforest. Its hidden hand alters flow down the River Nile, triggers rains in the hills of

Palestine and damps down hurricane formation in the North Atlantic.

Typically, an individual El Niño event lasts twelve to eighteen months. After it has abated, the system often goes into sharp reverse, with exceptionally wet conditions in Indonesia and fierce drought further east. This is called La Niña. Together El Niño and its sister constitute a vast oscillation of ocean and atmosphere that in recent times has been the most intense fluctuation in the world's climate system.

Scientists first became aware of the oscillation we now call El Niño in the nineteenth century. But they have been uncertain about how far back El Niño goes. Is it a permanent feature of the climate system or an aberration? Does it have long-term variability tied to global climate changes? Does the Pacific ever get 'stuck' either in a permanent El Niño or a permanent La Niña?

Reliable climate and ocean records cover only a couple of centuries or so. Delving further requires alternative sources of information. To this end, Donald Rodbell of Union College in Schenectady, New York, dug up the bed of a lake in southern Ecuador to chart its past flood levels in the expectation that, as today, floods would be a feature of El Niño episodes. In 1998, he published a remarkable 12,000-year record of the lake's floods. They showed that for the first half of the period, they came roughly once every fifteen years, suggesting a near-dormant El Niño. Then they speeded up quite abruptly to settle at an average return period of about six years – the classic El Niño pattern until recently. This pattern has been confirmed by Lonnie Thompson's ice cores from nearby glaciers.

The change in the flood pattern from fifteen to six years

also seemed to coincide with the same precession shift in the Earth's tilt that caused the desertification of the Sahara and the advance of tropical glaciers spotted by Thompson. This was a major breakthrough, linking long-term trends in El Niño to a key driver of the global climate system. El Niño was no longer just a short-term cycle played out over a few months in one ocean: it had global and long-term meaning. Then came Schrag's chunk of coral.

Through isotopic analysis Schrag extracted an El Niño signal from his piece of jetsam. When water evaporates, molecules containing the lighter isotope of oxygen – oxygen-16 – evaporate slightly faster, leaving behind sea water that is rich in the heavier oxygen-18. When it rains, the oxygen-16 is returned. So in the Indonesian islands during El Niños, when rainfall ceases, both the sea water and the coral growth in those years contain more oxygen-18. Schrag measured the ratio of the two oxygen isotopes in the sixty-five annual growth rings in his ancient chunk of coral. He found two things of importance. First, he found that there was indeed an El Niño cycle back then. That pushed the longevity of the phenomenon back to before the last ice age, further establishing it as a permanent feature of the climate system. And second, he found that the El Niño cycle looked exactly like that of the modern period from the mid-nineteenth century to the mid-1970s, in which El Niño returned on average about every six years. This underlined the idea that six years is the natural length of the cycle – and made the post-1976 period, during which El Niño has developed a return period averaging 3.5 years, appear increasingly unusual.

This sense that El Niño may have changed in some fundamental way in the last thirty years has been reinforced by another observation. The earliest records of the El Niño phenomenon are from the Pacific shores of South America, where a cold ocean current normally works its way north, bringing waters rich in nutrients that sustain one of the world's largest fisheries, off Peru. But during El Niños, the flood of warm water from the west overrides this cold current for a while, and the fish disappear. That has been the classic pattern. But since 1976, the underlying state has changed. The cold current has been pushed to ever greater depths, even during normal times. The ocean system appears to have become stuck in a quasi-permanent El Niño state.

What lies behind these recent changes? Some say that El Niño is simply on a short-lived, exuberant joyride. They point out that there have always been decades when it is unusually quiet or busy or just plain weird. Schrag thinks this is unlikely to explain recent events. Publishing his Sulawesi findings, he said: 'In 1982–83 we experienced the most severe El Niño of the 20th century. According to previous records you wouldn't expect another that powerful for a hundred years. But 15 years later, in 1997–98, we have one even larger.' And since then, in 2002 and 2004, there have been two more minor El Niños, not as large as those before, but turning up with ever greater frequency.

Kevin Trenberth, head of climate analysis at NCAR, was one of the first researchers to claim that the Pacific had entered an unusual state after 1976. He believes that the recent spate of strong and frequent El Niños could well be due to the hand of man. It looks as if global warming, which only gathered real pace in the 1970s, is generating so much warming in the tropical Pacific that the old 'flywheel' pattern in which occasional El Niños distribute the heat that accumulates around

Indonesia is not sufficient to handle the amount of energy in the system.

Modellers have been testing this theory, with interesting results. Mojib Latif at the Max Planck Institute for Meteorology in Hamburg developed the first global climate model that was detailed enough to reproduce El Niño. His model predicts that the average climate in the twenty-first century will be more like the typical El Niño conditions of the twentieth century. Cold La Niña events will still happen occasionally, and may even be more intense. But they will become the break-out events, while the 'normal' situation will become more El Niño-like.

It would be wrong to suggest that science has somehow cracked the enigma of El Niño. There are still many mysteries. Certainly the idea that a strong El Niño is necessarily associated with warm times could be a gross simplification. Schrag's coral, along with other evidence, suggests that El Niño kept going right through the last ice age, when even in the western Pacific temperatures were several degrees lower than they are today. There is even some suggestion that El Niños were more common in the colder phases of the ice age, whereas La Niña held sway during the warmer periods. Likewise the warm early Holocene era, before 6,000 years ago, saw El Niño largely in abeyance. It recovered during a cooler period.

Clearly El Niño is not a simple planetary thermostat. But its operation in the past may have had more to do with changes in solar radiation that were reflected in alterations to the tropical hydrological cycle rather than in temperature fluctuations. It is possible to imagine a climate system in which those changes triggered different temperature signals at different times. So efforts to tie past El Niños to temperature trends may not provide a good guide to what happens in a world of pumped-up greenhouse gas concentrations.

But what is becoming clear is that El Niño is a phenomenon that influences basic planetary processes such as the transfer of heat and moisture in huge swathes of the tropics. That it has big swings that operate on timescales varying from months to thousands of years. That it leaves its calling card in different ways right round the planet. And that its variability seems to be keyed into the critical external drivers of past climate like the precession and Bond's 1,500-year solar cycles. You would not bet against it playing an equally important role in moderating or amplifying global warming caused by greenhouse gases. What is not yet clear is which way it will jump.

Perhaps scientists should put aside their models and search for some wisdom on El Niño from Peruvian farmers, who have grown potatoes high in the Andes for thousands of years. Throughout that time, El Niños have become stronger and weaker, more frequent and less frequent, and have influenced potato growing all the while. For many centuries now, farmers have gathered in mid-June (the southern winter) to gaze up at the night sky in the Andes and observe the eleven-star constellation known as Pleiades or the Seven Sisters. If the stars are bright, they get planting quickly, confident that there will be good rains and a healthy harvest. If the stars are dull, they delay planting.

For years this folklore was dismissed by agriculturalists as mumbo-jumbo. Until Mark Cane, one of the world's foremost modellers of El Niño, heard about it from a guide while travelling in the Andes. Intrigued, he checked meteorological records, and discovered that typically about six months before an El Niño, thin, high and almost invisible clouds form above the Andes. These dim the brightness of the constellation. So a dim constellation means a dry spring, while clear skies and a bright constellation mean good rains.

The farmers had, it seems, perfected many hundreds of years ago what climate modellers like Cane have only fitfully managed in the past twenty years – a way of forecasting El Niño. Cane says the Peruvian potato farmers' forecast is better than his. 'It's a brilliant scheme, really quite a feat. I still wonder how they possibly worked it out.' Perhaps, he muses, the Peruvian potato farmers have known the key to the world's climate all along.

31

FEEDING ASIA

WHAT HAPPENS IF THE RAINS FAIL?

More than 3 billion people today are fed and watered thanks to the Asian monsoon. It is the greatest rain-making machine on the planet – and possibly one of the most sensitive to climate change. Its mechanism is extremely simple. It is like a giant sea breeze operating over the world's largest continent. In winter, the vast Asian land mass becomes cold – extremely cold over the high ice caps of Tibet, the largest area of ice outside the polar regions. This cools the air above. That air descends, in turn forcing cold dry winds to blow off the land and out across the Indian and Pacific Oceans. Asia is mostly rainless for nine long months. But come the summer, the land warms up much faster than the oceans. Warm air rises, and as it does the winds reverse and moist winds blow in off the oceans. For about a hundred days, monsoon rains fall across Asia. The rains burst rivers, fill irrigation canals and water fields. Across the continent, rice farmers take their chance to grow the food that sustains half the world's population.

A failed monsoon has devastating consequences. It happened repeatedly in the nineteenth century. British colonial administrators in India watched in bemusement as tens of millions died in the famine of 1837–8, and again in 1860–61, 1876–8 and 1896–1902. The Asian monsoon remained an unruly beast through the twentieth century. But despite tenfold increases in the populations of most monsoon countries, the death toll from famine has fallen. There are many reasons for this, one of which is that the rains proved more reliable in the twentieth century than in the nineteenth. That is a good news story. The question is: can it last? The Asian monsoon has appeared for the past century to be self-contained and invulnerable. But, like other big features in the global climate system, it may have an Achilles' heel. If the monsoon proves less reliable in the twenty-first century, there could be real trouble ahead – for about 3 billion people.

The monsoon's vulnerability in past centuries seems to lie with its links to two other parts of the global climate system. One is to El Niño. Strong El Niños historically seem to have switched off the Asian monsoon. British imperial scientists discovered more than a century ago that most of the great Indian famines coincided with marked climatic fluctuations in the Pacific. El Niños seemed to draw heat away from Asia and so drain the monsoon's strength. But recently that link seems to have broken. El Niño has intensified without there being any widespread weakening of the Asian monsoon. The break in the old link has been both a scientific surprise and a humanitarian godsend. But nobody knows what has caused it and whether it will last. If the Pacific climate system does what many predict, and in the twenty-first century leans heavily towards a permanent El Niño-like state, and if the monsoon resumes its former relationship, then the rains may soon be failing over Asia more often than they succeed. We can hope they do not, but we cannot be sure.

The second link is with the Atlantic. This was dramatically established in 2003, when Indian and US researchers assembled a 10,000-year record of the strength of the Indian monsoon. They did it by counting fossilized plankton found in ancient marine sediments off the Indian coast. The plankton thrive when strong monsoon winds cause an upwelling of the nutrients that provide their food. The study found huge variability in the monsoon's strength over the centuries. And it confirmed that, over timescales longer than individual El Niño years, 'weak summer monsoons coincide with cold spells thousands of miles away in the North Atlantic,' according to Anil Gupta of the Indian Institute of Technology in Kharagpur, who worked on the project. Strong monsoons go hand in hand with warm waters off Europe and North America.

It had been known for a while that the Indian monsoon had turned off during the last ice age but probably flickered on briefly during the warm episodes that punctuated the glaciation. The new study showed that the strength of the monsoon also shadowed the flutters of the Atlantic system during the post-glacial era, faltering during the Younger Dryas and the chill of 8,200 years ago, for instance. The changes clearly followed Bond's 1,500-year solar pulse. Thus the last faltering of the monsoon came during Europe's little ice age, which came to an end in the final decades of the nineteenth century.

But this pattern, impressive though it is, does not explain how the link with the Atlantic works. Does the Atlantic tell the monsoon what to do? Does the monsoon tell the Atlantic what to do? Does Bond's solar pulse independently determine both? Or is there another element not taken into account? Where does El Niño fit in, for instance?

Jonathan Overpeck of the University of Arizona, one of the authors of the monsoon history, holds that the Atlantic has the whip hand. He says that a warm North Atlantic sends heat east on the winds, warming Asia in spring, and allowing a rapid melt of the Tibetan plateau and an early start to the rain-giving monsoon winds. But when the Atlantic is cold, 'more snow on the Tibetan plateau in spring and early summer uses up all the sun's heating, because it has to be melted and evaporated before the land can warm.' If he is right, then if the ocean conveyor falters in the coming years, the effects for Asia could be even more grievous than for Europe. 'There could be a weakened monsoon and less water for all the people who depend on it,' says Overpeck.

But the tropical school disagrees with this analysis. It holds that both the cooling of the Atlantic and the weakening of the monsoon are likely to be triggered by changes in the heating of the tropics. According to this theory, a cooling of the tropics will weaken monsoon winds and rains, while at the same time sending less warm water north in the Gulf Stream.

The theories of the polar and tropical schools are on this occasion not mutually exclusive. In fact, they are mutually reinforcing. But right now, for anyone living in India, neither theory offers much enlightenment about what might happen to the Asian monsoon in the coming decades. Global warming driven by accumulating greenhouse gases without a solar component may have different features and different outcomes from the solar-dominated scenarios of the past. The situation is further complicated because across much of monsoon Asia warming is itself severely compromised and sometimes extinguished by the aerosols in the Asian brown haze. As we have seen, the haze's biggest impact is on the radiation balance between the land surface and the air aloft – a vital parameter in determining the strength of the monsoon. The fear is that the haze may break the seasonal heating cycles between land and ocean, and turn off the monsoon. It hasn't yet, but it may. And, valuable though reconstructed histories of the Asian monsoon may be, it is unlikely that they will ever provide an answer to that puzzle.

PART SEVEN

AT THE MILLENNIUM

32

THE HEATWAVE

THE YEAR EUROPE FELT THE HEAT OF GLOBAL WARMING

At a zoo near Versailles outside Paris, keepers kept twenty-seven polar bears cool by feeding them mackerel-flavoured ice. In Alsace, the electricity company trained water cannon on the roof of a nuclear power reactor as temperatures outside soared to 48 degrees C. In Rome, tourists queued up to pay the fine for bathing in the Trevi fountain. It seemed like a good deal, they said. Crops died; forests burned; power blacked out as office air conditioners were turned to full power; rivers from the Danube to the Po and the Rhine to the Rhone were at or near record lows.

This was by no standards an ordinary summer heatwave. For one thing, it killed at least 35,000 people: 20,000 in Italy and 15,000 in France. Old people, many of them abandoned in apartments without air conditioning as their families took their August holidays, suffered most. Dehydrated and short of breath, they died in their thousands in temperatures than often exceeded 40 degrees C during the day and stuck close to 30 degrees at night. It was Europe's hottest summer for at least half a millennium. At the heatwave's peak, on 13 August 2003, the twenty-four-hour death toll in Paris was eight times the norm. In parts of the city, there was a waiting list of three weeks for funerals.

It wasn't just the mortuaries who were rewriting their record books. This was the first single weather event that climate scientists felt prepared to say was directly attributable to man-made climate change. In the past, the mantra had always been that individual weather events could be a product of chance. But the 2003 heatwave was different, says Oxford University climate scientist and statistician Myles Allen. 'The immediate cause, I agree, was a series of anticyclones over Europe. They always raise temperatures in summer and we can't say those were made any more likely by climate change. But we can say that climate change made the background temperatures within which those anticyclones operated that much higher.'

There is no doubt that average temperatures have been rising strongly for years. In much of Europe, the summer average at the start of the new century was between 0.5 and 1 degree C warmer than it was in the first half of the twentieth century. In the summer of 2003, temperatures averaged 2.3 degrees warmer. On the basis of past averages, the heatwave was probably a once-in-a-thousand-year-event. But, says Allen, 'Small changes in average temperatures make extreme events much more likely.'

One of the nicest confirmations of how exceptional the summer of 2003 was came from a study published at the end of 2004. French mathematician Pascal Yiou of the

Laboratoire des Sciences du Climat et de l'Environnement in Paris had collected more than six hundred years of parish records showing when the Pinot Noir grape harvest began in the Burgundy vineyards of eastern France. There is a clear relationship between summer temperatures and the start of the harvest, so he extrapolated backwards to produce a temperature graph from the present to 1370. The results showed that temperatures as high as those typical in the 1990s were unusual, but had happened before several times in individual years. 'However, the summer of 2003 appears to have been extraordinary, unique.' Temperatures in Burgundy that year were almost 6 degrees C above the long-term average. And if Yiou's formula was accurate, the highest previous temperature had been just 4 degrees above the average. That happened in 1523, during a warm interlude of the little ice age.

'The 2003 heatwave was far outside the range of normal climate,' says Allen. It was not impossible that it could have happened without global warming, but it was very improbable. 'Our best estimates suggest the risk of such a heatwave has increased between four and sixfold as a result of climate change.' Many scientists continue to argue about how we might recognize 'dangerous' climate change, he told me. 'Well, for the thousands of victims in Europe in the summer of 2003, it is clear we have already passed that threshold.'

And the big heat is only just beginning. Allen says that by mid-century, if current warming trends persist, the extreme temperatures experienced in 2003 in Europe could be happening every other year. Richard Betts at Britain's Hadley Centre says that for people living in cities the risks are even greater. They are already feeling the worst of climate change because they also suffer the 'urban heat island effect'. During heatwaves, the concrete, bricks and asphalt of buildings and roads hold on to heat much better than the natural landscape in the countryside. In the typically windless, anticyclonic conditions of a European heatwave, the effect is even more marked. The air just stays in the streets and cooks. The effect is especially marked at night, which doctors say is a critical time for the human body to recover from daytime heat.

Betts says global warming will push the urban heat island effect into overdrive. Even as the countryside warms, the additional dose of heating experienced in the cities will increase – especially at night.

33

THE HOCKEY STICK

WHY NOW REALLY IS DIFFERENT

It was a seductive image. So seductive that the IPCC put it right at the front of its thousand-page assessment of climate change, published in 2001. The panel hoped that it would become as talked about as the Keeling curve. And scientists gave it a snappy caption: this was the graph they called the 'hockey stick'. As I don't play hockey, I was initially left wondering what this meant. But if you lay a hockey stick on the ground and look at its shape as a graph, you will see that the long flat shaft has at the end of it a short but sharply upturned blade, the bit you hit the ball with. And that, according to the IPCC authors, is the shape of the world's temperatures over the past thousand years: about nine hundred years of little or no change, followed by a century with a short, sharp upturn.

The assembly of the data behind the hockey stick graph has become a political cause célèbre. It began with high hopes: it was to be the first serious attempt to piece together a global picture of climate over the past millennium from a wide variety of different kinds of sources. Rather than carrying on the well-established work of reconstructing past temperatures from analysis of tree rings, it sought to add in other proxy data based on ice cores, coral growth rings and lake sediments. The idea was to lose the inbuilt bias of tree-ring chronologies, which mostly rely on trees from northern hemisphere regions outside the tropics, because that is where trees have well-defined annual growth rings.

The hockey stick graph was first put together in 1998. That year turned out to be the warmest in the instrumental record. So it wasn't much of a stretch to argue that the hockey stick revealed 1998 to be the warmest year in the warmest century of the last millennium. That got headlines. And brought trouble – not least for the voluble, self-confident and likeable collator of the hockey stick data, Mike Mann. Even though the IPCC published other data sets showing much the same, it was Mann who was accused of concocting a spurious case that late-twentieth-century warming was exceptional and therefore, presumably, a result of man-made pollution.

It probably didn't help that Mann was at the time based at the University of Virginia, home of the biggest voice among the climate sceptics, Pat Michaels. Soon Mann was fraud-of-the-month on the websites of the climate sceptics. But it wasn't just the usual suspects who criticized him: some serious climate researchers expressed misgivings about Mann's methods.

When I finally met Mann, he had moved from Virginia to Penn State University, where he is now director of the Earth System Science Center. But the flack had followed. Some was fair, some was unfair, some was deployed as political hand grenades, some was just a part of the normal adversarial flow of scientific debate and some was just plain personal – like Wally Broecker's bad-mouthing of Mann, quoted at the start of Chapter 23. Mann was even damned in Washington, where Senator James Inhofe of Oklahoma accused him of playing fast and loose with the data, and Representative Joe Barton from Texas summoned him to provide voluminous details of his working procedures and funding. Some called it a McCarthyite vendetta. But Mann seemed up for it, dismissing Inhofe as 'the single largest senate recipient of oil industry money'.

I will now entertain some of the criticisms that have rained on Mann, because they matter. But it is worth saying first that nothing I have heard impugns Mann's scientific integrity, credentials or motives. He is just braver than some, and more willing to have his debates in public – and to fight back when the brickbats start flying. (You can read him in action on the website he started with scientific colleagues at www.realclimate.org) Some researchers have suffered real personal and psychological damage from attacks by sceptics. I hope that won't happen to Mann. I wish more scientists were like him.

First, does the hockey stick fairly represent the temperature record? Does Mann's take-home conclusion, that the last century warmed faster and further than any in the past thousand years, stand up to scrutiny?

The world of proxy data trends is a statistical minefield. This is partly because the physical material that shows past climate loses detail with time. Tree rings, for instance, get smaller as the tree gets older, so annual and even decadal detail gets lost. 'You lose roughly 40 per cent of the amplitude of changes,' says tree-ring specialist Gordon

Jacoby at Lamont-Doherty. But it goes far beyond that. To make any sense, analysis of a single data set – for instance, from the tree rings in a forest – involves smoothing out the data from individual trees to reveal a 'signal' behind the 'noise' of short-term and random change. The kind of analysis pioneered by Mann, in which a series of different data sets are merged, involves a further sorting and aggregation of these independently derived signals, and smoothing the result. And Mann's work involves a further stage, meshing that proxy synthesis with the current instrumental record.

Some, including Jacoby, complain that by combining smoothed-out proxy data from past centuries with the recent instrumental record, which preserves many more short-term trends, Mann created a false impression of anomalous recent change. 'You just can't do that if you are losing so much of the amplitude of change in the rest of the data,' Jacoby told me. Mann argues the contrary, that in fact he was one of the first analysts in the field to include error bars on his graph. 'The error bars represent how much variance is lost due to the smoothing,' he says.

But the accusation that he has somehow fixed the data analysis continues to dog him. The most persistent line of criticism, and the one most widely championed by anti-IPCC lobbyists, came from two Canadians: Stephen McIntyre, a mathematician and oil industry consultant, and Ross McKitrick, an economist at the University of Guelph. They claimed to have found a fundamental flaw in Mann's statistical methodology that biased the temperature reconstruction towards producing the hockey stick shape.

The argument is a technical one that hangs on how Mann used well-established mathematical techniques.

McIntyre and McKitrick claimed that Mann's method had the effect of damping down unwanted natural variability, straightening the shaft of the hockey stick and accentuating twentieth-century warming. Mann agrees there was some truth in this charge. He analysed the data in terms of their divergence from twentieth-century levels. And this had the inevitable effect of giving greater significance to data showing the biggest differences from that period.

But the critical charge was that he had somehow created the hockey stick out of nothing, 'mining' the data for hockey-stick-shaped trends, as his critics put it. McIntyre and McKitrick produced their own analysis that showed an apparent rise in temperatures in the fifteenth century, which they claimed may have been as warm as the twenteith century. The shaft of their hockey stick had a big kink in it. When it was published in 2005, this analysis was hailed by some as a refutation of Mann's study.

But while Mann was open to attack, so were McIntyre and McKitrick. Would their 'refutation' of Mann stand up to critical attention? During 2005, three different research groups concluded that Mann's findings stood up much better than his critics'. They had bent the statistics more than he had, arbitrarily leaving out certain sets of data to reach their conclusion. Remove all the biases and the real data looked more like Mann's – a conclusion underlined in early 2006, when Keith Briffa, a respected British tree-ring analyst from the University of East Anglia, published the most complete analysis to date, showing the twentieth century to have been the warmest era for at least the last 1,200 years.

If the key to successful science is producing findings that can be replicated by other groups, using different methodologies, then again Mann is on a winning streak. Upwards of a dozen studies using different collections of proxy data, as well as different analytical techniques, have now all produced similar graphs to Mann's original hockey stick. Not identical, for sure, but with the same basic features of unremarkable variability for 900 years followed by a sharp upturn in temperatures in the final decades.

The one unexplained factor is the paltry evidence in most of these studies for the medieval warm period and the little ice age. But an answer to that conundrum now seems at hand. There is growing agreement that the most substantial evidence about the existence of both a medieval warm period and a little ice age comes from the northern latitudes. 'What we know about the cold in the little ice age era is primarily a European and North Atlantic phenomenon,' says Keith Briffa. Most interestingly, there is growing evidence from a range of new proxy data that other parts of the world were seeing climate trends that were the opposite of those going on in Europe. The tropical Pacific appears to have cooled during the medieval warm period and warmed during the little ice age. One ice core from the Antarctic shows temperatures during the medieval warm period that were 3 degrees C colder than those in the little ice age. Under the circumstances, says Mann, it is not surprising that his more global assessment of temperatures does not spot much difference during these earlier climatic shifts. They undoubtedly had major influences on regional climate, but the cumulative effect on global temperature was small.

It is no part of this book's case that climate didn't change in the past. Parts of the world clearly saw substantial warming and cooling during the medieval warm period and the little ice age. Other parts saw other changes. In the American West, there were huge century-long droughts during the medieval warm period. Even Broecker, who holds that the little ice age was global, admits that the evidence of a global medieval warm period is 'spotty and circumstantial'. But there is a good case for saying that over the millennium until the mid-twentieth century, most climate change concerned the redistribution of heat and moisture around the globe rather than big changes in overall heating. Only recently has substantially more heat been added to the system through the introduction of hundreds of billions of tonnes of greenhouse gases into the atmosphere. Recent warming may be the first global warming since the closure of the ice age itself.

The argument over the hockey stick is an interesting sideshow in the debate about climate change. But it remains a sideshow. It matters little right now for the planet as a whole whether the medieval warm period was or was not warmer than temperatures today – or indeed whether it was a warm period at all. The subtext of the climate sceptics' assault on Mann's hockey stick has always been that if the current warming is shown not to be unique, then somehow the case that man-made global warming is happening evaporates. But this is a spurious argument. Briffa is not alone in arguing precisely the opposite. What would be most worrying would be the discovery that the medieval warm period was actually as warm as some sceptics claim, he says. How so? Because 'greater long-term [natural] climatic variability implies a greater sensitivity of climate to forcing, whether from the sun or greenhouse gases. So greater past climate variations imply greater future climate change.'

34

HURRICANE SEASON

RAISING THE STORM CONES AFTER KATRINA

Corky Perret lost everything when Hurricane Katrina hit. His house on the beachfront out on Highway 90 between Gulfport and Biloxi, Mississippi, was reduced to match-wood by the 220-kilometres-per-hour winds, and sucked away by a 10-metre storm surge that washed up the beach and over the highway. 'Nothing is left: it was totally destroyed,' he told me weeks later. Out in the Gulf of Mexico, barrier islands that once provided protection against storms had also succumbed. Perret didn't know if the hurricanes would be worse in future, but without the islands the effects would probably be worse anyway.

The houses along Highway 90 where Perret lived, along with the hotels and resorts, had been built mostly between the 1970s and 1990s, a period of quiet in the Gulf when there were few hurricanes. Hearing reports that a let-up is unlikely any time soon, some of his neighbours were going for good. They could see only more hurricanes and more havoc. They were off to Jackson or Dallas or Memphis, or anywhere inland. But when we spoke in late 2005, Perret still had his job as director of marine fisheries for the state of Mississippi, and was unsure what to do. He wanted to stay and rebuild, but was that wise?

The year 2005 had been an extraordinary one in the Atlantic. There were so many tropical storms that for the first time forecasters ran out of names for them. Wilma became the most powerful Atlantic storm ever recorded. Katrina brought an entire US coastline to its knees, including the great city of New Orleans. It was the second successive hurricane year to be described by forecasts as 'exceptional' and 'unprecedented', and it came after a decade of rising hurricane activity that stretched the bounds of what had previously been regarded as natural. So what is going on? Are hurricanes becoming more destructive as global warming kicks in? Is there worse to come? The answer matters not just to the people in the firing line around the Gulf of Mexico and the Caribbean, or across the tropics in the Indian Ocean and the Pacific: if there's more severe disruption to oil production in the Gulf, or supertyphoons hit economic powerhouses such as Shanghai or Tokyo at full force, we'll all feel the impact.

Until 2005, most of the world's leading hurricane experts were sanguine. The upsurge in the number of hurricanes in the North Atlantic in the previous decade had been just part of a normal cycle. Hurricanes had been strong before, from the 1940s through to the 1960s. Climate models suggested that even a doubling of carbon dioxide levels in the atmosphere would increase hurricane intensity by only 10 per cent or so. But that year the consensus was shattered. A flurry of papers claimed that hurricanes had grown more intense during the past thirty-year surge in global temperatures. Not more frequent, but more intense, with stronger winds, longer durations, more unrelenting rains and even less predictable tracks. The trend was apparent in all the world's oceans, they said. From New Orleans to Tokyo, nobody was immune.

One of the authors, Kerry Emanuel of the Massachusetts Institute of Technology, said: 'My results suggest that future warming may lead to an upward trend in tropical cyclone destructive potential and – taking into account an increasing coastal population – a substantial increase in hurricane-related losses in the twenty-first century.' Coming just weeks after the destruction of New Orleans, that sounded like a clear message to Corky Perret and the people of the Gulf coast. No point in rebuilding, because the next superhurricane could be just round the corner. But the claims produced a schism among the high priests of hurricane forecasting. Many, like veteran forecaster William Gray of Colorado State University, said that they saw no upward trend and no human fingerprint. They accused the authors of the latest papers of bias and worse. So who is right?

Hurricanes are an established part of the climate system. There have always been hurricanes. They start off as clusters of thunderstorms that form as warm, humid air rises from the surface of the tropical ocean. As the air rises, the water vapour condenses, releasing energy that heats the air and makes it rise even higher. If enough storm clouds gather in close proximity, they can form what Emanuel calls a 'pillar' of humid air, extending from the ocean surface for several kilometres into the troposphere. The low pressure at the base of the pillar sucks in more air, which picks up energy in the form of water vapour as it flows inwards, and releases it as it rises. This lowers the pressure still further.

Meanwhile, the rotation of the Earth, acting on the inward-flowing air, makes the cyclone spin. If conditions are favourable, a tropical storm can rapidly turn into a hurricane as wind speeds pick up. Its power is staggering: Chris Landsea of the National Oceanic and Atmospheric Administration in Miami has calculated that an average hurricane can release in a day as much energy as a million Hiroshima bombs. Luckily for all concerned, only a tiny fraction of this energy is converted into winds.

Worldwide there are about eighty-five tropical cyclones each year, of which about sixty reach hurricane force. That figure has been fairly stable for as long as people have been counting hurricanes. But the distribution of the hurricanes varies a great deal from year to year. In 2005, for example, the Atlantic was battered but the Pacific was relatively peaceful. And much of that variability seems to be tied to ocean temperature. The initial pillar of humid air forms only when the temperature of the sea surface exceeds 26 degrees C. What is more, every degree above the threshold seems to encourage stronger hurricanes. When Katrina went from a category 1 to a category 5 hurricane back in August 2005, the surface of the Gulf of Mexico was around 30 degrees C, which so far as anyone knows was a record. Whether or not the record sea temperatures can be blamed on climate change (and most would guess that they can), those record temperatures certainly helped Katrina strengthen as it slipped across the Gulf from Florida towards the Louisiana coast.

As the world's oceans warm, ever larger areas of ocean exceed the threshold. There has been an average ocean warming in the tropics of 0.5 degrees already. The simple link between sea surface temperatures and hurricane formation and strength has encouraged the view that a warmer world will inevitably lead to more hurricanes, stronger hurricanes and the formation of hurricanes in places till now outside their range. But the world is not that simple, says William Gray. What actually drives the updraughts that create the storm clouds, he says, is not the absolute temperature at the sea's surface but the difference between the temperature at the sea's surface and the temperature at the top of the storm. Climate models suggest that global warming will raise air temperatures aloft. So, if he is right, while the current sea surface temperature when hurricanes start to form may be 26 degrees C or more, it could in future rise to 28 degrees or more. In the final analysis, Gray argues, the hurricane-generating potential of the tropics may remain largely unchanged.

There are other limitations on hurricane formations and intensity. However hot the oceans get, air cannot rise everywhere. It has to fall in some places, too, whatever the ocean temperature. And many incipient hurricanes are defused by horizontal winds that lop off their tops. Climate models suggest that global warming will increase wind speeds to levels where they would disrupt hurricanes. Other disruptions include dust, which often blows across the Atlantic during dry years in the Sahara.

But some trends will make big storms more likely. Most tropical storms fizzle out because they lose contact with their fuel – the heat of warm ocean waters. This happens most obviously when a hurricane passes over land, but it also happens at sea. As the storm grows, its waves stir up the ocean, mixing the warm surface water with the generally cooler water beneath. The surface water cools and that can be the end. In practice, a hurricane can grow only if the warmth extends for tens of metres or more below the surface. And with every year that passes warm water is penetrating ever deeper into the world's oceans. That is clearly tied to global warming. And it is setting up ideal conditions for more violent thunderstorms. Katrina is again an object lesson here. It continued to strengthen as it headed towards New Orleans because it moved over water in the Gulf of Mexico that was very warm, not just at the surface but to a depth of more than 100 metres.

The past decade in the North Atlantic has seen a string of hurricane records broken. The period from 1995 to 1998 experienced more Atlantic hurricanes than ever before in such a short time – a record broken only in 2004 and 2005. The 1998 season was the first in a 100-year record when, on 25 September, four hurricanes were present on weather charts of the North Atlantic all at one time. And not long afterwards came Hurricane Mitch, the most destructive storm in the western hemisphere for 200 years. Feeding on exceptionally warm waters in the Caribbean, it ripped through Central America in the final days of October 1998, its torrential rains bringing havoc to Honduras and Nicaragua and killing some 10,000 people in landslides and floods.

The Atlantic is also generating hurricanes in places where they have never been seen before. In March 2004, the first known hurricane formed in the South Atlantic, striking southern Brazil. The formation of the hurricane, later named Catarina, was startling enough. What caused the greatest frisson was that it developed very close to a zone of ocean pinpointed a few years before by Britain's Hadley Centre modellers as a likely new focus for hurricane formation in a warmer greenhouse world. But they had predicted that the waters there wouldn't be up to the task till 2070. Many saw Catarina as a further sign that global warming was making its presence felt in the hurricane world rather ahead of schedule.

The billion-dollar question (literally so for insurance companies) is whether there is now a discernible climate change component at work in the frequency and intensity of hurricanes. Kerry Emanuel for one argues that, whatever the natural variability, the 'large upswing' in hurricanes in the North Atlantic in the last decade is 'unprecedented, and probably reflects the effect of global warming'. Jim Hansen weighed in at the end of 2005, insisting that climate change was the cause of a warmer tropical Atlantic and that 'the contention that hurricane formation has nothing to do with global warming seems irrational and untenable.'

The matter of North Atlantic hurricane trends is likely to be debated for many years yet. The 'signal' of climate change will be difficult to disentangle from the 'noise' of natural variability. But while it is easy to become obsessed with hurricanes in the North Atlantic, they amount to only around a tenth of the global total – and a rather smaller proportion of those that make landfall in a typical year. The biggest source of hurricanes is, and is likely to remain, in the western Pacific, where they terrorize vulnerable and densely populated nations like the Philippines, Vietnam and China. So it is the global picture that both matters most and is most likely to resolve the issue of the impact of climate change.

Several research groups have been scouring records of past hurricanes worldwide to see if there is any evidence of a trend as the world has warmed. Emanuel has concluded that on average storms are lasting 60 per cent longer and generating wind speeds 15 per cent higher than they were back in the 1950s. The damage done by a hurricane is proportional not to the wind speed but to the wind speed cubed. And Emanuel's results suggest that the destructive power of a typical hurricane has increased by an alarming 70 per cent. 'Global tropical cyclone activity is responding in a rather large way to global warming,' he says.

Others are coming to agree. Only weeks after Emanuel's paper appeared in the autumn of 2005, three other leading hurricane researchers published a similarly alarming conclusion. Peter Webster and Judy Curry of the Georgia Institute of Technology and Greg Holland of NCAR concluded that while there had been no overall increase in the number of hurricanes worldwide, the frequency of the strongest storms – category 4 and 5 – had almost doubled since the early 1970s. They made up 35 per cent of the total compared to 20 per cent just three decades before. The trend, they said, was global, and they agreed with Emanuel that it was clearly connected to the worldwide rise in sea surface temperatures. That made it extremely unlikely to be caused by natural cycles, which are relatively short-term and confined to single ocean basins. 'We can say with confidence that the trends in sea surface temperatures and hurricane intensity are connected to climate change,' Curry declared.

William Gray and some other traditional hurricane forecasters have contested the findings, claiming that some of the data, particularly old estimates of wind speed from the Pacific in the 1970s, are flawed. In an increasingly vitriolic exchange, Gray argued that the papers simply could not be true. Emanuel and Webster agree that the data are not as good as they might like. But 'Gray has not brought to my attention any difficulties with the data [of] which I was not already aware,' Emanuel said, with some irritation. Webster says Gray is 'grasping at thin air'.

So where does that leave us? There is as yet nothing unique about recent individual hurricanes, though Katrina, Wilma and Mitch clearly stretch the bounds of what can be regarded as normal. The largest and most powerful hurricane ever recorded, Typhoon Tip, with wind speeds of more than 300 kilometres per hour, grazed Japan a quarter of a century ago, in 1979. The storm that hit Galveston in 1900 killed 10,000 people, many more than Katrina. Both pale compared with the hurricane of 1970, which may have killed half a million people in what is now Bangladesh.

But even if we don't yet see superhurricanes, evidence is nonetheless emerging of a human fingerprint in the rising number of stronger, longer-lasting hurricanes. It is not yet proof of a long-term global trend tied to global warming, but the striking finding from both Emanuel and Webster of the consistent, global link between rising sea surface temperature and rising storm strength is strong evidence of such a link. Whatever the theoretical concerns, for now it seems that, as climatologist Kevin Trenberth of the National Oceanic and Atmospheric Administration in Boulder, Colorado, puts it: 'High sea surface temperatures make for more intense storms.'

One puzzling question is how scientists have until now failed to spot the sharply increased destructiveness of modern hurricanes. There is no dispute that, taken together, hurricanes have been doing a lot more damage in recent years. But the prevailing view has until recently been that the problem is one of bad planning, rising populations and more people putting themselves in harm's way. The beach resorts along Highway 90 and the large squatter colonies spreading along low-lying coastal land in Asia give some support to that view. But the new data suggest that there is more to it than that. A lot more. And that most of the extra damage is being caused by the storms themselves becoming more intense. The trend seems set to continue.

35

OZONE HOLES IN THE GREENHOUSE

WHY MILLIONS FACE RADIATION THREAT

Joe Farman is a boffin of the old school. String and sealing wax. Smokes a pipe and drinks real ale. He has the faraway look in his eyes that you often see in men who have spent any length of time in Antarctica. He is retired now from the British Antarctic Survey (BAS), where he spent virtually his entire working life in a worthy though less than exalted capacity. Or he did until 1985, when he wrote one of the decade's most quoted research papers. He is the man who discovered the ozone hole over Antarctica. And the way it happened – or rather almost didn't happen – is revealing.

A quarter of a century ago, Farman was in charge of the BAS's Dobson Meter, which for many years had been pointing up into the sky measuring the depth of the ozone layer in the stratosphere from the BAS's Halley Bay base on an ice shelf off West Antarctica. For several years his bosses had been trying to halt the observations and bring the old instrument home. After all, they pointed out, nothing interesting had happened for years, and satellites orbiting the Earth were by then measuring ozone levels routinely. Ground-based observations were deemed superfluous.

But Farman resisted and in 1982 he noticed a series of unusual and abrupt fluctuations in the ozone readings, just after the sun reappeared following the long polar night. It happened again the following year.

'I asked the Americans if they had seen anything similar from their satellites,' he told me later. 'They said they hadn't. So I assumed that my old machine was on the blink.' But he was intrigued enough not to leave it at that. He found another Dobson Meter back in Cambridge and took it south in 1984 to check the readings. It recorded the same thing – only more so. Farman's data were by now unambiguous. He was seeing a deep hole opening in the ozone layer over the base. It lasted for several weeks before closing again. 'We were sure then that something dramatic was happening,' Farman said. In places, more than 90 per cent of the ozone was disappearing in what appeared to be runaway reactions taking place in just a few days.

The ozone layer protects the Earth's surface from dangerous forms of ultraviolet radiation from the sun. Without this filter, there would be epidemics of skin cancers, cataracts and many other diseases, as well as damage to vital ecosystems. Life on Earth has evolved to live under its protection and would find things much harder without it.

For more than a decade scientists had been concerned about the ozone layer, fearing that man-made chemicals such as CFCs in aerosol cans and refrigeration units might cause it to thin. But nobody had thought of a hole forming. Least of all over Antarctica, which was as far from the source of any ozone-destroying chemicals as you could get. And certainly not in a runaway reaction over just a few days. The Earth was simply not supposed to work that way. Farman bit his pipe and got to work. No more checking with NASA. He had his data and was intent on an urgent publication in the scientific press. Perhaps he sensed it was his moment of fame. He was certainly scared by what he had found; and scared enough to miss all the office parties in Cambridge in 1984 to finish his paper on 'Large Losses of Total Ozone in Antarctica'. He posted it to *Nature* on Christmas Eve.

The editors didn't quite share Farman's sense of urgency. It took them three months to accept his paper, and another two months to publish. When the paper finally appeared, NASA scientists were bemused. They still had no inkling of anything amiss over Antarctica. But they could hardly ignore the findings of two Dobson Meters, however ancient. They re-examined the raw data from their satellite instruments and were shocked to find that their satellites had seen the ozone hole forming and growing over Antarctica all along, even before Farman had spotted it. But the computers on the ground that were analysing the streams of data had been programmed to throw out any wildly abnormal readings. And the data showing the ozone hole had certainly fitted that category. The episode, as Farman was not slow to point out, was a salutary lesson for high-tech science. It was also a triumph for the string-and-sealing-wax school, and for the dogged collection of seemingly boring and useless data about the environment.

Farman's findings were swiftly tied by Paul Crutzen – who had unravelled much of the complex chemistry of the ozone layer – to specific chemical reactions involving CFCs that took place only in the uniquely cold air over Antarctica each spring. Below temperatures of about minus 90 degrees C, unique clouds form in the stratosphere above Antarctica. These are called polar stratospheric clouds. It turns out that the runaway reactions happen only on the surface of the frozen particles in these clouds. The reactions require both the cold to create the clouds and solar energy to fuel them. And there is a window of a few weeks when both are supplied – after the sun has risen, but before the air has warmed enough to destroy the clouds. After that, the air warms and the ozone recovers, though the repair job takes some months.

Farman's discovery and Crutzen's analysis finally pushed the world into taking tough action against ozone-eating chemicals. The Montreal Protocol was signed in 1987. Slowly, very slowly, the amount of CFCs and other ozone-eaters in the stratosphere are now declining. And the Antarctic ozone layer is equally slowly starting to heal, though it could be a century before it is fully repaired, even if every promise made by government negotiators is met. But it had been a close call.

And things could have been a lot worse, says Crutzen. 'Looking back, we were extremely lucky that industrialists chose chlorine compounds, rather than the very similar bromine compounds, to put in spray cans and refrigerators early in the last century.' Why so? Bromine compounds make refrigerants that are at least as effective as their chlorine equivalents. But atom for atom, bromine is about a hundred times more effective than chlorine at destroying ozone. Pure luck determined that Thomas Midgley, the American chemist who developed CFCs, did not opt for their bromine equivalent. 'It is a nightmarish thought,' says Crutzen, 'but if he had chosen bromine, we would have had something far worse than an ozone hole over Antarctica. We would have been faced with a catastrophic ozone hole, everywhere and at all seasons during the 1970s, before we knew a thing about what was going on.'

The world has been very lucky. Or has been lucky so far. The same combination of low temperatures and accumulating gases that combined so devastatingly over Antarctica can also occur over the Arctic some years. The conditions are not quite so favourable for ozone destruction, because the atmosphere is not quite so stable and the extremely cold temperatures occur less frequently. But they can, and there have been some near misses.

One occurred in January 2005. Anne Hormes, who runs the German research station in Ny-Alesund, Svalbard, told me the story when I visited there a few months later. Temperatures in the lower stratosphere above Svalbard had for a few days fallen to minus 98 degrees C, fully 8 degrees below the threshold necessary for the formation of polar stratospheric clouds, and extremely low even by the standards of Antarctica. 'We feared that a real big ozone hole would form,' she said. 'And if the temperature had stayed that cold for a few more weeks, till the sun came up to drive the chemical reactions, we would certainly have seen one.' It would have been the Arctic's first fully fledged ozone hole, and a major world environment story.

Her concern is shared. At NASA's Goddard Institute for Space Studies in New York, ozone expert Drew Shindell says: 'Overall winter temperatures are going down in the Arctic stratosphere. 2005 was very cold. But actual ozone loss is very time-critical. So far we have been lucky.' But he doubts that our luck will hold. How so? How come the risks of an ozone hole are still growing even though the chemicals that cause it are now in decline in the stratosphere?

The problem is this. In the lower atmosphere greenhouse gases trap heat, but in the stratosphere they have the opposite effect, causing an increase in the amount of heat escaping to space from that zone of the atmosphere. This is happening worldwide, but some of the most intense cooling is over areas with the greatest warming at the surface. Like the Arctic, which increasingly resembles the air high above Antarctica. As the stratosphere cools the risk of formation of stratospheric clouds, and massive ozone loss, increases.

There is another risk factor, too. The warmer troposphere, with stronger convection currents taking thunderstorm clouds right up to the boundary with the stratosphere, may be injecting more water vapour into the stratosphere. So far as we know, the stratosphere has always been very dry in the past. So extra water vapour is potentially a big change. And more water vapour will also make more likely the formation of the polar stratospheric clouds. 'If it gets a lot wetter that will make ozone depletion much worse,' says Shindell. There is some evidence that that is happening, though data are scarce. 'Water vapour levels in parts of the lower stratosphere have doubled in the past sixty years,' he says.

No hole formed in the Arctic ozone layer in 2005, because the sun did not rise when the air was at its coldest. But the spring of 2005 nonetheless saw the largest Arctic ozone loss in forty years of records. More than a third of the ozone disappeared, and losses reached

70 per cent in places. Air masses containing the reduced ozone levels spread south across Scandinavia and Britain and even as far south as Italy for a few days. One year soon, the sun will rise when temperatures are still cold enough for major runaway ozone destruction. And when it does, there could be millions of people living beneath. It will be another unexpected consequence of global warming.

PART EIGHT

INEVITABLE SURPRISES

36

THE DANCE

POLES OR THE TROPICS? WHO LEADS IN THE CLIMATIC DANCE?

As we have seen, researchers into the global history of climate, especially in the US, divide into two camps. One believes that the key drivers for past, and therefore probably future, climate change lie in the polar regions, especially the far North Atlantic. The other believes that the real action happens in the tropics.

The most outspoken advocate for the polar school is Wally Broecker at Lamont-Doherty. As described in Chapter 23, he is the man behind the idea of the ocean conveyor, which begins in the far North Atlantic and which, he argues, is the great climatic amplifier. It has, he says, a simple on-off switch. It pushed the world into and out of ice ages; it modulates the effects of Bond's solar pulse, including its most recent manifestations in the medieval warm period and the little ice age; and it could be a big player in directing the consequences of global warming. Around Broecker is a whole school of researchers who have spent their careers investigating the dramatic climate events of the North Atlantic region, as recorded in the ice cores of Greenland.

The rival tropical school has often looked to two characters. One, just down the hill from Broecker at Lamont-Doherty, is Mark Cane, a leading modeller of El Niño, the biggest climate fluctuation in the tropics. The other is Lonnie Thompson, the man who decided thirty years ago to stop investigating polar ice cores and switch instead to drilling tropical glaciers. They argue that Broecker's ocean conveyor is at best a sideshow, relevant to the North Atlantic and the countries that border it but not the great global player that is claimed. For them, the important climatic levers must be in the planetary heat and hydrological engine round the Earth's girth. The debate between the two schools has, at various stages, got quite personal. 'It all came from one man: Wally Broecker,' says Cane. 'You were for him or against him. And I found myself against.'

The polar people deploy their polar ice core data to show that climate change has been more dramatic and sudden in the far north, so it must be the cockpit of climate change. This is where the Gulf Stream turns turtle and drives the ocean conveyor; this is where ice melting and changes in fresh-water flow can freeze the ocean virtually overnight and send temperatures tumbling tens of degrees; this above all is where the great ice sheets of the ice ages form and die. They have a point. There can be little doubt about the importance of ice formation to the ice ages. Virtually the whole world did cool then, and two-thirds of that cooling was caused by the feedback of growing ice sheets and their ability to reflect solar radiation back into space. And nothing except a huge rush of meltwater from the receding ice caps could have plunged the world into the Younger Dryas 12,800 years ago.

But that doesn't mean that the Arctic tells the whole story. What pulled the world out of the Younger Dryas, for instance – an event that happened even faster than our entry? And while big climate change during and at the close of the ice ages does seem to be associated with polar events, the evidence about events since is far less secure. Thompson argues that most of the global climatic shudders of the Holocene, such as events at 5,500 and 4,200 years ago, must be tropical in origin. 'In climate models you can only make such things happen in both the northern and southern hemisphere by forcing events from the tropics, and I am convinced that is what is happening.'

Hockey stick author Mike Mann, though not a fully paid-up member of the tropical school, says: 'I think increasingly that the tropical Pacific is the key player. When you see La Niña dominating the medieval warm period and El Niño taking hold in the little ice age, it begins to look like the tropics rather than the North Atlantic rules.' The argument is that heat flows from the tropics are the true intermediaries between Bond's solar pulse and temperature fluctuations in the North Atlantic.

The tropical school also accuse the polar fraternity of being blinkered about what constitutes climate change. Besides an over-focus on events in North America and Europe, Broecker and Co. stand accused of being overly concerned with temperature. In the tropics, the hydrological cycle matters more than the temperature. Megadroughts are as damaging as little ice ages, and it is rains rather than extra warmth that bring plenty. Witness the drying of the Sahara 5,500 years ago, and the importance of the vagaries of the Asian monsoon.

The tropical school don't stop there. They argue that many of the big climatic events in the northern polar regions have their origins in the tropics. The tropics, through their delivery of warm water into the North Atlantic, are just as capable of flipping the switch of the ocean conveyor as ice formation in the far North Atlantic. And if there is a tropical equivalent of Broecker's switch in the North Atlantic, they say, it is probably the warm water pool around Indonesia – an area they often call the firebox. This is the greatest store and distribution point for heat on the surface of the planet, with a known propensity for threshold changes via the El Niño system. It is also the biggest generator of water vapour for the atmosphere, which is both a potent greenhouse gas and a driver of weather systems.

If this region can trigger short-term El Niños that warm the whole planet, and La Niñas that cool it again, then might it not also trigger long-term climate changes? Might not events here have been important in turning a minor orbital wobble into the waxing and waning of the ice ages? The waning, certainly. For recent cores of ocean sediment taken from the tropical Pacific suggest that temperatures started to rise there a thousand or more years before the northern ice sheets began to shrink.

After some years of stand-off, many protagonists in this debate are now seeking common ground. Not Broecker, of course. But Richard Alley, a polar man but also a fan of Thompson, now thinks that the location of the climate system's driving seat may change with time. During the glaciations, when a third of the northern hemisphere was covered with ice, it is easy to imagine the power of ice and meltwater to hijack the world's climate. But with less ice around in the interglacials, he concedes that the argument is less persuasive. And with characteristic pithiness he admits to past regional bias. 'Suppose the North Atlantic circulation did shut down. Sure, Europe would care. They might have a mid-season break in football in Britain. Manchester United wouldn't be playing on Boxing Day. But in the Great Plains of the US and in the Pacific Ocean, would it be so important?'

Meanwhile, on the tropical side, Cane admits: 'I am less absolutist than I used to be.' He concedes that his great enthusiasm, El Niño and the tropical Pacific, might not be behind everything. He still believes that the role of the ocean conveyor is hyped, but he concedes the possible importance of the 'sink or freeze' switch for sea ice in the North Atlantic. Peter deMenocal of Lamont-Doherty says the divide between the polar and tropical schools is 'a slightly false separation. You cannot at the end of the day change one bit without changing the other. They are all part of the same pattern, whether leading or following.' The Earth functions as an integrated system, not a series of discrete levers.

That view seems to be confirmed by Steve Goldstein of Columbia University, who has used analysis of a rare earth called neodymium, which has different isotopic ratios in different oceans, to unpick the order of events at the start of the ice ages. He argues that orbital changes, as expected, lead events. But the first feedback to respond was the ice-albedo. It caused an initial cooling at the start of the last ice age that was most pronounced in the far north. Prompted by that initial cooling, the chemistry and biology of the oceans started to change, removing carbon dioxide from the atmosphere and accentuating the cooling further. Only then, some thousands of years later, did the ocean conveyor start to shut down. 'The conveyor

follows; it does not lead,' he says. If his analysis is confirmed, it would be a blow to Broecker, but it would also
confirm that both the tropics and the polar regions were
deeply implicated in the elaborate dance that took the
world into and out of the ice ages.

Paul Crutzen has been in the forefront of research in
both the tropical and polar spheres, helping crack the
mysteries of the Antarctic ozone layer while making a
strong case for the dynamic properties of the tropical heat
engine. 'Big planetary changes happen in both the tropics
and the very high latitudes,' he says. 'The tropics are
where the high temperatures drive a lot of the chemistry
and dynamics of the atmosphere. And the polar regions
are the homes of the big natural feedbacks that could
accelerate climate change: things like melting ice and
permafrost and alterations to ocean currents.' That is probably as good a compromise statement as can be found
right now. At the end of the day, the system is bigger than
the individual parts.

37

NEW HORIZONS

FEEDBACKS FROM THE STRATOSPHERE

Is that the end of the story? I don't think so. Constantly, in writing this book, I have been struck by how little we know about the way the Earth's climate and its attendant systems, feedbacks and oscillations function. This story contains some heroic guesses, brilliant intuition and no doubt occasionally some dreadful howlers – because that is where the science currently lies. More questions than answers. Beyond the cautious certainties of the IPCC reports, there is a swathe of conjecture and scary scenarios. Some criticize the scientists who talk about these possibilities for failing to stick to the certainties, and for rocking the IPCC's boat. But I suspect we still need a good deal more of the same, because we may know much less than we think. I think Wally Broecker and his colleagues deserve praise for developing their scenarios about the global conveyor. They have produced a persuasive narrative that has transformed debate. Of course, producing a convincing story doesn't make it right, but it does generate new research and new ideas that can be tested. It is time someone in the tropical school produced something comparable.

Equally importantly, there may be other narratives that need developing. Richard Alley must be right that there are more 'inevitable surprises' out there – planetary control systems and outcomes that nobody has yet thought of, let alone tested. One area where unconsidered triggers for global climate change may lie is in and around Antarctica. While sinking cores into Antarctica as well as Greenland, the polar school has yet to devote as much attention to generating theories about events in the South Atlantic as they have in the North. This may have been a mistake. Much of the scientific action in Earth system science in the next few years will happen there, I am sure. Any place capable of producing something as remarkable as the ozone hole in the stratosphere is surely capable of storing up other surprises.

One new idea emerging from the battle between the polar and the tropical schools is that the real driver of climate change up to and including the ice ages might actually lie in the far south. During ice ages, the theory goes, the ocean conveyor did not so much shut down as switch where it got its new 'deep water' from the Arctic to the Antarctic. There has always been a certain amount of deep water formed around Antarctica, though in recent times it has played second fiddle to the North Atlantic. But, as the ice sheets grew across the Arctic and the chimneys in the North Atlantic shut down, the zone of deep-water formation in the Southern Ocean seems to have strengthened and may have taken charge of the conveyor.

Some go further and say that there must be a 'bipolar see-saw', in which warming in the southern hemisphere is tied to cooling in the north and vice versa. That would certainly make sense of some of the Antarctic ice cores that show warming while the north is cooling. The question then is: which pole leads? Does the North Atlantic end of the system shut down, closing off the Gulf Stream's northward flow of warm water, leaving more heat in the South Atlantic? Or does some switch in the south trigger the shutdown of the Gulf Stream and leave the northern hemisphere out in the cold with the North Atlantic freezing over?

The idea that the south may lead in this particular dance gained ground late in 2005, when results were published from new ice cores in Antarctica. A European group found that the tightest 'coupling' between temperature and carbon dioxide levels in the atmosphere is to be found in Antarctic cores, rather than their Greenland equivalents. 'The way I see things is that the tropics and Antarctica are in phase and lead the North Atlantic,' says Peter deMenocal of Lamont-Doherty. 'Even though we may see the largest events in the North Atlantic, they are often responding, not leading.' By this reading, the onset of the northern glaciation may have its origins in the southern hemisphere.

This apparently obscure debate could matter a great deal in the twenty-first century. Right now, the world has become worried that melting ice in the Arctic could freshen the far North Atlantic and shut down the Gulf Stream. This is a real fear. But maybe while we are researching that possibility we are ignoring the risk that large stores of fresh water in the Antarctic might break out and disrupt deep-water formation there. Arguably the risks are far greater in the south where, besides the potential breakout of ice from Pine Island Bay, recent radar mapping studies have revealed a large number of lakes of liquid water beneath the ice sheets of Antarctica. They might set off a cascade of fresh water into the Southern Ocean similar in scale to the emptying of Lake Agassiz, which triggered the Younger Dryas cold snap. Yet nobody, so far as I am aware, has studied what the effects of such a breakout might be for deep-water formation and the southern arm of the ocean conveyor – still less the global climate.

Or, rather than shutting down deep-water formation in Antarctica, might we be about to trigger a switch in the polarity of the bipolar see-saw, so that deep-water formation in the south takes over from that in the far north? Could we flip that switch in the south, rather than the north? And if so, how? And what might happen? It would certainly lead to the southern hemisphere hanging on to very large amounts of heat that currently head north on the Gulf Stream. The Southern Ocean might warm dramatically while the North Atlantic froze. And if the Southern Ocean were to warm substantially, says former International Geosphere Biosphere Programme boss Will Steffen, 'it could result in the surging, melting and collapse of the West Antarctic ice sheet.' Ouch.

If anybody doubts that there are plenty of new surprises waiting to be discovered, then the work by Drew Shindell of NASA's Goddard Institute for Space Studies (GISS) in New York should offer food for thought. His story starts with an apparent success for climate modellers. From the days of Arrhenius, most climate models have predicted that global warming will be greatest at high latitudes, where known feedbacks like ice-albedo are most pronounced. So rises in temperatures of up to 3 degrees C over parts of the Arctic and the Antarctic peninsula in recent decades have often been taken as the first proof of man-made climate change.

But there has been a persistent and troubling counter-argument. The warming in the two polar regions appears to be linked to two natural climatic fluctuations, one in the far north and one in the far south. In the north, the fluctuation is known as the Arctic Oscillation, an extension of the better-known North Atlantic Oscillation. It is the second largest climate cycle on Earth, after El Niño. The oscillation itself, as measured by meteor-ologists, is a change in relative air pressure, but its main impact is to strengthen or weaken the prevailing westerly winds that circle the Arctic. Like El Niño, the Arctic Oscillation flips between two modes. In its positive mode, air pressure differences between the polar and extra-polar regions are strong and winds strengthen. Especially in winter, the winds take heat from the warm oceans and heat the land. So, during a positive phase of the Arctic Oscillation, northern Europe, Svalbard, Siberia, the Atlantic coast of North America and Alaska all warm strongly. Likewise, when the oscillation is in its negative phase, the winds drop and the land cools.

The strength of this effect depends on the warmth of the oceans, and in particular on the Gulf Stream and the health of the ocean conveyor. But for most of the past thirty-five years, the Arctic Oscillation has been in a strongly positive mode, helping sustain a long period of warming. Modelling studies suggest that at least half of the warming in parts of the northern hemisphere is directly due to its influence, leaving global warming itself apparently a bit-part player. Except that there is growing evidence that global warming is driving the Arctic

Oscillation, too. And it does it from a surprising direction.

Enter Shindell. He likes to occupy the unpopular boundaries between scientific disciplines. His particular interest is the little-studied relationship between the stratosphere, the home of the ozone layer, and the troposphere, where our weather happens. He studies this with the aid of the GISS climate model, one of the few that can include the stratosphere fully in its calculations. Most models show little relationship between global warming and the Arctic Oscillation. The GISS model is the same when the stratosphere is not included. But Shindell discovered that when the stratosphere is hooked up, global warming causes a huge intensification of the Arctic Oscillation and the westerly winds round the Arctic. In fact, with current levels of greenhouse gases, he has reproduced a pattern very similar to the current unusually strong positive state of the oscillation.

What is going on? One of the problems with climate models is that it is not always easy to unpick exactly which of the elements in the model is causing the effects that you see in the printout. But here the role of the stratosphere is clear. And Shindell reckons he has the steps in the chain explained. Greenhouse gases cool the stratosphere, as we have seen. And this cooling alters energy distribution within the stratosphere so as to strengthen winds. In particular, a wind called the stratospheric jet that swirls around the Arctic each winter picks up speed. This wind in turn drives the westerly winds beneath, in the troposphere. So they go faster, too. In this way, a stratospheric feedback is amplifying global warming in the Arctic region by pushing the Arctic Oscillation into overdrive and strengthening the winds that warm the land. It is a brilliant, startling and until recently entirely unexpected feedback.

Might the same apply to events in Antarctica? The GISS model suggests so. There, the dominant climatic oscillation is the Southern Hemisphere Annular Mode, or SAM. Like the Arctic Oscillation, the SAM is a measure of air pressure difference between polar and non-polar air that drives westerly winds sweeping around Antarctica. The geography is somewhat different from the Arctic. The winds whistle round the Southern Ocean and hit land only on the Antarctic peninsula, which juts out from the Antarctic mainland towards South America.

Climatologist John King has studied the SAM for the British Antarctic Survey in Cambridge. He says that, like the Arctic Oscillation, it has been in overdrive since the mid-1960s, driving stronger westerly winds. And, again like the Arctic Oscillation, it is amplifying warming along its path. The Antarctic peninsula has seen air temperatures rise by 3 degrees C since the 1960s – the only spot in the southern hemisphere to show warming on this scale. The effects include the melting of the peninsula's glaciers and the dramatic collapse of its floating ice shelves, such as the Larsen B. Additionally, by bringing more warm air further south, the SAM winds are warming the waters that wash around the edges of Antarctica and beneath its ice – helping destabilize the West Antarctic ice sheet.

Here again, Shindell's model suggests that the strengthening of the SAM is the product of a cooling stratosphere and a strengthening of stratospheric jets. There is an important additional element too in the thinning ozone layer, which makes an additional contribution to stratospheric cooling.

All this is alarming evidence of a new positive feedback

that intensifies warming in two particularly sensitive regions of the planet, where that extra warming could unleash further dangerous change. Glaciologists say that the Greenland ice sheet could collapse if warming there reaches 3 degrees C. The huge stores of methane beneath the Siberian permafrost and the Barents Sea could be liberated by similar warming. And, says Shindell's boss Jim Hansen, 'the SAM warming now includes parts of the West Antarctic ice sheet, as well as the Antarctic peninsula. This is a really urgent issue.'

The discovery of the stratospheric feedback also helps answer another question that has long bothered climate scientists: why do variations in solar output that are probably no more than half a watt per square metre cause the big climate fluctuations in the North Atlantic identified by Gerard Bond in his analysis of the 1,500-year solar pulse? Conventional climate models without a stratospheric dimension suggest that such a solar fluctuation shouldn't produce temperature changes of more than 0.2 degrees C. But, while the global temperature change may well have been close to that, in parts of Europe and North America the pulses produce changes ten times greater.

Researchers have struggled to find amplifying mechanisms that might have caused that. Sea ice, the ocean conveyor and tropical flips like El Niño have all been suggested, but none seems up to the task. Shindell says the answer is his stratospheric feedback. The heart of the mechanism this time is ultraviolet radiation. While the total solar radiation reaching the Earth's surface during Bond's pulses varies by only a tenth of a percentage point, the amount of ultraviolet radiation reaching the Earth changes by as much as 10 per cent. Most of the ultraviolet

radiation is absorbed by the ozone layer in the stratosphere, so its impact at ground level is small. But the
process of absorption causes important changes in energy
flows in the stratosphere. These eventually change the
stratospheric jets and with them the Arctic Oscillation in
the northern hemisphere and the SAM in the south.

Shindell modelled the likely effects of the last reduction
of solar radiation at the Maunder Minimum in the depths
of Europe's little ice age 350 years ago. The GISS model
without the stratosphere was unmoved by the tiny change
in solar radiation. But with the stratosphere included, it
delivered a drop in temperatures in Europe of between 1
and 2 degrees C, but only a tenth as much globally –
results remarkably close to likely events in the real world.
The declining flows of ultraviolet radiation into
the stratosphere triggered a slowdown in the westerly
winds at ground level, says Shindell. That in turn caused
winter cooling, particularly over land, in the higher
latitudes of the northern hemisphere.

The stratosphere and its influence on polar and mid-
latitude winds thus seems to be a hidden amplifier that can
turn small changes in solar radiation into larger changes
in temperature in the polar regions of the planet. This is
not the only amplifier in those regions. Ice and snow are
important, along with the ocean conveyor and maybe
methane. But it appears to be the critical ingredient that
turns minor solar cycles into big climatic events. It makes
sense of Bond's solar pulse and perhaps other solar cycles.

Climate sceptics have sometimes argued that sunspot
cycles correlate so well with warming in the twentieth
century that greenhouse gases could be an irrelevance.
Climate scientists couldn't understand what mechanisms

might be involved. The changes in solar radiation seemed much too small. So they dismissed the sceptics' claims out of hand. Shindell's findings of a powerful stratospheric feedback to the solar signal have forced a rethink. But Shindell has not joined the climate sceptics. Far from it.

His own conclusion is that for the first half of the twentieth century, the correlation between estimated solar output and Earthly temperature is not bad. And the stratospheric feedback might show how the sun could have driven some warming early in the century, followed by a mid-century cooling that made some fear an on-coming ice age. But after that, there is no change in the solar signal that can be amplified to explain the recent warming. During the final three decades of the twentieth century, average solar output has if anything declined, while global temperatures – not just at high latitudes, but almost everywhere – have surged ahead at what has probably been a record rate. So, Shindell says, 'although solar variability does impact surface climate indirectly, it was almost certainly not responsible for most of the rapid global warming seen over the past three decades.'

For that most recent period, it is clear, he says, that rising concentrations of greenhouse gases are the primary driver. But besides producing a general global warming, they have also generated changes in the stratosphere that have produced a specific positive feedback to warming in the polar regions and mid-latitudes. The positive feedback has manifested itself through the apparently natural Arctic Oscillation and the SAM. Cycles that appear to have gone into overdrive.

Only a fool would conclude from Shindell's work that we don't need to worry so much about man-made climate change. On the contrary, Shindell's dramatic discovery of the stratospheric feedback suggests that the natural processes of temperature amplification are much stronger than those in most existing climate models. His new feedback seems set to continue, driving up temperatures in Arctic regions beyond the levels previously forecast. That additional warming is likely to unleash other feedbacks that will melt ice, raise sea levels, release greenhouse gases trapped in permafrost and beneath the ocean bed, and perhaps cause trouble for the ocean conveyor.

Relieved? I don't think so.

CONCLUSION

ANOTHER PLANET

Over the past 100,000 years, there have been only two vaguely stable periods of climate, according to Richard Alley. The first was 'when the ice sheets were biggest and the world was coldest. The second is the period we are living in now.' For most of the rest of the time, there has been 'a crazily jumping climate'. And now, after many generations of experiencing global climatic stability, human society seems in imminent danger of returning to a world of crazy jumps. We really have no idea what it will be like, or how we will cope. There is still a chance that the jumps won't materialize and that instead the world will warm gradually, even benignly. But the chances are against it. There are numerous feedbacks – waking monsters, in Chris Rapley's words – waiting to provide the crazy jumps. Climatically, we are entering *terra incognita*.

I have called this book *The Last Generation* not because I believe we humans are about to become extinct, but because we are in all probability the last generation that can rely on anything close to a stable global climate in which to conduct our affairs. Jim Hansen gives us just a decade to change our ways. Beyond that, he says, the last thing we can anticipate is what economists call 'business as usual'. It will be anything but. 'Business as usual will produce basically another planet,' says Hansen. 'How else can you describe climate change in which the Arctic becomes an open lake in the summer, and most land areas experience average climatic conditions not experienced before in even the most extreme years?'

I am sorry if you have got this far hoping for a definitive prognosis for our planet. Right now, there is no such prognosis except uncertainty. The Earth system seems chaotic, with the potential to head off in many different directions. If there is order, we don't yet know where it lies. No scenario has the ring of certainty. No part of the planet has yet been identified as holding an exclusive key to our future. No feedback is predestined to prevail. Some areas have 'form' from climatic history, and may continue to matter more than others. But as Alley puts it, 'The story of abrupt climate change will become more complicated before it is finished. We have to go looking for dangerous thresholds, wherever they may be.'

For now we have checklists of concerns. Melting Arctic ice, whether at sea or on land, could have huge impacts either by raising sea levels or by amplifying global warming itself. In Antarctica, glaciological 'monsters' could be lurking in Pine Island Bay or the Totten glacier. The whole West Antarctic ice sheet could just fall apart one day. El Niño may get stuck on or off, triggering megadroughts or superhurricanes. The Amazon rainforest may be close to disappearing in a rage of drought and fire that would impact weather systems round the world. The oceans may turn into a giant lifeless acid bath. Smogs may cripple the hydroxyl cleaning service or shut down the Asian monsoon. And the stratosphere may yet contain more surprises.

Methane is always lurking in the background, ready to repeat the great fart of 55 million years ago, if we allow it out of its various lairs. And the North Atlantic seems to hold a particular thrall. I keep coming back to Alley's disturbingly simple choice for the Gulf Stream as it surges north: sink or freeze? And Peter Wadhams' lonely chimney stuck out off Greenland somewhere north-east of Scoresby Sound, endlessly delivering water to the ocean floor. Until it stops. Who knows when? And who knows what will follow?

Quite a lot of this book has been taken up with climatic history. This is deliberate. The past shows more clearly than any computer model how the climate system works. Generally it does not work through gradual change, but through periods of stability broken by sudden drunken lurches. And the past operation of the climate system reveals in their fully conscious state the monsters we may be in danger of waking.

But past climate does not provide a blueprint for the future. There are no easy analogues out there. We have already strayed too far from the tracks created by Bond's solar cycles and the other natural oscillations of the Earth system. Greenhouse gas concentrations are already probably at their highest level for millions of years; temperatures will soon join them. But the distinctive nature of our predicament goes a long way beyond that. Give or take the occasional asteroid impact, past changes have almost all been driven by changes in solar radiation, beamed down to us through the stratosphere. Earthly feedbacks such as biological pumps and spreading ice sheets, and threshold changes to marine currents and terrestrial vegetation, followed on the solar signal. This time, we are starting from the ground up, with a bonfire of fossil fuels that has shaken the carbon cycle to its core. Not only that: we are filling the atmosphere with aerosols, destroying carbon stores like the rainforests and pumping ozone-eating chemicals into the stratosphere. There can be no certainty how the monsters of the Earth system will respond. We can still learn from the past, but we cannot expect the past to repeat itself.

When I first wrote at length about climate change back in 1989, in a book called *Turning up the Heat*, I warned how we passengers on Spaceship Earth could no longer sit back for the ride. We needed to get hold of the controls or risk disaster. But it was at heart an optimistic book. I figured that if *Homo sapiens* had survived through the last ice age as a mere novice on the planet, then we could make it this time, too. We had the technology; and the economics of solving the problems wouldn't be crippling. I compared the task facing us to getting rid of the old London pea-souper smogs of half a century ago. Once the decision was taken to act, the delivery would be relatively easy. We'd soon be wondering why we dawdled for so long.

Fifteen years on, the urgency of the climate crisis is much clearer, even if the story has grown a little more complicated. But we are showing no signs yet of acting on the scale necessary. The technology is still straightforward, and the economics is only easier, but we can't get the politics right. Even at this late hour, I do believe we have it in our power to set Spaceship Earth back on the right course. But time is short. The ship is already starting to spin out of control. We may soon lose all chance of grabbing the wheel.

Humanity faces a genuinely new situation. It is not an environmental crisis in the accepted sense. It is a crisis for the entire life-support system of our civilization and our species. During the past 10,000 years, since the close of the last ice age, human civilizations have plundered and destroyed their local environments, wrecking the natural fecundity of sizeable areas of the planet. Nevertheless, the planet's life-support systems as a whole have until now remained stable. As one civilization fell, another rose. But the rules of the game have changed. In the Anthropocene, human influences on planetary systems are global and pervasive.

In the past, if we got things wrong and wrecked our environment, we could up sticks and move somewhere else. Migration has always been one of our species' great survival strategies. Now we have nowhere else to go. No new frontier. We have only one atmosphere; only one planet.

APPENDIX

THE TRILLION-TONNE CHALLENGE

All the world's governments are committed to preventing 'dangerous' climate change. They made that pledge at the Earth Summit at Rio de Janeiro in 1992. The signatories included the US and Australia, which both refused to ratify the subsequent Kyoto Protocol and its national targets for emissions reductions. But what constitutes dangerous climate change? And how, in practice, can we prevent it?

For some people dangerous climate change is already a reality. Many devastated by recent hurricanes, floods and droughts believe they are victims. Such claims are usually impossible to prove. But that doesn't mean that our weather is not changing, says Myles Allen of Oxford University. In essence, climate change is already loading the dice in favour of weird and dangerous weather. 'The danger zone is not something we are going to reach in the middle of this century. We are in it now,' he says. The 35,000 Europeans who died in the heatwave in 2003 were victims of an event that would almost certainly not have happened without the insidious increase in background temperatures that turned a warm summer into a killer.

But, despite such local disasters, most would argue that the critical aim in the quest for the prevention of dangerous climate change is to avoid crossing thresholds in the climate system where irreversible global changes occur – especially changes that themselves trigger further warming. There is no certainty about where such 'tipping points' lie. But there is a growing consensus, especially in Europe, that the world should try to prevent global average temperatures rising by more than 2 degrees C from pre-industrial levels, or about 1.4 degrees above current levels.

Unfortunately, there is no certainty either about what limits on greenhouse gases will achieve that temperature target. We don't yet know how sensitive the climate system is. Current estimates suggest that to stack the odds in favour of keeping below a 2-degree warming, we probably need to keep concentrations of man-made greenhouse gases such as carbon dioxide and methane below the heating equivalent of 450 parts per million of carbon dioxide. In practice, that probably means keeping carbon dioxide levels themselves below about 400 ppm. Let's call this the 'safety-first' option.

Forgive me if I now abandon this language of parts per million. I find it an irritating and unnecessary abstraction. It seems to me much more sensible to talk in terms of tonnes of carbon rather than parts per million. Then we can establish how much there is in the atmosphere and see more clearly how much more we can afford to add before the climate goes pear-shaped.

The simple figures are these. At the depths of the last ice

age, there were about 400 billion tonnes of carbon dioxide in the atmosphere. As the ice age closed, some 200 billion tonnes switched from the oceans to the atmosphere, raising the level there to about 600 billion tonnes. That's where things rested at the start of the Industrial Revolution, when humans began large-scale burning of carbon fuels. Today, after a couple of centuries of rising emissions, we have added another 200 billion tonnes to the atmospheric burden, making it about 800 billion tonnes. If we want to keep below the safety-first concentration, we have to keep below 850 billion tonnes. So we have only about another 50 billion tonnes to go.

Currently, we pour about 7.5 billion tonnes of carbon into the atmosphere annually. Of this, a bit over 40 per cent is quickly taken up by the oceans and vegetation on land. The rest stays in the air, where its life expectancy is more than a century. So, for practical purposes, we are adding about 4 billion tonnes of carbon dioxide a year to the atmosphere. Even at current rates of emissions, that means that we will be above our 850 billion tonnes safety-first target before 2020; and assuming emissions continue to rise as they currently are, we will be there in less than a decade. Frankly, barring some global economic meltdown, there is now very little prospect of not exceeding 850 billion tonnes. If we had acted quickly after 1992 we could have done it. But the world failed.

If we are lucky – if climate sensitivity turns out to be a little lower than the gloomier predictions suggest – the 2-degree target might still be achieved while we allow carbon dioxide levels to rise significantly above 850 billion tonnes. We cannot be sure. There is already about 0.6 degrees of warming 'in the pipeline' that we can no longer prevent. But if we are feeling lucky – and with a nod to both round numbers and political reality – we might allow ourselves a ceiling of a trillion tonnes. Some would call that a 'realistic' target, though others would brand it a foolish bet on climate systems we know little about.

The 'trillion-tonne challenge' is still a tough call. Literally whatever target we set will require drastic cuts in emissions. Nature will probably continue to remove a certain amount of our emissions. But experts on the carbon cycle say that we must reduce emissions to around a quarter of those today before nature can remove what we add each year. Only then will atmospheric levels stabilize; only then will climate start to stabilize. The quicker we can do it, the lower the level at which carbon concentrations in the air will even out. Reaching the safety-first target of 850 billion tonnes of carbon dioxide would require an immediate and dramatic ditching of business as usual in the energy industry worldwide. Global emissions would need to peak within five years or so, falling by at least 50 per cent within the next half-century, and carrying on down after that. A trillion-tonne target could be achieved with more modest early cuts and greater reductions later.

Another consideration is the danger posed by the sheer speed of warming. Many climate scientists say that rapid warming may destabilize vulnerable systems like carbon stores and ice caps more than slower warming. For this reason, it could be important to take some urgent steps to limit short-term warming while we get carbon dioxide emissions under control. And there is a way of doing that, through a concerted assault on emissions of gases other than carbon dioxide that have a big short-term 'hit' on climate.

Let me explain. Different greenhouse gases have different lifetimes in the atmosphere, ranging from thousands of years to less than a decade. For convenience, climate scientists usually assess their warming impact as if it operated over a century, the average lifetime in the atmosphere of carbon dioxide. But this is rather arbitrary. And it has the effect of 'tuning' the calculations to make carbon dioxide look of maximum importance, and to reduce the apparent importance of other gases. Most important here is methane. Methane is, however you measure it, the second most important man-made greenhouse gas after carbon dioxide. Measured over a century, the warming caused by a molecule of methane is about twenty times greater than that from a molecule of carbon dioxide. But methane does most of its warming in the first decade, its typical lifetime in the atmosphere. It has a quick hit. Measured over the first decade after their release, a molecule of methane causes a hundred times more warming than a molecule of carbon dioxide.

By following the scientists' conventional time frame, the Kyoto Protocol emissions targets have underplayed the potential short-term benefits of tackling methane emissions. It is unlikely that the politicians who signed the protocol were even aware of this. But underplaying the benefits has had an important effect on policy priorities. To take one example, if the British government decided today to eliminate all methane emissions from landfill sites, it would meet only a fraction of the country's Kyoto targets, because the Kyoto rules measure the impact of the foregone emissions over the whole of the coming century. If the initiative were measured instead on its impact over the first decade, the benefits would be five times greater. Methane specialist Euan Nisbet of

Royal Holloway College in London reckons that the short-term hit would be almost as great as banning all cars on the streets of Britain. And, if the rules had been drawn up differently, it would have been enough to meet Britain's Kyoto target entirely.

If the world is concerned solely about the effect of greenhouse gases in fifty to a hundred years' time, then we should probably stick with the existing formula. But if we are also concerned about having a quick hit on global warming to stave off more immediate disaster, then there is strong case for acting hard on methane now – on leaks from landfills, gas pipelines, coal mines, the guts of ruminants and much else. 'Cutting carbon dioxide emissions is essential, but we have neglected methane and the near-term benefits [acting on] it could bring,' says Nisbet. He wants the Kyoto Protocol rules changed to a twenty-year time horizon. Jim Hansen takes a similar view. 'It makes a lot of sense to try to reduce methane because, in some ways, it's easier,' he says.

Hansen also advocates action on soot, which he calculates to be the third biggest man-made heating force in the atmosphere. Soot, as we saw in Chapter 18, has a local cooling effect but a wider and more considerable warming effect. It sticks around in the atmosphere for only a few days, but while it is there its effects are large. Action against soot and methane would not stop global warming. But it would give the world time to introduce measures against the chief culprit, carbon dioxide.

Kyoto politics

The Kyoto Protocol, signed in 1997, was the first, tentative step towards implementing the Rio pledge to prevent dangerous climate change. Some forty industrialized nations promised to make cuts in their emissions of six greenhouse gases, including the 'big two', carbon dioxide and methane. Different countries accepted different targets, and the countries of the European Union later internally reallocated theirs. Those cuts averaged about 5 per cent, measured between 1990 and the first 'compliance period', which runs from 2008 to 2012. The protocol included various 'flexibility mechanisms' aimed at making more effective use of clean-up investment funds. They allow countries to offset emissions by investing in clean-up technology abroad and in planting trees to soak up carbon dioxide from the air, and to trade directly in pollution permits.

The protocol did not impose targets on developing countries, because their emissions per head of population are mostly much lower than those of the rich, industrialized world (though there are some conspicuous exceptions, including South Korea, Singapore and several oil-rich Gulf states). The US and Australia originally signed up to Kyoto targets, but then pulled out. The protocol came into force in 2005; and at the end of the year, its signatories agreed to start negotiations on tougher cuts to come into force after 2012.

So far, so good. But the current Kyoto targets are very small compared with the cuts in emissions that will eventually be needed to control climate change. And the delay in implementing them has effectively shut off the option of a safety-first limit on carbon concentrations in the atmosphere. Some European countries have set themselves informal targets for 60 per cent emissions reductions by mid-century, which is a better measure of what is needed. But even if all the Kyoto nations did likewise, they are only responsible for a minority of today's emissions. So more would still be needed by other nations.

Eventually, if the climate regime develops as many hope, every country and every major energy and manufacturing company will need a licence to emit greenhouse gases. If we are to stop dangerous climate change, the number of licences available will need to be very limited. So the question of how they should be shared out becomes critical. It is political dynamite. In particular, the very suggestion sets the industrialized and developing worlds at loggerheads. This is partly because the industrialized countries of Europe and North America have already used up most of the atmospheric 'space' available for emissions, and partly because developing nations are coming under pressure to reduce their emissions before they have had a chance to industrialize.

Big developing nations like China and India may rank high in the emissions league table. But measured per head of population, their emissions remain low. While the US and Australia emit around 5 tonnes a year for every citizen, and European countries average under 3 tonnes, China is still below 1 tonne and India below half a tonne. Developing countries feel they are being asked to forgo economic development to help clean up a mess they did not create. On the other hand, they increasingly see that climate change threatens their prospects for economic development. The only solution is to institute a rationing system for pollution entitlements, based on a shared view of fairness.

Perhaps the simplest blueprint is called 'contraction and convergence'. Developed by a small British group called the Global Commons Institute, it is attracting support round the world. The contraction half of the formula would establish a rolling programme of annual targets for global emissions. The targets would begin roughly where we are today and then fall over the coming decades. They would be set so as to ensure that the atmosphere never passed whatever limit on carbon dioxide concentrations the world chose.

The convergence half of the formula would share out those allowable global emissions each year according to national population size. So national targets might begin at about 1 tonne of carbon per person and then fall to maybe half a tonne by 2050 and much less again by 2100, depending on the global target chosen. Of course, at the start that would leave rich nations with too few permits and many poor nations with more than they needed. So they would trade. The price of buying and selling pollution licences would be a powerful incentive for a global clean-up.

Fantasy politics? Maybe. But something on this scale will be needed if we are to prevent climatic disaster. And if the rich world wants the poor world to help clean up its mess, and save the world from dangerous climate change, then some such formula will be needed.

Technological fixes

Politics aside, what are the practicalities of stabilizing climate? President George W. Bush may have become a pariah in environmental circles for refusing to sign the Kyoto Protocol, but he is right on one thing: ultimately, it will be technologies that solve the problem more than politics. The only question is what politics will best deliver the technologies that will allow us to 'decarbonize' the world energy system. Those technologies fall into four categories. They are much more efficient use of energy; a switch to low-carbon and carbon-free fuels; capturing and storing or recycling some of the emissions that cannot be prevented; and finding new methods of storing energy, such as hydrogen fuel cells.

The task sounds daunting. But in truth, much of it goes with the grain of recent economic and industrial development. In the past thirty years, global carbon dioxide emissions have grown only half as fast as the global economy because of improved energy efficiency. And many of the new energy technologies we will need are already in use, offering benefits such as cheaper or more secure supplies. The replacement of coal with lower-carbon natural gas, the development of wind power and biofuels, the proposed expansion of nuclear energy and investment in energy efficiency all fall into this category. What is needed first is faster progress in a direction we are already headed.

The top priority should be energy efficiency. More than half the immediate cheap potential for reducing carbon dioxide emissions lies in improving energy efficiency in buildings, transport and industry. Much of it could be done at zero or even negative cost, because the cost savings would outweigh the investment. It is also the area where we as individuals can most easily make a difference, by buying energy-efficient light bulbs and appliances, insulating our homes properly, cutting down on car use and choosing energy-efficient models such as hybrids.

Also in the short term, there is huge potential to fit the world's fossil-fuel-burning power stations with 'scrubbers' to remove carbon dioxide and deliver it via pipelines for burial underground. The technology is already developed and only needs scaling up. The potential global storage capacity in old oil and gas wells alone is approaching a trillion tonnes of carbon. The British government's chief scientist David King says that by 2020 Britain could be burying a quarter of its power station carbon dioxide emissions in old oilfields beneath the North Sea and a pilot programme was launched in early 2006.

Other technologies will take more development before they become cost-effective on a large scale. These include the widespread use of solar power, which is available but currently too expensive, and turning hydrogen into the fuel of the future for transport. The idea here would be to manufacture hydrogen in vast quantities for use in batteries, known as fuel cells, that power cars. Hydrogen would become the 'new oil'. Hydrogen is manufactured by splitting water into hydrogen and oxygen, which is a very energy-intensive process. So if the energy for splitting water were generated by burning fossil fuel, there would be little environmental gain; but if the energy came from renewables, such as solar or wind power, that would change everything.

The hydrogen fuel cell is not so much a new source of energy as a new way of storing energy. It could be the only way of making cars truly greenhouse-friendly. And it may turn out to be the best way of utilizing fickle renewable energy sources such as the wind and sun. The big problem for these energy sources is that the wind cannot be guaranteed to blow (nor the sun to shine) when the energy is needed. But by converting the energy into hydrogen, it can be kept for future use.

So what exactly would it take to deploy all these technologies in order to bring climate change under control? The most ambitious attempt so far to produce a simple global blueprint comes from Robert Socolow, an engineer at Princeton University. He admits that when he checked out the plethora of options for cutting greenhouse gases he was overwhelmed, and figured that most politicians and industrialists would be too. So he decided to break the task down into a series of technological changes that, over the coming fifty years, would each cut global emissions of carbon dioxide by about 25 billion tonnes. He called them 'wedges' because the impact of each would grow gradually from nothing in the first year to a billion-tonne emissions cut in the fiftieth year. They would each cut a 'wedge' out of the graph of rising carbon dioxide emissions.

Socolow proposed more than a dozen possible wedges, but said seven would be necessary to prevent rising emissions over the coming fifty years and stabilize them at current levels. But we need to do more than that. We don't just need to stabilize emissions: we need to stabilize actual concentrations of greenhouse gases in the atmosphere, and that requires reducing emissions from their current 7.5 billion tonnes a year to around 2 billion tonnes. So I have adapted Socolow's blueprint to allow for that tougher target. We might choose the following twelve wedges, each of which is able to cut emissions by 25 billion tonnes over the coming half-century, reducing global emissions by 2060 from the projected 14 billion tonnes a year to 2 billion tonnes:

- universally adopt efficient lighting and electrical appliances in homes and offices;
- double the energy efficiency of two billion cars;
- build compact urban areas served by efficient public transport, halving future car use;
- effect a fifty-fold worldwide expansion of wind power, equivalent to two million 1-megawatt turbines;
- effect a fifty-fold worldwide expansion in biofuels for vehicles;

- embark on a global programme of insulating buildings;
- cover an area of land the size of New Jersey (Socolow's home state) with solar panels;
- quadruple current electricity production from natural gas by converting coal-fired power stations;
- capture and store carbon dioxide from 1,600 gigawatts of natural gas power plants;
- halt global deforestation and plant an area of land the size of India with new forests;
- double nuclear power capacity;
- increase tenfold the global use of low-tillage farming methods to increase soil storage of carbon.

Economics of the greenhouse

How much might all this cost? In 2001, a team of environmental economists assembled by the IPCC reviewed estimates for stabilizing atmospheric concentrations of carbon dioxide by 2100. They ranged from a low of $200 billion to a high of $17 trillion – almost a hundred times greater. It seems extraordinary that there could be such a large range of estimates. But, when these are boiled down to their basics, it appears that much of the difference depends on whether the modellers assume that the necessary technical and social changes will 'go with the flow' of future change, or whether everything will have to be grafted onto a society and economy heading fast in a different direction.

Put simply, the high estimates guessed that, under business as usual, rising wealth will produce and require almost equally fast rises in emissions from burning cheap carbon fuels. Diverting from that path would thus require preventing the emissions of trillions of tonnes of carbon using expensive technologies that would not otherwise have been developed. The lower estimates assumed that the world is already slowly losing its addiction to carbon fuels, and that all we need to do is make the switch faster. They also had a rather different view of technological development, seeing it as moulded by a range of economic incentives. In this version, governments can shape techno-logical development by stimulating markets. Once this process is under way, innovation will go into overdrive and prices will fall away.

Some of the people involved in the IPCC study were instinctively hostile to major efforts to cut carbon dioxide emissions. Yale environmental economist William Nordhaus suggests that 'a vague premonition of potential disaster is insufficient grounds to plunge the world into depression.' But let us assume that the real costs are towards the top end of the range. Would their adoption really push the world into economic depression?

Veteran climate scientist Stephen Schneider of Stanford University re-did the arithmetic in 2002, assuming it would cost $8 trillion to stabilize carbon dioxide concen-trations by 2100. He found that the same economists who predict doomsday if we try to tackle climate change also believe that, under business as usual, an average citizen of the world will be five times richer in a hundred years' time than they are today. So he took them at their word and asked: how much would the $8 trillion bill for halting climate change delay those riches? The answer was just two years.

'The wild rhetoric about enslaving the poor and bank-rupting the economy to do climate policy is fallacious, even if one accepts the conventional economic models,' he told me on publication of his analysis. Coincidentally, it came out in the week that the Australian prime minister

John Howard announced that his country would not ratify the Kyoto Protocol because it would 'cost jobs and damage our industry'. Poppycock, said Schneider. 'To be five times richer in 2100 versus 2102 would hardly be noticed.' It was a small price to pay.

A small price to pay for what? What would we be buying with this trillion-dollar investment in a stable climate? That is, of course, impossible to answer, because we don't know the extent of the climatic catastrophes that would be avoided. But we can easily see the scale of things, even today. The evidence of the cost of extreme weather is everywhere. The 1998 El Niño cost Asia at least $20 billion. Insured losses from extreme weather in 2004 hit a record $55 billion, which was promptly exceeded by an estimated $70 billion for 2005. Total economic losses, including uninsured losses, are expected to be three times higher: cleaning up after Hurricane Katrina alone may eventually cost $100 billion. Incidentally, a simple extrapolation of trends in insurance claims from extreme weather in recent years suggests that they will exceed global gross domestic product by 2060. That may be slightly wacky maths, but it is sobering nonetheless.

Not surprisingly, economists disagree about the cost of inaction on climate change as much as they do about the cost of action. Some have attempted to assess the 'social cost' of every tonne of carbon put into the air. One recent review found a range from $1,666 per tonne down to zero. The British government, which commissioned the review, settled on a figure of $70 per tonne. One of the reasons for the wide range is accounting practices. Economists routinely apply a discount to the cost of anything that has to be paid for in the future. Dealing with climate change that may happen decades or even centuries ahead allows for huge discounts. Some economists say that very long-term impacts – such as rising sea levels as ice caps melt – should be discounted to zero.

This discounting of the future may be a convenient device for corporations, or even governments. But it is less clear how sensible it is for the management of a planet. If it all goes wrong, shareholders can sell their shares and governments can print money or go cap in hand to the International Monetary Fund. But the planet, our only planet, is rather different.

Moreover, the existing estimates of social cost are based on IPCC studies that so far have not included many of the irreversible positive feedbacks to climate change that this book has concentrated on. So nobody has yet even asked what price should be attached to a century-long drought in the American West; or an enfeebled Asian monsoon; or a permanent El Niño in the Pacific; or a shut-down of the ocean conveyor; or the acidification of the oceans; or a methane belch from the ocean depths; or a collapse of the West Antarctic ice sheet; or sea levels rising by half a metre in a decade. Though, on reflection, these are perhaps questions best not answered by accountants.

GLOSSARY

Aerosol Any of a range of particles in the air – including soot, dust and sulphates – that can intercept solar energy, sometimes scattering it and sometimes absorbing and re-radiating it. Under different circumstances it can either warm or cool the ground beneath it and the air around it.

African Humid Period Period that began at the close of the last ice age and culminated about 5,500 years ago, characterized by wet conditions in Africa, notably in the Sahara.

Albedo A measure of the reflectivity of a surface.

Anthropocene New term to describe the past two centuries or so, during which human activities are seen to have dominated some key planetary processes, such as the carbon cycle.

Arctic Oscillation A climate oscillation that occurs on timescales from days to decades. Measured by differences in air pressure between polar and non-polar areas, and manifested in changing wind patterns which alter temperature. Related to (and sometimes synonymous with) the North Atlantic Oscillation.

Biological pump The process by which living organisms in the ocean draw carbon dioxide out of the atmosphere as they grow and then deposit carbon as their bodies float to the ocean floor following their death. Has the effect of moderating the accumulation of the gas in the atmosphere.

Biosphere That part of the Earth's surface, atmosphere and oceans that is inhabited by living things.

Carbon dioxide fertilization effect What happens when high concentrations of carbon dioxide in the air 'fertilize' the faster growth of plants or other organisms.

Carbon cycle The natural exchange of carbon between the atmosphere, the oceans and the Earth's surface. Carbon may be dissolved in the oceans, absorbed within living organisms and soils, or float in the air as carbon dioxide.

Carbon sink Anything that absorbs carbon dioxide from the air.

Carbon source Anything that releases carbon dioxide.

Chimneys A term coined by Peter Wadhams for the giant whirlpools in the far North Atlantic that take dense water to the sea bed. The start of the ocean conveyor.

Climate model Normally computerized simulation of the workings of the atmosphere. Often used to predict the effect of future changes such as an accumulation of greenhouse gases.

El Niño Periodic switch in ocean currents and winds in the equatorial Pacific Ocean. A major perturbation in the global climate system.

Feedbacks Any by-product of an event that has a subsequent effect on that event. A positive feedback amplifies the original event, while a negative feedback dampens it. Key climate feedbacks include ice, water vapour and changes to the carbon cycle. See also ice-albedo feedback.

Fossil fuel Fuels made of fossilized carbon (the remains of ancient vegetation), including coal, oil and natural gas.

Gaia The idea, developed by James Lovelock, that the Earth and its living organisms act in consort, like a single organism, to regulate the environment of the planet, including atmospheric chemistry and temperature.

Global warming Synonym for the greenhouse effect and climate change.

Greenhouse gas Any one of several gases that trap heat in the lower atmosphere, including water vapour, carbon dioxide and methane.

Gulf Stream Tropical ocean current that keeps Europe warm, especially in winter. It is part of the ocean conveyor and may be turned off at times, such as during ice ages.

Holocene Geological era from the end of the last ice age. Sometimes regarded as being recently succeeded by the Anthropocene.

Hydrological cycle The movement of water between the oceans, the atmosphere and the Earth's surface through processes such as evaporation, condensation, rainfall and river flow.

Ice ages Periods of several tens of thousands of years when ice sheets spread across the northern hemisphere and the planet cools. Believed to be triggered by Milankovitch wobbles and amplified by positive feedbacks. Recent ice ages have occurred roughly every 100,000 years. The last finished 10,000 years ago.

Ice-albedo feedback Positive feedback on air temperature caused by the presence or absence of highly reflective ice. Thus, during warming, ice melts and is replaced by a darker surface of ocean or land vegetation that absorbs more heat, amplifying the warming. The reverse happens when cooling causes ice to form.

Ice sheets The largest expanses of ice on the planet. There are currently three: Greenland, West Antarctica and East Antarctica.

Interglacials Warm periods between ice ages.

Intergovernmental Panel on Climate Change (IPCC) Panel of scientists appointed by the UN through national science agencies to study the causes, impacts and solutions to global warming.

Isotope One of two or more atoms with the same atomic number but containing different numbers of neutrons. For example: oxygen 16 and oxygen 18. The ratio of the isotopes in the air or oceans can vary according to environmental conditions, but will be fixed when the isotopes are taken up by plants or air bubbles are trapped in ice. Thus, isotopic analysis of ocean sediments, ice cores and other leftovers from the past can be a valuable way of reconstructing past temperatures, etc.

Kyoto Protocol 1987 agreement on climate change. Provisions include cuts in emissions by most industrialized nations during the first compliance period – 2008 to 2012. US and Australia initially signed the protocol but subsequently pulled out.

Little ice age Period from the fourteenth to the nineteenth century when parts of the northern hemisphere were cooler than today.

Medieval warm period Period from the ninth to the thirteenth century when parts of the northern hemisphere were notably warm.

Methane clathrates Crystalline lattices of ice that trap large volumes of methane. Usually found at low temperatures and high pressures beneath the ocean bed or in permafrost.

Milankovitch wobbles Various wobbles in the orbit of the Earth than can influence climate over timescales of thousands of years. Believed to be the trigger for ice ages. Named after Serbian mathematician Milutin Milankovitch but originally investigated by forgotten Scottish amateur scientist James Croll.

Nuclear winter Theory that in a nuclear war there would be so many fires that smoke would blanket the planet, causing massive cooling.

Ocean conveyor Global ocean circulation in which dense surface water falls to the ocean floor in the Arctic and near Antarctica before travelling the oceans and resurfacing about a thousand years later in the warm Gulf Stream of the Atlantic. Prone to switching on and off, and perhaps a major determinant of global climate.

Ozone hole Extreme sign of thinning of the ozone layer seen in recent decades. Found each spring over Antarctica, but potentially could occur over the Arctic, too. Caused when man-made 'ozone-eating' chemicals accumulate in the ozone layer of the lower stratosphere, and triggered by low temperatures and sunlight.

Ozone layer The ozone within the lower stratosphere that protects the Earth from harmful ultraviolet radiation from the sun.

Permafrost Permanently frozen soil and rock found in the tundra regions of Siberia, Canada, Antarctica and some mountain regions. Can reach a depth of more than two kilometres.

Precession One of the Milankovitch wobbles that effects the axis of the Earth's rotation. Changes the season when the Earth is closest to the sun. Implicated in some climate changes during the Holocene.

Rainforest Forest that depends on frequent rainfall but also generates rain by recycling water into the atmosphere from its leaves.

Southern Hemisphere Annular Mode (SAM) Antarctic equivalent of the Arctic Oscillation. Responsible for strong warming of Antarctic peninsula in recent decades.

Stratosphere Layer of the atmosphere that starts about 10–15 kilometres above the Earth's surface. Home of the ozone layer. The greenhouse effect causes it to cool but it may act to amplify warming in the troposphere beneath.

Thermal expansion The warming and resulting expansion of water in the oceans. Along with the melting of land ice, it is causing a worldwide rise in sea levels.

Troposphere The lowest layer of the atmosphere, occupying the 10–15 kilometres beneath the stratosphere. The area within which our weather occurs. The greenhouse effect causes it to warm.

Ultraviolet radiation Solar radiation with wavelengths shorter than light but longer than x-rays. Harmful to living organisms, which are largely protected from it on Earth by the ozone layer.

NOTES ON REFERENCES

It would be impossible for me to list all the sources I have used in the process of researching and writing this book. What follows here is a summary of the reference material and further reading that you may find most useful.

Preface

Wadhams' work on 'chimneys' appears at greatest length in 'Convective Chimneys in the Greenland Sea: a Review of Recent Observation', (*Oceanography and Marine Biology: An Annual Review*, 2004, vol. 42, pp. 29–56) and also in *Geophysical Research Letters*, 2002 (vol. 29, p. 76). He also spoke to me at length. For more on William Scoresby, see my article 'Hell with a Harpoon' in *New Scientist*, 18 May 2002.

Introduction

The proceedings of the British government's Dangerous Climate Change conference appear at **www.stabilisation2005.com/**. The resulting book can also be found at **www.defra.gov.uk/environment/**

climatechange/internat/dangerous-cc.htm. Hansen's address to the AGU in late 2005 is at www.columbia.edu/~jeh1/keeling_talk_and_slides.pdf. Three overviews on abrupt climate change are: Richard Alley's *Abrupt Climate Change: Inevitable Surprises* (National Academies Press, 2002), especially chapter four; 'Abrupt Changes: The Achilles' Heels in the Earth System' by Steffen *et al.* in *Environment* (vol. 46, p. 9) and Rial *et al*'s 'Non-Linearities, Feedbacks and Critical Thresholds with the Earth's Climate System', (*Climate Change*, vol. 65, p. 11).

1. The Pioneers

The journal *Ambio* had a special issue on Svante Arrhenius and his legacy in 1997 (vol. 26, no. 1). I wrote about him in *New Scientist* in 'Land of the Midnight Sums', 25 January 2003. Other sources include Gale E. Christianson's book *Greenhouse: The 200-Year Story of Global Warming* (Constable, 1999); he is also good on Callendar and Keeling. Many useful obituaries of Keeling were posted on news websites following his death in June 2005 – for instance in the *Daily Telegraph* (www.telegraph.co.uk/news/main.jhtml?xml=/news/2005/06/24/db2402.xml). And a good personal description of his early work appears at: www.mlo.noaa.gov/HISTORY/PUBLISH/20th%20anniv/co2.htm.

2. Turning Up the Heat

The British newspaper mentioned in the first paragraph is the *Daily Mail*. The column by Melanie Phillips, 'The Global Warming Fraud', can still be read at her website: www.melaniephillips.com/articles/archives/000255.html. Christianson covers much of the early history of researching greenhouse gases. Brindley's paper on the planet's radiation balance is in *Nature*, vol. 410, p. 355. See also **www.imperial.ac.uk/P2641.htm**.

The definitive consensus overview of the science of climate change in 2001 is provided by the Third Assessment Report of the Intergovernmental Panel on Climate Change (**www.ipcc.ch/**), which will be superseded during 2007 by the Fourth Assessment. However, the Fourth Assessment is already out of date. It only accepted evidence published in peer-reviewed literature by the summer of 2005 – missing much new evidence of 'tipping points' in the climate system.

Sherwood's 2005 research appears in *Science* (vol. 309, p. 1556). Parker's work on the urban heat island appears in *Nature* (vol. 432, p. 290). For references to Mann's work see chapter thirty-three. Lassen and Friis-Christensen's original 1991 paper was in *Science*, vol. 254, p. 698. Lindzen is better known as a polemical and op-ed writer (for instance, **www.cato.org/pubs/regulation/reg15n2g.html**). But he does have a track record of interesting research, such as 'Does the Earth Have an Adaptive Infrared Iris?' (*Bulletin of the American Meteorological Society*, vol. 82, p. 417).

Pat Michaels (**www.cato.org/people/michaels.html**) is another media regular, whose exposition of the 'paradigm problem' appears in his diatribe on climate science, *Meltdown: The Predictable Distortion of Global Warming by Scientists, Politicians and the Media* (Cato, 2004). For a vigorous attack on Michael Crichton's book *State of Fear*, read Jeremy Leggett in *New Scientist*, 5 March 2005.

Oreskes' review of the scientific literature on climate change appeared in *Science*, vol. 306, p. 1686.

3. The Year

I visited Honduras after Hurricane Mitch for the Red Cross. I wrote up my findings at **www.redcross.int/EN/ mag/magazine2001_2/heating.html**. First reports on how exceptional 1998 was appeared the following year (e.g., **www.sciencedaily.com/releases/1999/03/ 990304052546.htm**). This was underlined in 2001 in the Third Assessment Report of the IPCC.

4. The Anthropocene

The proceedings of the Dahlem conference, at which I was introduced to many of the topics discussed here, are published as *Earth System Analysis for Sustainability*, ed. Schellnhuber *et al.* (Dahlem University Press, 2004). Crutzen discussed his work at length in his Nobel Lecture (**www.nobelprize.org/nobel_prizes/chemistry/laureates /1995/crutzen-lecture.html**). His discussion of the Anthropocene first appeared in print in 2000 in the newsletter of the International Geosphere-Biosphere Programme (IGBP), no. 41. I interviewed him for *New Scientist*: 'High Flyer', 5 July 2003. Alley's report is *Abrupt Climate Change: Inevitable Surprises* (National Academies Press, 2002). Many of the remarks by Alley and Steffen come from my interviews with them in 2003 and 2005.

5. The Watchtower

The reportage follows a visit to Ny-Alesund in September 2005. Kim Holmen discusses its role as 'a watchtower for human-induced climate change' in *Polar Science in Tromso* (Polarmiljosenteret, 2004). Kohler's mass balance study appears in *Polar Research* (vol. 22 (2), p. 145). Dobson's story can be read at **www.atm.ox.ac.uk/user/**

barnett/ozoneconference/dobson.htm. The Bear Island research appeared in *Environmental Pollution*, vol. 136, p. 419.

6. Ninety Degrees North
McCarthy revealed the ice-free North Pole at news.bbc.co.uk/1/hi/world/americas/888235.stm. Scamdos's work is being updated all the time and appears at: nsidc.org/. Polyakov's warm-water pulse is reported in 2005 in *Geophysical Research Letters*, vol. 32, L17605. The statement by glaciologists on the transformed state of the Arctic appeared in *Eos* in August 2005 (vol. 86, p. 309).

7. On the Slippery Slope
Hansen's 'slippery slope' essay appears in *Climate Change*, vol. 68, p. 269. His 'dangerous anthropogenic interference' remarks appeared in a lecture of that name to the University of Iowa, available, with much else of interest, from his website at: www.columbia.edu/~jch1/.

Box's remarks, and those of Bromwich and Alley, are from interviews conducted in 2005. Zwally's research was published in 2002 in *Science* (vol. 297, p. 218). Data on movement of the Jakobshavn glacier appear in *Nature* (vol. 432, p. 608), and the new findings on Kangerdlugssuaq from measurements by Gordon Hamilton of the University of Maine on a Greenpeace cruise in 2005 at www.greenpeace.org.uk/climate/climate.cfm?UCIDParam=2005072 1151314.

8. The Shelf
The demise of Larsen B is described by Hulbe at web.pdx.edu/~chulbe/science/Larsen/larsen2002.html. Alley discusses mechanisms at igloo.gsfc.nasa.gov/wais/

pastmeetings/abstracts04/Alley.htm. I learned more from interviews with scientists at the British Antarctic Survey, and from Rignot and others at a conference on the Antarctic ice held at the Royal Society in London in late 2005 (www.royalsoc.ac.uk/news.asp?year=&id=3831).

9. The Mercer Legacy
I heard the story of Mercer from Thompson during interviews at his lab in 2005, and in correspondence with Hughes. Mercer's 1978 paper is in *Nature* (vol. 271, p. 321), and Hughes's 1981 'weak underbelly' paper was in the *Journal of Glaciology*, vol. 27, p. 518. Pine Island Bay was a major talking point at the Royal Society conference mentioned above, along with the state of the Totten and Cook glaciers. Vaughan's initial findings first emerged at igloo.gsfc.nasa.gov/wais/pastmeetings/abstracts05/Vaughan.pdf. Davis's paper on the East Antarctic ice sheet appeared in *Science* (vol. 308, p. 1898).

10. Rising Tides
The Carterets' plight reached the world via the BBC. See www.sidsnet.org/archive/climate-newswire/2000/0093.html. Plans to abandon the islands and Tuvalu were reported by Reuters on 24 November 2005. I interviewed Teuatabo for *New Scientist* in 2000 ('Turning Back the Tide', 12 February 2000). Hansen discussed the history of sea-level rise in his December 2005 lecture: www.columbia.edu/~jeh1/keeling_talk_and_slides.pdf.

11. In the Jungle
Nepstad's drought experiment is discussed in *Science*, vol. 308, p. 346, and at earthobservatory.nasa.gov/Study/AmazonDrought/. His plans for an experimental burn are

discussed at www.eurekalert.org/pub_releases/2005-07/
whrc-whr071905.php. The 2005 Amazon drought was
widely reported, e.g. news.bbc.co.uk/1/hi/world/americas
/4344310.stm. The Hadley Centre predictions appear in
its report 'Stabilising Climate to Avoid Dangerous Climate
Change', published in January 2005. The report by
Gedney and Valdes appears in *Geophysical Research
Letters*, vol. 27, p. 3053.

12. Wild Fires of Borneo
I visited Palangkaraya for the *Guardian* newspaper shortly
after the fires of 1997–8 and received first-hand reports
from locals. See also reportage in *Nature* in 2004 (vol. 432,
p. 144). Rieley's calculations of emissions from the fires
appeared in *Nature* (vol. 420, p. 61). The US research cor-
roborating his findings appeared in *Science* (vol. 303, p. 73).

13. Sink to Source
Fan's explosive *Science* paper appeared in vol. 282, p. 442.
Ciais' work for CarboEurope (www.carboeurope.org/)
appeared in *Nature* (vol. 437, p. 529), while Angert's
paper appeared in the *Proceedings of the National
Academy of Sciences* (PNAS), vol. 102, p. 10823, and
Zeng's findings were in *Geophysical Research Letters*, vol.
32, L22709. Lawrence's work on permafrost is publicized
at www.ucar.edu/news/releases/2005/permafrost.shtml
and in *Geophysical Research Letters* (vol. 32, L24401).
Peter Cox presented his findings at the Dangerous Climate
Change conference (see Introduction above) and published
in *Geophysical Research Letters* (vol. 30, p. 1479). I found
Canadell's work at www.esm.ucsb.edu/academics/courses
/595PP-S/Readings/VulnerabGlobalC.pdf. Kirk's findings
on British carbon appeared in *Nature*, vol. 437, p. 245.

14. The Doomsday Device
My story on melting permafrost appeared in *New Scientist* on 11 August 2005. Kirpotin's findings have yet to find a peer-reviewed publication in English at press time, but a revised version of his translated Russian paper appears at **www.mindfully.org/Air/2005/Palsas-Climate-Changes11aug05.htm**. His findings were corroborated by Ted Schuur a year later in *Nature* (vol. 443, p. 71). I learned of Larry Smith's findings in e-mail interviews. The report suggesting that all plants make methane appeared in *Nature*, vol. 439, p. 187. I interviewed Christensen extensively during my visit to Stordalen in late 2005. His papers include *Geophysical Research Letters*, vol. 31, L04501.

15. The Acid Bath
The Royal Society's study 'Ocean Acidification Due to Increasing Atmospheric Carbon Dioxide', appeared in June 2005, and can be found at **www.royalsoc.ac.uk**. Turley presented her findings at the Dangerous Climate Change conference. Orr reported in *Nature* (vol. 437, p. 681). Falkowski's paper appeared in *Science* (vol. 290, p. 291).

16. The Wind of Change
Kennett and Stott's 1991 paper appeared in *Nature*, vol. 353, p. 225. Dickens has published, for instance, in *Geotimes*, November 2004, pp. 18–22. Alan Judd's seabed explorations were written up by Joanna Marchant in *New Scientist* on 2 December 2000. Norman Cherkis's paper was presented at the American Geophysical Union Spring Meeting 1997. Mienert discussed the Storegga slide in *Marine and Petroleum Geology* (vol. 22, p. 1) and

in *Oceanography* (vol. 17, p. 16). Some other material comes from unpublished research he provided me with during interviews. Nisbet discussed methane releases in a paper in the Royal Society *Transactions*, vol. 360, p. 581. And David Archer produced an inventory of methane clathrates in *Earth and Planetary Science Letters*, vol. 227, p. 185.

17. What's Watts?

Hansen's work on this is synthesized in his paper 'The Earth's Energy Imbalance: Confirmation and Implications', published in *Science* (vol. 308, p. 1431) and available at **www.columbia.edu/~jeh1/hansen_imbalance.pdf**. Read about the Global Albedo Project at **www-c4.ucsd.edu/gap/**. Chapin's findings on Arctic albedo were in *Science* (vol. 310, p. 627), while Betts's findings are in *Nature*, vol. 408, p. 187.

18. Clouds from Both Sides

The 2004 Exeter meeting was a closed session of IPCC scientists. I was the only outsider attending. But most of the findings have since been made public. Stainforth's work appeared in *Nature* (vol. 433, p. 403), and Murphy's in the same journal, vol. 430, p. 768. Likewise I was the only journalist attending sessions of the 2003 Dahlem conference (see chapter four), where Crutzen and Cox made their first calculations about the 'parasol effect', later written up by Cox in *Nature* (vol. 435, p. 1187). Wielicki responded in e-mail interviews and outlined some issues in *Science* (vol. 295, p. 841). Schwartz's remarks were made in an interview coinciding with his paper in the *Journal of the Air and Waste Management Association* (vol. 54, p. 1). Hansen wrote about black soot in the *Journal of Geophysical Research*, vol. 110, D18104.

19. A Billion Fires

The INDOEX website is at **www-indoex.ucsd.edu/**. Remanathan and Crutzen discussed its findings in 2002 in *Current Science*, vol. 83, p. 947. Dale Kaiser's work on dimming appeared in *Geophysical Research Letters*, vol. 29, p. 2042. Hansen's ideas appear in *Science*, vol. 297, p. 2250.

20. Hydroxyl Holiday

Prinn gave his warning in *Science* in 1995 (vol. 269, p. 187) and returned to the issue in the IGBP Newsletter no. 43 in 2000, and in *Science* in 2001 (vol. 292, p. 1882). Madronich raised his fears in 1992 in *Geophysical Research Letters*, vol. 19, p. 465, and also a year later at **www.ciesin.org/docs/011-457/011-457.html**. I wrote a somewhat fanciful 'doomsday scenario' for hydroxyl in a *New Scientist* supplement in April 2001. It can be found at **www.gsenet.org/library/04chm/hydroxyl.php**.

21. Goldilocks and the Three Planets

Read all about Snowball Earth in the book of that name by my former *New Scientist* colleague Gabrielle Walker (Bloomsbury, 2003). And more from Kirschvink at **www.pr.caltech.edu/media/Press_Releases/PR12723.html**. Lovelock gave his Gaian interpretation of the planet's history in books such as *The Ages of Gaia* (1995). His most recent book is *The Revenge of Gaia* (Allen Lane, 2006). I explored Retallack's ideas about the Kingdoms of Gaia in *New Scientist*, 10 June 2001.

22. The Big Freeze
The best read on the ice ages and Agassiz and the intriguing James Croll is in *Frozen Earth* by Doug Macdougall (California UP, 2004). Shackleton's ground-breaking paper appeared in 1976 in *Science* (vol. 194, p. 1121). I took Berrien Moore III's analysis of carbon movements from the *Global Change Newsletter* no. 40 (December 1999, p. 1).

23. The Ocean Conveyor
Broecker's writings on the conveyor are extensive. Some key early papers are in *Nature* in 1994 (vol. 372, p. 421), *Scientific American* in 1995 (vol. 273, p. 62) and *Science* in 1997 (vol. 278, p. 1582). I interviewed him in late 2005. Schlesinger's paper appears on the website of the Dangerous Climate Change conference, along with Challoner's. Ruth Curry's paper on the great salinity anomaly was in *Science*, vol. 308, p. 1772. And Bryden's paper appeared in *Nature*, vol. 438, p. 655.

24. An Arctic Flower
Alley splendidly describes the science of the Younger Dryas (and many other things) in his book *The Two-Mile Time Machine* (Princeton UP, 2000). Read about how humans fared in William Burroughs' *Climate Change in Prehistory* (Cambridge UP, 2005). The latest thinking on the emptying of Lake Agassiz is in *Eos*, vol. 86, p. 465. Chiang's paper appeared in *Climate Dynamics* (vol. 25, p. 477). Alley explored events 8,200 years ago in *Quaternary Science Reviews*, vol. 24, p. 1123.

25. The Pulse
The best study of the events of the little ice age remains the book of that name by Jean Grove (Routledge, 1989).

Bond's pioneering work on 'the pulse' and its links to the era appeared in *Science* (vol. 278, p. 1257 and vol. 294, p. 2130). His work is summarized at **www.ldeo.columbia.edu/news/2005/07_11_05.htm**. Read too Peter deMenocal's paper with Thomas Marchitto in *Geochemistry Geophysics Geosystems* (DOI: 10.1029/2003GC000598) and his essay 'After Tomorrow' in *Orion*, January 2005, plus Shindell's 'Glaciers, Old Masters and Galileo' at **www.giss.nasa.gov/research/briefs/shindell_06/**, and Christina Hulbe in *Paleoceanography* (vol. 19, PA1004).

26. The Fall
Useful analyses of how the Sahara became a desert include Robert Kunzig's 'Exit from Eden' in *Discovery*, January 2000, Claussen's paper in *Climate Change* (vol. 57, p. 99), and deMnocal in *Quaternary Science Reviews*, vol. 19, p. 347. Haarsma's theories are articulated in *Geophysical Research Letters*, vol. 32, p. L17702. DeMenocal looks at megadroughts through the late Holocene in *Science* (vol. 292, p. 667); and Richard Seager's study is at **www.ldeo.columbia.edu/res/div/ocp/drought**.

27. See-Saw across the Ocean
The Bodele dust reservoir is discussed in *Nature* as 'the dustiest place on Earth' (vol. 434, p. 816). I learned of Schellenhuber's ideas on links between the Sahara and Amazon in conversations. They seem intuitively sensible but remain, so far as I know, unquantified.

28. Tropical High
I interviewed Thompson at length about his career and ideas in 2005. There is also a highly readable book about

him called *Thin Ice* by Mark Bowen (Henry Holt, 2005). Key papers include those in *Climatic Change*, vol. 59, p. 137, and *Quaternary Science Reviews*, vol. 19, p. 19. His website is at **www-bprc.mps.ohio-state.edu/Icecore/GroupP.html#lonniethompson.**

29. The Curse of Akkad
The story of Akkad and other tales of climate and civilization appear in *The Winds of Change* by Eugene Linden (Simon & Schuster, 2006). DeMenocal looks at the collapse of Akkad in *Geology*, vol. 28, p. 379. Weiss's original paper appeared in the *Journal of the American Oriental Society*, vol. 95, p. 534. Issar explores similar collapses in the Middle East at the time with Mattanyah Zohar in *Climate Change: Environment and Civilization in the Middle East* (Springer, 2004).

30. A Chunk of Coral
I wrote about Dan Schrag's find and its implications for El Niño in *New Scientist*, 9 October 1999. He published his findings in *Geophysical Research Letters* (vol. 26, p. 2139). El Niño has many chroniclers these days, including Richard Grove and John Chappell's *El Niño: History and Crisis* (White Horse Press, 2000) and *El Niño in History* by Cesar Caviedes (UP Florida, 2001). Rodbell's compelling paper is in *Science* (vol. 283, p. 516). Latif modelling of El Niño's future appeared in *Nature* (vol. 398, p. 694). Read about the Peruvian potato farmers at **www.columbia.edu/cu/pr/00/01/pleiades.html.**

31. Feeding Asia
Mike Davis wrote passionately about the effects of El Niño and failed monsoons in the late nineteenth century

in *Late-Victorian Holocausts* (Verso, 2001). Overpeck's analysis of the monsoon's potentially troubled future appeared in *Nature*, vol. 421, p. 354. Analysis of the different interpretations of the links that sustain the monsoon emerged from conversations with Mark Cane, Broecker, Alley, Thompson and others.

32. The Heatwave
The 2003 heatwave was summed up at **www.earth-policy.org/Updates/Update29.htm**. The link to global warming was articulated by Allen in *Nature* (vol. 432, p. 610). The study of Burgundy vineyards appeared in Nature (vol. 432, p. 289). Betts warned about the extra threat to cities in *PNAS* (DOI 10.1073/pnas.0400357101).

33. The Hockey Stick
Read the IPCC summary for policymakers at **www.ipcc.ch/pub/spm22-01.pdf**. Early versions of the hockey stick were parlayed in *Nature* (vol. 392, p. 779) and *Geophysical Research Letters* (vol. 26, p. 759). Other write-ups of Mann's work and the controversy it created include those in *Scientific American* (March 2005, p. 34) and *Mother Jones* (18 April 2005). McIntyre and McKitrick set out their case in 2003 in *Energy and Environment*, vol. 14, p. 751. Mann's side of the debate, with commentary from some critics, appears on a website run by him with others: **www.realclimate.org**. Recent scientific analyses of the debate include Osborn and Briffa in *Science* (vol. 311, p. 841).

34. Hurricane Season
I spoke to Corky Perret for a feature in *New Scientist*: 'Is Global Warming Making Hurricanes Stronger?' (3

December 2005). Webster's paper appeared in *Science*
(vol. 309, p. 1844). Emmanuel first predicted a big
increase in hurricane destruction in *Nature* in 1987 (vol.
326, p. 483).   He was more sanguine when, with
others, he reported in the *Bulletin of the American
Meteorological Society* in 1998 (vol. 79, p. 19), but
returned to the barricades in *Nature* in 2005 (vol. 436,
p. 686). Trenberth made his warnings earlier that year in
Science (vol. 308, p. 1753). Gray's efforts to refute
these claims were not carried in the major journals, but
can be seen at his website: **typhoon.atmos.colostate.edu/**.
The story of 'hurricane' Catarina is told at
www.met-office.gov.uk/sec2/sec2cyclone/catarina.html.

35. Ozone Hole in the Greenhouse
Farman's landmark paper on the ozone hole appeared in
Nature (vol. 315, p. 207). Crutzen discussed how lucky
the world had been in his Nobel lecture (see chapter four).
Hormes and Shindell's thoughts come from personal interviews in Ny-Alesund and New York respectively. The
mechanisms that might cause ozone depletion to produce
rapid climate change were discussed by Hartmann *et al.* in
PNAS, vol. 97, p. 1412.

36. The Dance
The debate between the polar and tropical schools
has never been properly articulated in the journals.
So this chapter is pieced together from interviews
with the participants, many of them in New York.
Goldstein's paper appears in *Science* (vol. 307,
p. 1933). Crutzen's comments came in an interview
with me.

37. New Horizons
Similarly, much of this chapter derives from conversations rather than written papers. The idea of a bipolar see-saw was discussed by David Sugden in *Planet Earth*, journal of the Natural Environment Research Council, in autumn 2005. Read about lakes beneath the Antarctic ice at www.earth.columbia.edu/news/2006/story01-26-06.html. Recent changes to SAM are reviewed by King in *Geophysical Research Letters*, vol. 32, L19604. Shindell's key papers appear in *Science* (vol. 284, p. 305. and vol. 294, p. 2149), with useful summaries at www.giss.nasa.gov/research/news/20041006/ and www.giss.nasa.gov/research/briefs/shindell_04/.

Conclusion
My earlier book, *Turning Up the Heat*, long out of print, was published by The Bodley Head in 1989 and in paperback by Paladin later the same year.

Appendix
Much of what appears here was presented at the Dangerous Climate Change conference, whose proceedings appear at www.stabilisation2005.com/.

INDEX

INDEX